NEUROLOGICAL FOUNDATIONS
OF ANIMAL BEHAVIOR

NEUROLOGICAL FOUNDATIONS
OF ANIMAL BEHAVIOR

BY

C. JUDSON HERRICK

PROFESSOR OF NEUROLOGY IN THE UNIVERSITY OF CHICAGO

HAFNER PUBLISHING COMPANY
New York and London
1962

Reprinted by Arrangement
1962

HAFNER PUBLISHING COMPANY, INC.

Printed in U.S.A. by
NOBLE OFFSET PRINTERS, INC.
NEW YORK 3, N. Y.

INTRODUCTION

This reprinting of C. Judson Herrick's "Neurological Foundations of Animal Behavior" fills a gap that existed in this area. This book presents in broad outline the basic principles that relate the nervous system to behavior.

From an evolutionary point of view the nervous systems of animals as seen by Herrick, not only are presented comparatively in relation to behavior, but they are shown to be progressive. There is a creativity innate in nature at all levels, ascending to the human brain, which is more efficient in its operation than the brains of lower forms. Man can do more with it than the great apes. He can transform his natural and cultural environment to suit his purposes. This premise was Professor Herrick's message that had its first expression in this book.

Recently much interest has been focused on the behavioral sciences. This intense preoccupation with behavior includes the entire range of the animal world. Studies of this nature are being carried on in the basic sciences of anatomy, biochemistry, physiology, psychology, psychiatry, etc., culminating in human sociology with considerable time given to the narrow field of decision making. Large nations have been forced to consider seriously the problems involved in this area, not only for the advancement of knowledge, but for their survival.

In this reprint, one table (page 24) and one figure (page 182) have been changed. Because of these two changes, dates and a few physical data were altered in the text. With these minor revisions, the book is reprinted as it was published in 1924. Its thought content and approach remain valid.

Students of animal and human behavior will find in this book the framework upon which to build soundly a more understandable structure, because behavior is, after all, structured in relation to the nervous system through which it operates. American neurology can be proud of such pioneers as C. Judson Herrick, George Ellett Coghill, Elizabeth Crosby, J. B. Johnston and Stephen Ranson. Of this group Professor Herrick has the honor of being referred to as the father of The American School of Neurology.

Paul G. Roofe, Professor and Chairman
Department of Anatomy
University of Kansas, Lawrence, Kansas

PREFACE

Several years ago the author of this book, in response to requests for an account of the nervous system especially adapted for the use of zoölogists, physiologists, comparative psychologists and students of allied sciences, prepared a brief outline of the general physiology of protoplasmic response to stimulation and the broader aspects of the special functions and structures of the nervous system from the comparative standpoint. This outline was entitled, "Biological Foundations of Animal Behavior." As the manuscript developed under repeated revision it became more and more evident that the treatment of the general physiology of excitation and conduction was inadequate.

The appropriate reaction to this situation was to seek the coöperation of some recognized authority with first-hand experimental knowledge in this field of inquiry. Accordingly, the difficulty was laid before my colleague, Professor C. M. Child, who consented to prepare an independent book on "Physiological Foundations of Behavior," which is published simultaneously with this work. Taking its departure from this more general discussion of protoplasmic response to stimulation, the present work concerns itself with nervous functions in particular, their precursors, origin, and evolutionary history, together with a schematic analysis of the related structures.

Students of behavior are of necessity continually searching out the underlying causes of behavior. And the insistent intrusion into behavioristic literature of formulations of objective psychology and mechanistic conceptions of life, on one hand, and of doctrines of orthogenesis and vitalism with their numerous accompanying familiars, entelechies, and other metaphysical dæmons, on the other hand, indicates that these basic problems lie, not only in the background, but also often in the foreground of research in behavior, sometimes playing a decisive part in shaping research programs. This is, accordingly, an opportune time to pass in review some fundamental features of the organization of the animal body and to inquire how the principles of general physiology actually work out, when examined in a critical spirit, in action systems of various grades of complexity.

The materials for this book have been drawn from a wide field and my indebtedness to the works of the authors cited in the Bibliography is very inadequately expressed by these references. The sources of the numerous figures copied from other works are acknowledged in their descriptions and the courtesy of the authors and publishers who have granted permission to use them is appreciated. The manuscript, or parts of it, has been read by many of my colleagues and friends, whose kindly criticisms have spared the reader many errors and infelicities of expression which would otherwise have been overlooked. My deepest obligation is to Professor Child, who has repeatedly read the manuscript and generously collaborated during the entire course of its preparation. Chapters five to nine especially have benefited by his critical revision.

The Index has been prepared with special care and with it is combined a brief Glossary of some of the more commonly used technical terms, the simple catch-word definitions being followed by the numbers of the pages upon which fuller account will be found.

C. J. H.

Chicago, Ill.
January, 1924.

CONTENTS

CHAPTER I

CHAPTER II

CHAPTER III

CHAPTER IV

CHAPTER V

CHAPTER VI

LIST OF ILLUSTRATIONS

NEUROLOGICAL FOUNDATIONS OF
ANIMAL BEHAVIOR

NEUROLOGICAL FOUNDATIONS OF ANIMAL BEHAVIOR

CHAPTER I

THE PROGRAM

Introductory — The evidence — Physiological factors in evolution — General behavior of protoplasm

Introductory. — While watching on a summer day the evolutions of half-a-dozen hawks soaring placidly in great circles above my head, an aviator swept into the field of view, weaving in and out amongst them and flying with equal assurance and even greater freedom and range of movement. I am interested in the maneuvers of both the hawk and the airplane, in their striking resemblances and fundamental differences, and I wonder how it is that so similar behavior can be manifested by so diverse mechanisms. A little further analysis of this question may assist in the formulation of the theme of this work.

The behavior of the hawk can readily be studied and recorded in a descriptive way, and more detailed observation with the aid of instruments and mathematical armament permits quantitative expression of much of this behavior. It is possible to ascertain the amount and character of food necessary to keep the body in health, its energy equivalent, the optimum times of feeding, the flying radius, the ratio of weight of body to wing expanse, the effects of wind and other weather conditions, and numberless other factors in the complex problem of the flight of the bird.

The airplane in flight can similarly be studied as a problem of behavior. The fuel requirements, radius of action, powers and limitations of flight in various weathers, ratio of load to engine capacity and expanse of wing, etc., are all matters of record. The engineers also possess a large fund of knowledge regarding tensile strength of materials, design and theory of heavier-than-air machines in general.

A good scientific knowledge of the machine involves all this and more. We want to know the history of its design and construction,

1

the mistakes which have been made and rectified, with a view to additional experimentation in the directions offering greatest promise of further improvement.   In all these respects our knowledge of the mechanics of aviation is far advanced.   The whole history of human aviation is an open book before us, and we can follow the progress of improvement from the mythical failures of Icarus and Darius Green to the triumphs of the transcontinental mail service.   But the history of flight in birds goes back to an antiquity of which we have scanty records and these much defaced by time.

The biologist who investigates animal behavior soon reaches a limit beyond which simple observation cannot carry him.   He, too, requires certain engineering facts regarding the organization of the body whose activities he is studying—its anatomy, physiology and evolutionary history.   Descriptive anatomy, it is true, is a dead science, and pure physiology has no *raison d'être;* these highly specialized disciplines must play into each other's hands, for only so can we obtain a true picture of the body in action.   Animal behavior as commonly studied in this country gives such a picture of the more obvious external manifestations of the organism, but these are only the end-products of a complex series of recondite internal processes whose mechanisms are not easily understood.

The plane and the bird are obviously units and the first question to confront us relates to this unity—in what does it consist, what are the integrating factors, and how do they operate?

Looked at from the human standpoint the purpose of the plane is to fly, and if it fails in this it is worse than a tangle of junk.   One such failure broke the heart of a noble man who as a pioneer in the theory of aviation probably contributed more than any other single individual to its ultimate success; and the fact that Langley's machine salvaged from the Potomac did later make a successful flight only adds poignancy to the tragedy of its initial failure.

Biologically considered, the hawk, too, is adapted for flight and deprived of this function it is a failure.   What may be the philosophical significance of this apparent purposefulness in nature we need not here inquire, though it may be remarked in passing that I believe it to be in some sense a real factor in evolution.

A successful airplane flight requires a suitable machine and a competent pilot.   A perfectly constructed plane without the pilot and a highly trained aviator without a machine are alike unable to leave the ground.   Here the integrative factor which is the *sine qua non* of aviation is evidently the human intelligence in two of its manifestations: first, during the long history of experimental aërodynamics in the course of which a practicable design was slowly evolved by the coöperative labors of many men and a serviceable plane was actually built, and, second, through the skill of the pilot in the control of the finished mechanism. These psychic factors can be further analyzed and are matters of record; but only in part, for human intelligence has not yet been wholly reduced to rule. Moreover, to any unprejudiced observer the human intelligence is just as truly and in just the same sense a causative factor in aëronautics as is the muscular work of the pilot or the driving power of the engine.

Of course, this simple statement by no means exhausts the matter. For instance, in the realm of simple mechanics there are within the plane numerous subsidiary systems of mechanical control upon whose proper construction and coördinated operation the stability and efficiency of the whole apparatus depends. These, however, have been intelligently fabricated and must be intelligently operated.

From the standpoint of aviation, accordingly, the pilot and his plane constitute a single individual. One is reminded of James' discussion of human individuality (1890,[1] Chap. 10), where it is contended that the man as we know him is his personal self with all that pertains thereto—body, clothes, house, bank account and all. So the aviator *qua* aviator is naught without his highly trained neuromotor bodily mechanisms plus his wings, motors and all their appurtenances. The whole must function in flight as one mechanism or it crashes to the ground in disaster.

Now, returning to the bird, have we anything to learn from our analogy? The individuality of the bird is a more closely knit affair than that of the aviator and his plane. The feathers, it is true, can be clipped from his wings without evoking any expression of pain; but no one questions that the pinions are part of the bird, and the clipped hawk set free in nature soon becomes no bird at all but food of some hungry beast.

The integrating forces which keep the bird alive and a going concern have, like those of the airplane, grown up gradually, very gradually in this case, through long cycles of evolution. But they are also resident in the vital mechanism as an immanent and unitary directing control not altogether unlike the intelligence which guides the airplane to its destination. We have here an organism which

---

[1] Citations of literature are made in the text by reference to the name of the author followed by the date of publication; for the compléte references consult the Bibliography at the close of the volume.

has grown up in nature and there a mechanism skillfully fabricated by artifice of man and guided by a different and apparently adventitious intelligence in the person of the aviator who now enters it and grasps the controls and anon leaves it to go about his other business.

The analogy between bird and bird-man may, it is true, seem far-fetched, but possibly it is more than a mere phantasy. The contrast in which we take so great delight between the natural and the artificial, between nature and the arts of man, flatters our complacency, but it may be the wiser part to look at the matter from the other side. Has not mankind grown up within that same nature whose minor children are the hawks and the other birds of the air? And if we look at man and all his works as integral parts of nature mayhap we shall see some things to which else our eyes are blinded.

In this work we are searching for foundations, for biological origins; it is not our purpose to review animal behavior in general, nor even to attempt to apply in detail in concrete instances of more complex behavior the elementary principles which may be formulated. But these principles appear to be widely applicable and some of the factors which can be shown to operate in maintaining the unity of the organism in plants and lower animals are found to be present also in the simpler neuromuscular mechanisms of higher forms as well. How far these same factors can be recognized in the complex life of man is an interesting speculation. The evidence so far as it goes suggests that mankind is organically related with the rest of nature and even his most artfully contrived mechanical and social fabrications may strike their roots down deep in to the biological soil from which the human race as a whole has sprung.

In brief, human aviation and the flight of birds, though differing profoundly in origin and in mechanism, may be found to spring from a common stock, and our search for elemental integrating factors in all protoplasmic activities may help to discover those hidden roots whose inflorescence and fruitage we recognize in the personal behavior and social conduct of the highest organisms.

The evidence. — The incessant ebb and flow of opinion regarding the nature of life and the processes and factors of evolution necessitate a preliminary survey of some general principles for purposes of definition of terms and general orientation. A few of these topics will first be touched upon very lightly.

In the condensed phraseology of current scientific exposition the biologist sometimes remarks loosely that a certain organ is formed thus-and-so in order to perform such-and-such a function or that the organism acts in this way because it has certain specified structure. Of course, nothing could be more unscientific. Probably no biologist understands the true nature of either purpose or cause, and it is certainly far from his thought to arrogate to himself any so profound philosophy. But it is a matter of unchallenged observation that certain anatomical structures and certain functions are invariably associated, and on this purely empirical basis current biological theory has been elaborated.

The present inquiry takes its departure from this simple proposition. Animals possessing certain types of structure manifest characteristic types of behavior not found elsewhere. A hound will follow the trail of a fox with superhuman acumen; but having brought the fox to bay and caught it, the hound does not remove and tan the pelt and fabricate from it a garment to keep out next winter's cold. The anatomical peculiarities correlated with these differences between the behavior of the hound and his master are obvious—some by casual inspection and some only through the refinements of scientific research. Our second task will be to pass briefly in review some illustrations of these structure-function correlations on the lower biological levels, where we may uncover some of the elemental processes out of which have developed all higher behavior complexes.

Now a further word regarding the nature of the evidence upon which we must depend in such studies. We are dealing with the problem of interrelation between structure and function. Where the organ can be observed in action, as a bird's wing in flight, the evidence is direct and satisfying as far as it goes, though often reaching its limits with disquieting promptness. Controversy is still active regarding the mechanism of soaring of birds. The more refined methods for the study of structure (anatomy) and function (physiology) usually require an elaborate special technique for each, and afterwards a logical synthesis is necessary to give a true picture of the organ in action. And the limitations of our technique are such that often our knowledge of the structure of one organ or the function of another far outstrips the correlated knowledge necessary in each case to permit us to picture the organ in function.

We are again reminded of the ancient fable of the six blind men who went to see the elephant. One grasped the sturdy leg and said, "The elephant is like a tree"; another seized the tail and reported, "The elephant is like a rope"; a third felt the flapping ear and decided, "The elephant is like a fan"; still another caught the squirming trunk and said, "The elephant is like a snake." The six blind men wrangled the rest of their lives over their observations and each was perfectly right as far as his experience went. But since they were unable to synthesize their different experiences they arrived nowhere. Much of our science is unfortunately in the same disjointed state.

We must, therefore make such use as we can of the inadequate observations available and all our concepts of biological things are elaborated from very incompletely observed data, much as a museum mount of an extinct vertebrate is fabricated from fragments of fossilized bone with wide stretches of plaster between. (But the honest paleontologist, let it not be forgotten, never paints his plaster so as to obscure the limits of the restoration.) In particular, the knowledge of function is far more advanced than that of the correlated anatomical structure at the two biological extremes, viz., in the domains of general physiology and of psychology. But in both cases this serves only to spur us to the more diligent and resourceful inquiry.

Physiological factors in evolution. — The problems of human evolution have been attacked from both flanks, first by advance from the lower positions represented by the known features of infrahuman ancestral types and second by approach from the higher ground of the intellectual and moral faculties, contrasting man in these respects with brutes and endeavoring to determine the existing relationships. Some ground has been won and held in both of these positions, though of very unequal value and strategic importance.

Not only biologists, but sociologists and psychologists as well, have made serious and well planned attempts to trace the descent of man and his mind and institutions, with a gratifying measure of success on the structural side but, it must be admitted, far less satisfactorily on the functional side. The bodily evolution of man to-day presents no biological problems which are fundamentally different from those met in other departments of evolutionary theory, though, of course, many details remain to be worked out. The efforts of the physiologists and psychologists to deduce human behavior from complexes of reflexes, instincts and similar elemental functions have, however, not as yet had so fortunate an outcome. And the whole field of mental evolution, including the problem of psychogenesis, has so far remained almost impenetrable.

The mind of man seems so far removed from anything known in other animals and the animal mind seems so inaccessible to us that those who approach the problem from this side seem prone to seek a way out through metaphysics or mysticism, though relief of this sort is obtained only at the expense of profound narcosis of critical and scientific method.

Even Huxley, that valiant champion of Darwin's cause, in his later years suffered defeat upon entering this field when he admitted (1902) that, "The history of civilization details the steps by which men have succeeded in building up an artificial world within the cosmos," and again, "The ethical progress of society depends, not on imitating the cosmic process, still less in running away from it, but in combating it." The contrast here drawn between human culture and the "cosmos" betrays the cause of human evolution.[1] By what right does he separate human civilization from the rest of the cosmos? This civilization has grown up, not apart from the process of nature, but within it, and failure to recognize this fundamental principle has wrecked many a promising evolutionary enterprise. The solutions of the great problems of human evolution will not be facilitated by the fabrication of artificial barriers between "ape and tiger" aspects of evolution and the nobler functions of cultured humanity, but by searching for the nexus between these. And this search will not be in vain.

The fundamental unity of the entire evolutionary process is an indispensable feature of any broad conception of this doctrine, for this is merely one expression of the law of continuity in nature. The interruption of the process at any point breaks the chain and leaves in our hands only the useless fragments of discredited theories. Whatever justification (if any) there may be in philosophy for a pluralistic universe, science knows naught of it.

Evolution is coextensive with life; the mechanisms of evolution must, accordingly, be sought in all protoplasm, and an adequate understanding of protoplasm, the properties common to all protoplasms, will carry with it knowledge of the essential factors of evolution in all of its manifestations.

It follows that the approach to the problems of human evolution may be undertaken, not only from the two flanks to which reference

---

[1] This criticism holds, I think, in spite of the extended argument of the Prolegomena published the year after the address from which my quotations are taken, in which it is recognized (page 11 of the volume cited) that both the artificial garden and the ethical process in human affairs are themselves "part and parcel of the cosmic process." The conflict in each human life between the "ethical process" and the "cosmic struggle for existence" is all-of-a-piece with those more brutal conflicts of the primitive "gladiatorial" stages of existence, and we gain little but on the other hand lose much by placing the emphasis on the lack of genetic bonds between the highest and best of human life and the biological soil out of which these choice fruits of the spirit have grown.

has been made, but also by direct frontal attack through the study of the organization of protoplasm as such and of the mutual relations of the various different protoplasms of which the living body is composed.

Such is the task before us in this work, namely, a review of some recent advances in the analysis of the structure and behavior or properties of living substance and the application of these facts in a brief summary of the successive stages through which we believe that protoplasm has passed in the course of its différentiation into nervous tissues and the further elaboration of these as found in the brains of higher animals.

The common principles of the physiology of protoplasm in general and of nervous tissues in particular to which reference is here made are few in number and rather simple; but their applications are far-reaching and shed light upon some of the most recondite phases of the general theory of evolution. That they cannot be expected to lead directly to ultimate solutions of all of these problems, of course, needs no advertisement.

General behavior of protoplasm.— In a recent work Child [1] has elaborated the foundations of behavior in terms of the underlying general physiology of living substance with special reference to the immediate reactions of the protoplasm to external influences (external, that is, to the reacting substance, not necessarily to the body as a whole). These immediate responses to stimulation are, of course, expressed in characteristic behavior patterns which in the aggregate make up the action system of the species in question. These specific differences in the behavior patterns rest upon differences in the stable organization of the protoplasmic apparatus, that is, upon the structural substratum, which varies from species to species and from part to part of the same organism. These structural arrangements are apparently heritable and they establish more or less definitely the range of behavior patterns or the limits within which any organism or part can respond to external agents.

A difficulty arises here from the fact to which Child (1924, Chaps. 3, 9) has called attention that, if we accept current theories of heredity the protoplasm which is supposed to be the physical vehicle of the hereditary pattern is uniformly distributed throughout the develop-

---

[1] This work (Child, 1924) is a more comprehensive presentation of these general principles than are any of his previous publications. In it are found references to other publications presenting the details of experimental evidence and fuller discussion of many topics.

ing body, that is, the hereditary pattern is not different in the various parts of any given organism. But one may venture the opinion that there is room for doubt whether this assumption is true, and in any event there is urgent demand for an analysis of the factors operative in the process of the differentiation of parts of living bodies. One such factor which clearly is of prime importance in the fabrication of the body rests on differences in the rate of activity of the vital processes of growth, performance of the ordinary functions of the tissues, and response to changes in the surrounding medium—differences in short in the rate of living. These differences for the most part are in last analysis resolved into the local action of external agents upon the protoplasm of which the body is composed, that is, upon excitation; and since protoplasm is capable of transmitting these excitations through its own substance the effects of such stimulation are manifest most at the point of application and in diminishing degree as the excitation is transmitted away through the surrounding protoplasm.

Thus arise the *physiological gradients*, or lines of diminishing intensity of vital reaction to stimulation. These reactions are largely (though not exclusively) chemical activities within the protoplasm, that is, metabolism. Centers of high metabolic rate exert a wider influence upon the activities of surrounding parts than do regions exhibiting less energetic vital processes and in this way become centers of physiological dominance. The physiological gradients have been studied experimentally in a large number of organisms by a variety of methods with results of great significance to general physiology and to animal behavior in particular.

The actual behavior is a response to some stimulation, but the pattern of this behavior in each instance is always a joint product of the action of the exciting agent and the specific constitution of the reacting substance. There are certain broad similarities exhibited by all protoplasm under conditions of excitation and there are certain general laws of behavior, common to all specific protoplasms, which rest upon the fundamental nature of the excitation-conduction process—physiological gradients, relations of dominance and subordina-dination of parts, physiological integration, the mechanism and significance of physiological isolation, senescence and rejuvenescence of tissue, and the like. These in the aggregate Child calls organismic processes, or factors concerned with the maintenance and progressive elaboration of the individuality of the organism as a whole. It is to the analysis of these organismic processes especially that Child has devoted his comprehensive experimental studies.

The present work is built upon this foundation. Taking the mature organism as we find it, we shall examine its structure and behavior and endeavor to determine the relations between this behavior and specific structural mechanisms. Comparison of the results of such an examination of various lower and higher animals reveals some general laws of structure-function correlation and certain tendencies toward specialization in diverse directions. Study of the origins of these excito-motor mechanisms in the lowest animals clearly demonstrates that they are in large measure particular concrete expressions of the general principles of organismic integration of the excitation-conduction type to which Child has called attention in the course of his experiments on non-nervous protoplasms.

But our program is broader than this, for the structural mechanisms with which the comparative anatomist deals are apparently in large part very stable heritable fabrics, and we are interested to learn the steps through which these stereotyped structural patterns came into being, the parts which they play in behavior patterns, and to what extent and in what ways they are plastic and modifiable in the course of the individual experience. Obviously this leads us directly into the problems of the nature and apparatus of tropism, reflex, instinct, as illustrations of stabilized forms of behavior, in contrast with individual modifiability, habit, associative memory, learning by experience, intelligence, as illustrations of more labile behavior.

CHAPTER II

ANALYSIS OF BEHAVIOR

Behavior of the airplane — Behavior of the organism. Somatic, visceral and genetic behavior — The unit of behavior — Grades of behavior — The biological individual — Progressive factors in evolution. Spontaneity

Behavior of the airplane. — A simple analysis of the practical workings of the airplane, to which reference was made at the beginning, brings to light three aspects or phases of its career which are instructive for our present purpose. First, there is the process of practical flying, the control of the machine by a pilot. Second, there is the maintenance of the machine, the work of the mechanician. Third, we are interested in the origin of the machine, the history of its design and construction. These must all be taken into the reckoning before we can claim an adequate understanding of the flying machine.

Behavior of the organism. — In the behavior of the bird, man or other living thing we recognize three somewhat similar aspects. In the first place, there is the adjustment of the organism to the outside world in which it lives. This is fundamentally response to stimulating agents outside the body, and since it usually involves locomotion or other movements of the body as a whole or of its members in space it is called *somatic behavior* and the mechanisms involved are somatic organs.

In the second place, there are the internal processes of regulatory adjustment which maintain the body in health and vigor. These processes are usually initiated by changes in internal state and include nutrition, respiration, excretion, circulation and like activities concerned with the maintenance and propagation of the body. These in the aggregate constitute the *visceral behavior* and the organs concerned are viscera.[1]

Third, there is the genetic aspect, the processes involved in heredity, fertilization, embryological development and growth. These in the aggregate may be called *genetic behavior.*

[1] This physiological definition of the viscera conforms in general with current usage; but the word is commonly used so loosely that a more precise formulation seems desirable. This I have endeavored to do in a recent article entitled, "What are Viscera?" (1922 b).

Within recent years a new science has been born of the parent sciences, physiology and psychology, which has been named Animal Behavior. The activities of this lusty stripling at present lie almost wholly within the field termed above somatic behavior. This is merely an indication of the immaturity of the science, an age when the external and the obvious engross the attention. For, as Child has clearly shown (1924, Chaps. 2, 13, 14), the three types of behavior just enumerated all spring from a common root. The basic physiologic processes are identical, and somatic, visceral and genetic behavior, different as they are in their manifestations, not only conform to the same fundamental laws, but they are so inextricably interwoven in the complex fabric of life that in the study of behavior all must be reckoned with.

Behavior, in the larger view, includes every response of the living substance to stimulation and the general physiology of the process is not radically different whether the source of the excitation is outside or inside the limits of the body. As already mentioned, the character of these responses is determined in each case by (1) the action of the exciting agent and (2) the nature of the excited protoplasm. The analysis of these two factors will occupy our attention in the later chapters.

The unit of behavior. — The acts which in sum comprise behavior are in general either (1) immediate response to stimulation or (2) activities less directly resulting from such responses and their mutual interaction — their correlation, summation, interference, and the resulting more or less enduring modification of the stable physiological patterns which comprise the innate action system of the species. In this second category are included the mnemonic factors, organic memories of previous reactions which modify future behavior and form the physiologic basis of learning by experience.

The immediate response to stimulation may, therefore, be regarded as a convenient unit of behavior. In its definite form as seen in higher animals this unit includes the following processes: (1) The stimulus, a physical agent of some sort which impinges upon excitable protoplasm. (2) The excitation, or the direct effect of the stimulus upon the specific protoplasm which is affected. A special receptive apparatus is usually provided for each kind of stimulus to which the body is sensitive, namely, the sense organ or receptor. The sense organ is usually regarded as part of the nervous system, though it may contain a very complex assortment of non-nervous accessory tissues. (3) The afferent transmission. The apparatus is a sensory nervous pathway which transmits the excitation from the receptor to a center of correlation. (4) The central adjustment. The adjustor is a nerve center in which the afferent impulse is transferred to the efferent pathway, with or without more or less complex modification of the excitation in the center itself. (5) The efferent transmission. The apparatus is a motor nervous pathway which transmits the excitation to the peripheral organ of response. (6) The response. The specific apparatus of response is termed the effector, which is usually not a part of the nervous system — muscle, gland, electric organ, etc.

The apparatus of immediate reactions in its typical form is the familiar reflex arc; but the same schema lies at the basis of all higher forms of behavior (that is, it forms the foundation but not the superstructure of these higher forms), and also, at the other extreme, of the simplest responses of non-nervous organisms (with modifications to be noted). In the elementary protoplasmic animals like the ameba no such special tissues as have been mentioned exist, and the same protoplasm may perform any or all of the diverse functions appropriate to these tissues; nevertheless all of these processes are necessarily present in some form, however simplified and generalized.

This organization in all cases ensures effective interaction between the living body and the world about, from which it derives its food and the other raw materials of life and to which it returns certain waste products and, in many cases, various highly elaborated stuffs which play a significant part in the general economy of nature — starches and sugars used as food by other creatures, the rock-forming minerals of coral reefs and limestone, coal and graphite. The energy changes which go with this transmutation of substance constitute the process of living and they provide a quantitative measure of life.

Grades of behavior. — Life in its various manifestations cannot always be measured by the same yardstick. The rate of living may be expressed quantitatively in terms of the amount of energy turnover, as in the calorimeter experiments of Atwater and Benedict (1903); but, as has been pointed out elsewhere, this gives little insight into the real value of the work done. This latter is measured, rather, by the range and diversity of environmental contacts, to what kinds of natural forces adjustment is possible and how various and rapid are the possible modes of response to external changes.

Plants and animals are usually thought of as graded in ranks from low to high. The classifications in current use by biologists do not, however, imply anything of this sort; they aim, rather, to express the genetic relationships of the species. The surviving species of any branch of the plant or animal kingdom may be of very recent evolutionary origin, as illustrated by certain species which are peculiar to areas known to have been isolated by physical barriers until recent geological times, or they may be of very great antiquity. There are existing genera of lampshells (e. g., Lingula) of which we have fossil records extending back practically unchanged to Cambrian time, estimated at 540,000,000 years.

Any of these surviving species may be of high or low rank as compared with related species, living and extinct.

A group in which rapid diversification is taking place may quickly reach higher rank, while a related group may remain nearly stationary or it may even retrograde to a lower place. Diversification of species may take place by multiplication of lateral branches of the phylogenetic tree, each kind being nicely adjusted to some particular mode of life and therefore modified in some minor respects without great change in the fundamental characteristics of the group. This is well illustrated in the ants (Wheeler, 1913). Such a group as a whole may be very highly diversified and very successful biologically as measured by number of species and individuals, but it may rank lower in the zoölogical scale than the group next to be considered.

In case adjustment to various environmental conditions is brought about by an increase in the ability of each individual of the species to adapt his life to a wider range of natural forces with more plasticity of behavior, the evolutionary advance is in the vertical rather than in the horizontal direction and we call this behavior higher. This type of differentiation is illustrated by birds and more notably by mammals. Man is higher biologically than any of the other animals because he is individually capable of more diversified living. This, of course, implies greater structural as well as physiological complexity, as Darwin pointed out in the section of the Origin of Species entitled, "On the degree to which organization tends to advance."

In the broad view advance in evolution involves adjusting the whole organic realm, including the plant and animal kingdoms, to an increasing range of natural conditions. Individual species may be very perfectly adjusted to a limited and very special environment and still remain relatively low in the organic scale; and a species which can vary its behavior so as to adjust to a larger variety of environmental conditions is higher. On the whole, the history of life in our world as revealed by paleontology shows a trend toward biological advance in both of the senses just defined, that is, an increase, first, in the number of species exhibiting precise adaptation to diverse peculiar habitats and, second, in the biological efficiency of certain higher species as measured by their range and flexibility of behavior.

From the standpoint of behavior, accordingly, we estimate the biological rank of a species, not in terms of amount of energy transformed, of work done, but rather of the pattern in which this energy is liberated. An oak tree is capable of an immensely greater turn-over of energy and of material substance in a single day than is the ant crawling at its root; yet we regard the insect as a higher organism than the tree, for it can adjust to a greater variety of natural conditions more rapidly and in more diverse ways. The tree is a very successful organism, but only in its own natural habitat. It may withstand the buffeting of a harsh environment for centuries and its offspring may invade surrounding fields and ultimately people them with a mighty forest. Yet it is rooted to one place as long as it lives and can survive only by developing protective adaptations against wind, frost and drought and by accepting whatever of natural goods are brought to its station. The ant, on the other hand, is able to build for itself a shelter from the elements and actively to forage for food and other desirables.

Man ranks higher still. He seeks out and uses for his own advantage a greater variety of natural resources and in larger measure brings the forces of animate and inanimate nature under his own control. He is neither as strong nor as fleet as some of the creatures which he has subjugated. His success in life is measured by other standards. The energy expenditure of a single calorie in the brain of an engineer may be of more significance in the construction of a cantilever bridge than that of all the muscular work required in its fabrication.

Biological rank, as the term is here employed, is functionally defined. There is, of course, a corresponding structural differentiation which in general is a more convenient index of this rank, but only when properly evaluated in terms of function.

The biological individual. — Before proceeding further we must inquire briefly into the nature and organization of the biological individual. The definition of the animal or plant individual proves to be very difficult. Unicellular organisms undoubtedly are individuals and so are huge trees and human bodies with millions of cells of innumerable forms and functions. Between those extremes are all possible gradations — separate cells in communities and cells organically united in colonies and organs. Within the cells are smaller units sometimes regarded as organic individuals and at the other extreme complete individuals often remain in organic connection, like strawberry runners and coral polyps, and here there is sometimes great diversity in the persons represented in the composite individual. A highly complex social aggregate of separate persons, such as a hive of bees, a human family or nation, also has its own individuality.

The individuality of an organism is dependent upon the maintenance of a dynamic equilibrium of the internal forces with each other and with the environing forces. The preservation of this physiologic equilibrium under varying conditions of life requires a correlation of part with part and mutual readjustment as functional activity fluctuates in time, space and amount. This equilibrated correlation and mutual adjustment is termed biological regulation, and this is the most essential feature of the life process (see further in Chap. 20 and Jennings, 1905, Child, 1924, Chap. 13).

This regulatory control in its simplest form has been shown to be in part dependent upon the quantitative relations of chemical or metabolic changes within the protoplasm. High protoplasmic activity in one part exerts a regulatory control on other parts in proportion as free protoplasmic conduction between them is possible. The excitation-conduction phenomena to which reference has been made and the physiological gradients in the pathways of protoplasmic transmission are the chief integrating factors in the maintenance of the unity of the organism. In short, the individuality of the organism is dependent upon the organismic functions as these have already been defined (p. 9).

The unification of the organism is no mystic principle, no *deus ex machina*, nor is it to be conceived as an intrinsic agent or force immanent within the body and there exercising control as a supreme ruler of a realm in complete isolation from external influences. The body, rather, preserves its unity only by maintaining appropriate, that is adaptive, relations with the materials and energies of the world about. It is an equilibrated system whose integrity can be preserved only by incessant readjustment to the sequence of events in its natural environment.

The nature of this equilibrium and the reciprocal relation between the structural and functional aspects of organisms are graphically illustrated in Child's analogy of the river and its channel (see also beyond, pp. 75, 252). The river receives tributary water, suspended solids, and energy, here erodes its banks and there deposits the same material as a bar, and throughout its course exhibits the closest adjustment of energy of flow to configuration of channel. "The relation between structure and function in the organism is similar in character to the relation between the river as an energetic process and its banks and channel. From the moment that the river began to flow it began to produce structural configurations in its environment, the products of its activity accumulated in certain places and modified its flow, but just so long as the flow continues the process of equilibration goes on" (1911, p. 186; cf. 1915 a, p. 27).

The river is neither the water current nor the channel; it is both of these as they have developed together, and the only way the river can be fully understood is by the consideration of it as process. True, if the water were diverted, the empty bed would reveal much of the past history of the stream (as the "fossil rivers" of the physiographers illustrate), and so the study of the dead animal body is a useful branch of biology, though at best inconclusive and often misleading.

This analogy, of course, cannot be carried very far and we cannot continue the general exposition of biological individuality (see Child, 1915 a). But I wish to comment further on one characteristic of the living individual which has an important bearing on the course of evolution and of individual behavior.

Progressive factors in evolution. Spontaneity. — As we have seen, life is more than immediate reaction to stimuli. Moreover, energy is laid by in latent form as a reserve and movement is produced in excess of the requirements of immediate response (Ritter, 1919). This general motility and over-produced movement, this so-called spontaneity of action,[1] is an important factor in all higher forms of behavior. Even the lowest animals exhibit some rudiments of that spontaneity to which Max Eastman (1917) refers in an interesting passage:

"We shall find not only that experience as such is welcome to life, but that life of its own accord goes in search of experience. That 'general motility' which Jennings has to add to the specific reactions, in writing the biography of lower organisms, will, if separately dwelt upon, supply a standpoint from which life can be viewed as fruitfully as from the standpoint of adaptation to stimuli. We are not merely trying to adapt ourselves in order to stay alive,

[1] The concept of spontaneity to which reference is here made does not carry with it any implication of uncaused action. Physiologically, spontaneous acts are internally excited, as exemplified by the direct stimulation of the respiratory center by carbon dioxid dissolved in the blood. Similarly it is possible that many cortical activities are stimulated by local changes in the cortex itself. See the discussion of Automaticity by Child (1924, Chap. 11).

but we are trying even more energetically to live. Everything we do and think is not a reaction; a great deal of it is action. The 'Behaviorist' is not so much to be condemned for his refusal to observe or consider 'states of consciousness,' as for his totally inadequate view of what he does observe and consider. The interaction of organism and environment is for him carefully divided into reflex arcs, all operating in one direction. A stimulus to the end-organ, a commotion in the central-nervous system, then a response in the muscles — that is the whole story of life in his laboratory. But life interflows with reality in full circles. We do things not only because we have a sensation, but also in order to make a sensation. And so do the most elementary organisms. Any rubber ball can react, but it requires life to act. And life does act. It seeks experience."

Experience is not something to which the organism is passively subjected. In response to stimulation it reaches out actively to meet the exciting agent; but it does more than this, it is constantly seeking new contacts. And this restless search for food, mates and other desirables for the satisfaction of inner cravings leads up to higher manifestations in curiosity, the unquenchable impulse towards scientific discovery, and the divine fire of creative artistic genius. The evolutionary factor here is more than self-preservation; it is self-realization and fulfillment.

The increase in personal efficiency to which reference has just been made enlarges the scope of existence or the richness of life. The strivings of the individuals for self-preservation and for reproduction favor increase in their capacities. This self-aggrandizement or self-determination appears to be cumulative; it plays a larger part in higher animals than in lower. The joy of living expands in proportion to the wealth of life.

CHAPTER III

THE RECEPTIVE APPARATUS

Receptors — Analyzers — The analysis of vibratory energies — Classification of the sense organs

Receptors. — If, as is generally agreed, the process of living is the adjustment of the inner activities of the organism to the events taking place in that segment of the world which forms its natural habitat, evidently the receptive organs (sense organs) are critical points in this adjustment, for these are the places where external energies impinge upon the body surface and are transformed from inorganic physical or chemical forces into vital functions. The sense organs are the highest points in the excitation-conduction gradients to which reference has been made (p. 9) and they are centers of physiological dominance with reference to the apparatus of transmission and response which are immediately activated from them. Accordingly, they merit especial consideration in advance of the general review of the behavior mechanisms.

Since our unit of behavior is the total reaction, any analysis of the receptive organs is at best only a first step in the study of behavior mechanisms and it must be followed up by a complete synthesis of the relations of each of these organs to the apparatus of response and the intervening machinery of conduction and correlation. The unity of these processes is brought into clear relief by reference to their arrangement in the simplest organisms, where the same protoplasm performs all of these functions. As we follow the progressive differentiation of this primordial reacting stuff, the significance of the rôle played by each of the component subdivisions of the behavior unit in higher animals becomes more clearly defined.

Analyzers. — The sense organs and their related central apparatus are very aptly termed by Pavlov analyzers. Their function is to select from the infinite manifold of energy manifestations by which the body is surrounded those which have value for the body and to sort these selected forms and so distribute them to the different correlation centers that they may be recombined and discharged to the motor centers requisite to give the appropriate reactions. This is another way of saying that all stimuli in order to be effective

19

must be *adequate*, that is, they must bear some relation to the mode of life of the species.

The surface of organisms is commonly protected by a more or less impervious coverings, cuticle or shell. The sense organs may be thought of as windows, each of which can be penetrated by its own kind of physical energy — light waves, sound waves, pressures, various chemical substances, etc. Many of these organs have accessory parts by which the effective action of the exciting agents is modified, strengthened or concentrated, like the external ear of a rabbit, the refracting media of the eye, etc.

This analysis may be either peripheral or central. The peripheral analyzers are the sense organs, each of which is so constructed that it responds to only a certain kind and range of external energies, it may be mechanical pressures, air waves, light waves, chemical irritants, etc. In some cases, however, the same physical agent may excite more than one kind of sense organ, and here the analysis between the two stimuli is made in the central nervous system.

Slow mechanical vibrations of say 40 per second may be sensed as sound if they fall upon the ear and as touch if they fall upon the finger tips. The longer waves of the visible solar spectrum are sensed as red if they fall upon the retina and as warmth if they fall upon the skin. In each of these cases the same external agent initiates not only two different sensations, but also ordinarily two different kinds of motor responses, because the excitation is transmitted from each receptive end-organ to a different central apparatus of adjustment. The two sensory mechanisms excited by the red rays of the spectrum are very different, but these differences do not constitute the essential feature of the analyzer, for the physical stimulus is identical and the nervous impulses leading away from the retina and skin are, so far as we know, essentially the same. The analysis is central, as shown by the fact that stimulation of the optic nerve anywhere in its course by any means whatever leads to sensations of light, never to sensations of warmth.

On the other hand, a single sensory nerve ending may, apparently in some cases, be so connected centrally as to discharge into two or more centers of different physiological type, with resulting difference in both the sensory experience and the motor response. Stimulation of the olfactory organ, say by ethyl alcohol, leads to a locomotor reaction to locate the source of supply. Having found the bottle and sampled its contents, stimulation of the olfactory organ by identically the same substance within the mouth (through the posterior nasal apertures) leads to the visceral reaction of swallowing. (The illustration is an anachronism, I know, but it will suffice.) In the first case we say that we smelled the alcohol; in the second case we say, erroneously, that we taste it (erroneously, for the true taste of alcohol is subjectively quite different from the ethereal odor). The first is an exteroceptive stimulus (p. 26) leading, as Sherrington would say, to a distance-reaction; the second is an interoceptive stimulus leading to a visceral reaction. The mechanism of the discrimination in man is probably wholly central; in some other vertebrates with well developed vomeronasal organs it is probably largely peripheral (see p. 37).

The mechanism of analysis of painful and tactile sensibility of the skin is not fully understood (see Herrick, 1922, Chap. 18), and here apparently both peripheral receptors and central analyzers may come into play. In the skin there may be separate receptors for pain and touch — the so-called pain spots and tactile spots — and in some cases these may be connected with their respective cerebral centers by independent systems of nerve fibers. But that this is not universally the case is indicated by some recently published observations of Gerard (1923).

The skin of the face is supplied from the sensory root of the trigeminal nerve. It is known that each peripheral nerve fiber of this root divides upon entering the brain, one branch ascending to the so-called chief sensory nucleus of the trigeminus and one branch descending to the spinal nucleus of this nerve. Gerard in an analysis of numerous clinical cases of injury to this nervous pathway in man and experimental operations upon it in cats has shown that the ascending branches of its fibers and the chief sensory nucleus are concerned with tactile sensations and reflexes and that the descending branches and spinal nucleus are concerned with painful sensations and reflexes. These two types of sensibility are apparently conveyed by the same peripheral nerve fiber up to the point of its division within the brain, where they separate to reach their respective terminal nuclei (Fig. 1).

The analysis in this case is clearly effected in the central apparatus. It is very probable that something similar takes place in other cases of painful stimulation. Apparently most nerves, if stimulated above a certain intensity, may excite pain in addition to their proper sense qualities, and pain from over-stimulation is often conceived as an overflow of nervous impulses from the ordinary physiological path to another path of higher internal resistance. As illustrated in figure

1, the tactile path would be thought of as more readily traversed and the collateral pain path as activated with greater difficulty, so that under ordinary stimulation only the former could be traversed. If, however, under stronger stimulation the nervous impulses overflow into the pain path, these latter impulses reach a different cerebral center from the tactile impulses and the sensation of touch will be accompanied by a feeling of pain or discomfort. Under maximal

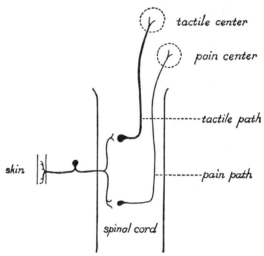

Fig. 1.—Diagram of the probable relations of the nervous pathways for pain and tactile sensibility.

stimulation the response of the pain center rises to so great intensity as to dominate the situation and this alone is perceived.[1]

The analysis of vibratory energies. — To bring the matter before us in concrete form the human receptors will next be reviewed, first taking up the receptors of vibratory stimuli. These include rhythmically repeated mechanical pressures sensed by the skin, more rapid

[1] This commonly accepted explanation of pain from over-stimulation encounters very grave physiological difficulties. The "all-or-none law" of nervous transmission (p. 263), states that every nerve fiber, if excited at all, must deliver its maximum nervous discharge. The universal validity of this law has not been proven, but if it applies in this case it is difficult to see how over-stimulation alone can lead to such an overflow into a collateral pathway. But nervous transmission is believed to be a series of rhythmic discharges and if maximal stimulation induces a different rhythm of transmission from the usual one (and there is some evidence that this is the case), the two nervous impulses of different rate may be filtered off into separate central pathways each of which is attuned to one of the rates of the primary fiber. For further consideration of these theoretic questions see page 116.

physical vibrations sensed by the ear, and the so-called electromagnetic vibrations. The skin can discriminate a series of contacts from single impacts up to vibration rates as high as 1552 per second. The human ear is sensitive to approximately ten octaves of the musical scale ranging from about 30 vibrations per second at the lower limit to about 29,000 at the upper limit. To all other frequencies it is insensitive. The so-called electromagnetic vibrations include the following classes. The lower members of the electromagnetic series are utilized in radiotransmission, then follow radiant heat waves, the visible spectrum, ultraviolet rays of the spectrum, and x-rays.

There is no human sense organ which can respond directly to the electric waves, the ultra-violet rays, and the x-rays. These have, accordingly, remained wholly unknown to us until revealed indirectly by the researches of the physical laboratories. Some ten octaves of their series are contained in the solar spectrum, from an infra-red wave length of about .1 mm. to an ultra-violet wave length of .0035 mm. The light from metallic arcs and from incandescent gases has, however, been found to contain wave lengths as short as .00006 mm. The human eye is sensitive to something over one octave of this series (waves from .0008 to .0004 mm. in length, whose rates lie between 375,000 and 750,000 billions of vibrations per second), with six octaves in the infra-red and three in the ultra-violet. The lower members of this series of vibrations of the solar spectrum, and to a less extent the higher also, are capable of stimulating the temperature organs of the skin.

Thus it appears that of the complete series of electromagnetic vibrations, we can sense directly only about one octave by the eye and a number of others through the sense organs for temperature in the skin, while to the lowest and highest members of the series our sense organs are entirely insensitive. The sensitivity of the skin to these vibrations is limited subjectively to a small range of temperature sensations, while the retinal excitations give us subjectively an extensive series of sensations of color and brightness. The human eye can discriminate from 150 to 230 pure spectral tints, besides various degrees of intensity and purity of tone, making a total of between 500,000 and 600,000 possible discriminations by the visual organs (von Kries). Some of the preceding data are summarized in the table [1] on page 24.

---

[1] This table and some of the accompanying paragraphs are taken by permission of the publishers from Chapter V of the author's Introduction to Neurology (third edition, Philadelphia, W. B. Saunders Co., 1922), where the classification here outlined is amplified.

TABLE OF PHYSICAL VIBRATIONS

Physical process	Wave length	Number of vibrations per second	Receptor	Sensation
Mechanical contact	- - - -	From very slow to 1552 per second	Skin	Touch and pressure
Waves in material media	Above 12,280 mm.	Below 30 per second	None	None
	12,280 mm.	30 per second to 20,000 per second	Internal ear	Tone
	Below 16 mm.	Above 30,000 per second	None	None
Electromagnetic waves	∞ to .2 mm.	0 to 1500 billion (1.5×10^{12})	None	None
	.1 mm. to .0004 mm.	3000 billion (3×10^{12}) to 750,000 billion (7.5×10^{14})	Skin	Radiant heat
	.0008 mm. to .0004 mm.	375,000 billion (3.75×10^{14}) to 750,000 billion (7.5×10^{14})	Retina	Visible light
	.0004 mm. to .000008 mm. (ultra-violet rays)	750,000 billion (7.5×10^{14}) to 37,500,000 billion (3.75×10^{16})	None	None
	.00002 mm. to .000000000004 mm. (x-rays)	15,000,000 billion (1.5×10^{16}) to 75,000 billion billion (7.5×10^{22})	None	None
	.0000014 mm. to .00000000005 mm. (gamma rays)	0.2 billion billion (2×10^{17}) to 6000 billion billion (6×10^{21})	None	None
	.000000005 mm. to .000000000008 mm. (cosmic-rays)	60 billion billion (6×10^{19}) to 40,000 billion billion (4×10^{22})	None	None

From these illustrations it is plain that the sensory equipment of the human body is adapted to respond directly to only a limited part of the environing energy complex, the remainder having little if any, practical significance in the natural environment of primitive man. Our human world, is, in fact, a very limited part of nature, and our furthest scientific advances and most recondite philosophical theories must be based in last analysis on such fragmentary knowledge of the cosmos as is revealed to us by our senses. During the progress of the development of human culture mankind has very considerably widened his contact with the environment by artificial aids to his sense organs. The range of vision has been extended by the microscope and the telescope, and of hearing by the microphone and the telephone. The photographic plate enables him to extend his knowledge of the solar spectrum beyond its visible limits, and the Marconi wireless apparatus brings the Hertzian electric waves under his control and thus enables him to put a girdle round about the earth in less than Puck's forty minutes.

The sensory equipment of the human race was thus established by the biological necessities of our immediate animal ancestors, and there is no evidence of subsequent improvement in these peripheral physiological mechanisms or of any increase in the number of our senses during the advancement of human culture. The advance in efficiency of the human race as compared with its brutish ancestors is to be sought rather in a more efficient central apparatus in the brain for the utilization of the sensory data for the welfare of the organism. What the progress of science has accomplished is to supplement the limited sensory equipment of primitive man by various indirect means. In short, by making more intelligent use of such experiences as our sense organs provide, mankind has acquired an increasing measure of control over inorganic nature and also over many other animals whose senses are in some respects superior to our own.

Classification of the sense organs. — Attempts to classify the sense organs appear to lead only to controversy, for their genetic and physiologic relationships are so involved as to preclude adequate analysis by any simple rule. If attention is directed only to the adequate stimuli, we have (Parker, 1922), (1) mechanicoreceptors, or organs of pressure, hearing, equilibration, muscle sense, etc., (2) radioreceptors, organs of vision and temperature, (3) chemoreceptors, organs of smell, taste, general chemical sensitivity and some others. The anatomical structure and distribution of the sense organs gives a very different grouping and one which as yet cannot be completed (for instance, the anatomical separation of the cutaneous senses has not been satisfactorily effected). The subjective qualities of sense give us, of course, our most direct evidence, but this is very incomplete, many physiologically demonstrable types of excitation normally not appearing in consciousness at all and others being incorrectly referred. (The enormous physiological importance of the muscle sense is everywhere recognized, though we are rarely aware of its action; smell and taste are unquestionably distinct sensations, though subjectively we often do not discriminate them.) Finally, the characteristic type of response is an important criterion of sense, and this physiological feature is perhaps, from our present viewpoint, the most significant of all.

We have seen (p. 11) that the bodily reactions fall into two great groups termed somatic and visceral, the first relating the body in general with its environment, the second concerned chiefly with matters of internal adjustment. All organs of the body may be arranged roughly in two corresponding series. The nervous system, accordingly, is similarly subdivided into somatic and visceral systems of reacting mechanisms.

The sense organs of the somatic group are termed by Sherrington exteroceptors, for they are typically excited by stimuli arising outside the body. The sense organs of the visceral group are similarly termed interoceptors, for the exciting agent is usually internal. Sherrington recognizes a third group of sense organs, the proprioceptors, whose most typical representatives are nerve endings found in muscles, tendons and joints which serve to regulate the movements of the body. The vestibular apparatus of the internal ear also belongs here. These sense organs are internally excited, but they are not properly classed as visceral, for their functions of control of equilibrium, locomotion and the movements of the skeletal musculature in general are called forth by the somatic movements, to which they are really ancillary. In addition to these there are less well known proprioceptive nerve endings in the visceral muscles which in a similar way regulate and coördinate visceral reactions. The proprioceptors, accordingly, fall into two groups which are subsidiary respectively to somatic and visceral reactions.

A list of the receptors of the human body will obviously include more than the organs of the traditional five senses. The following enumeration is by no means complete and is in some parts merely provisional. The organs of response, or effectors, are added and classified in accordance with the same physiological principles.

SOMATIC RECEPTORS

A. Exteroceptive group.

1. Organs of touch and pressure. These are numerous, widely distributed (both superficial and deep), and of very diverse form.
2. End-organs for sensibility to cold.
3. End-organs for sensibility to heat.
4. End-organs for pain.
5. End-organs for general chemical sensibility.

The anatomical analysis of these five systems of sense organs is by no means satisfactorily made out. The functions of some of the organs are accurately known, but there is considerable uncertainty about some of the others.

6. Organs of hearing.
7. Organs of vision.
8. Organs of smell.

B. Proprioceptive group.

9. End-organs of muscular sensibility.

10. End-organs of tendon sensibility.

11. End-organs of joint sensibility.

The last three are widely distributed in the deep parts of the body and are of very diverse forms.

12. Organs of postural and equilibratory sensations in the labyrinth of the internal ear.

VISCERAL RECEPTORS

A. General visceral group.

13. Organs of hunger. The stimulus is strong periodic contractions of the muscles of the stomach.

14. Organs of thirst. The stimulus is probably drying of mucous membrane of the pharynx, together with more general conditions.

15. Organs of nausea. The stimulus is probably an antiperistaltic reflex in the digestive tract.

16. Organs of respiratory sensations, suffocation, etc. Organs not well known.

17. Organs of circulatory sensations, flushing, heart panics, etc.

18. Organs of sexual sensations.

19. Organs of sensations of distension of cavities.

20. Organs of visceral pain.

21. Organs of obscure abdominal sensations associated with strong emotion, characterized (probably correctly) by the ancients by such expressions as "yearning of the bowels," etc.

B. Special visceral group.

22. Organs of taste.

23. Organs of smell. Smell is both a visceral and a somatic sense; its organs are both interoceptors and exteroceptors in Sherrington's sense.

SOMATIC EFFECTORS

Striated skeletal muscles of somatic type, with "motor end-plates" of nerves.

VISCERAL EFFECTORS

Involuntary visceral muscles of the digestive tract, blood-vessels, heart, etc. Glands.

Special striated visceral muscles of the head.

CHAPTER IV

COMPARATIVE REVIEW OF RECEPTORS

The senses of man and other animals — Organs of vision — The pineal eye — Invertebrate eyes — The skin as a photoreceptor — The origin of vertebrate eyes — Organs of hearing — Organs of smell — The vomeronasal organ — Organs of taste — General chemical sensibility — Kinesthetic and allied sensibility — Sense organs as windows of the mind.

The senses of man and other animals. — We know more about the human sense organs than about those of any other animals, first, because more attention has been paid to their anatomy and physiology and, second, because in the case of most of them we have direct subjective awareness of the results of their excitation. This second source of information is denied to us in the case of all other animals. All normal human eyes and ears are made according to very similar patterns and we have reason to believe by communicating with our fellows that the sensations arising from their excitation are in broad lines similar amongst all people. The brutes are unable to communicate to us any so direct information regarding their own subjective experiences and so we are obliged to depend almost exclusively upon evidence derived from anatomical structure and analysis of their objective behavior.[1]

So far as the eyes and ears of dogs, birds, fishes and insects are structurally similar to our own we may assume as a working hypothesis that their functions are similar. But these structures are in no cases identical with the human patterns and the physiological controls necessary to determine just what their functions are offer experimental problems of great difficulty. Our knowledge of the sensory physiology of animals other than man is so meager that it is difficult to picture to ourselves in what kind of a world these animals live, so far as their awareness of it goes, and in the case of the more lowly forms we can only conjecture whether they have any subjective experience at all.

In this chapter we shall pass in review a few illustrations of the sensory equipment of animals, illustrative samples merely of a very diverse

[1] For summaries of progress in this field see the works of Harris (1904), Hess (1912), Jennings (1906), G. L. Johnson (1901), Kafka (1914), Mast (1911), McIndoo (1922), Oppel (1896–1914), Pütter (1911), Sloanaker (1897), Vincent (1912), Washburn (1908), Watson (1914).

28

assortment of sense organs, some of which differ so widely from our own that we are quite unable to imagine just what functions they serve.

Few people question that man's most familiar friend among the brutes, the dog, who lives in the same houses with us, eats the same food, shares so largely in our daily occupations, and apparently has so sympathetic an understanding of our desires, moods and purposes, has conscious experiences which in some measure are coextensive with our own. But the dog looks at his world through different eyes from ours, he listens through different ears, and above all, nature as revealed to him through the olfactory sense includes realms of experience into which man can never hope to penetrate.

Organs of vision. — The eyes of the dog give to him sometimes a more intelligent expression than that of his master, and there is no doubt that he uses them to very good advantage; but they are not our eyes. The most careful experiments so far made fail to give any evidence that the dog possesses true color vision and his powers of discriminating visually any fine details of form are limited. He is sensitive to differences in form and size of objects, to differences in shading and illumination and to movement. His seeing, in short, resembles that of the margin of the human retina more closely than that of our acute foveal vision.

All mammals below the primates lack the human type of retinal macula lutea and fovea, that spot of most acute vision upon which is focussed the image of every object to which we closely attend. Mott (1907, p. 40) has called particular attention to the correlation between the differentiation of the fovea and of the hand in primates, and of both of these with a focal length of the eye for most acute vision just within the reach of the hand. This again brings into sharp relief the important part which the hand has played in preparing the way for the emergence of man from the anthropoid stock — the hand not merely as organ of prehension (for this function is shared by the foot in all anthropoids), but especially as an instrument of fine manipulation and skilled movements permitting correlations of eye and hand impossible and unnecessary when the fore limb is primarily an organ of locomotion. This in turn has influenced the course of differentiation of the cerebral cortex, for intentional control (of human type) of the delicate movements involved in the fabrication of shelters, tools and clothing must accompany the use of the hand as the executive organ, and until cortical structure has advanced beyond the pithecoid stage the powers of hand and eye are limited to the brutish level (Elliot Smith, 1912).

Studies on visual discrimination of animals are very numerous, but the difficulties in the way of a correct interpretation of the observed results have only recently been fully appreciated. Yerkes and Watson (1911; see also Watson, 1914, Chap. 3) have constructed a very complex apparatus designed to give monochromatic spectral light under controlled conditions of brightness, etc., for use in such studies; but as yet few experiments have been made with this or any other device adapted to overcome the obstacles inherent in any attempt to analyze color discrimination in animals. A notable step in advance has recently been taken by Hamilton (1922).

The sight of some birds is unquestionably more acute than our own, their powers of accommodation for distance being especially remark-

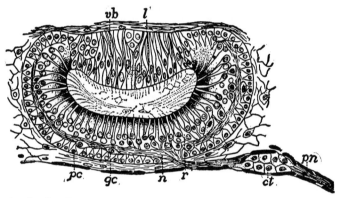

Fig. 2.—Section through the pineal eye of a lizard (Anguis fragilis): *ct*, connective tissue cells around the parietal nerve; *gc*, ganglion cells of the retina; *l*, lens; *n*, nerve fibers; *pc*, pigment cells; *pn*, parietal nerve from pineal eye to brain; *r*, retinal cells; *vb*, vitreous body. After Nowikoff.

able. The eyeball of birds of prey is strengthened by cartilaginous supports in the sclera and otherwise modified so as to give an astonishing range of accommodation. Birds in general have a retinal fovea, and in some species there are two. The visual acuity of the domestic fowl as measured by pattern discrimination appears to be distinctly inferior (Johnson, 1914, Bingham, 1922). Birds have been shown by adequate physiological tests to possess color discrimination, as also have fishes, though less rigorously.

The pineal eye. — The pineal body is present in more or less rudimentary form in nearly all vertebrates (the Crocodilia form an exception). In most of our common species of lizards it retains what was apparently its primitive function as a photoreceptor (Fig. 2), and in a few groups of fishes less well formed pineal eyes are present. The parietal eye of the New Zealand lizard, Sphenodon, is more perfectly formed than in most other reptiles (Dendy, 1910), having especially well developed retina, lens and nerve.

The pineal eye is fundamentally different from the lateral eyes (which are also present) in both embryological development and adult structure. It is located under the skin in the midline at the top of the head. In living species it is probably incapable of forming a clear image, though doubtless sensitive to changes in illumination. The history of its rise in ancestral vertebrates, its relation to the lateral eyes, and its subsequent decline in recent geological times, has not as yet been deciphered.

Invertebrate eyes. — Among the invertebrates there are many kinds of eyes, none of which are of the vertebrate type. The very efficient eyes of the squid and octopus resemble superficially vertebrate eyes, but internally they are of very different structure. Of the other Mollusca some are eyeless, while others have simple eyes placed where they will do the most good, as in snails on the ends of long tentacles or in scallops (Pecten) arranged as a fringe at the border of the mantle which projects beyond the edges of the open shell.

Spiders and insects have simple eyes similar to those of worms. Their focal length is very short, perhaps only an inch or two, and their image-forming powers are slight. The compound faceted eyes of crustaceans and insects are of quite different type, wholly unlike anything else in nature, and evidently they are very efficient. Their focal length is fixed, but apparently the effective range of vision extends to two or three meters. The convex corneal surface is broken up into from 7 to 27,000 lens-like facets, each of which transmits light into a subjacent cylindrical eye element with nerve ending, pigment and other accessories of a visual receptor. It is commonly believed that the image formed is a "mosaic" compounded of the fragments of the visual field received by the separate eye elements. A certain degree of accommodation is effected by migration of the optic pigment and color discrimination is possible (Hamilton, 1922).

The leeches have poorly developed simple eyes; many worms are eyeless yet are sensitive to changes in illumination. In planarian worms there is a pair of eyes (Fig. 35, p. 122) and experiments indicate that the general body surface is also sensitive to light, though less so than are the eyes.

In leeches there are rows of sense organs segmentally arranged along the dorsal aspect of the body. These are small patches of hair-cells which are apparently tactile in function. In Clepsine Whitman

(1892) has described the gradual transition, as the head end of the worm is approached, of these simple sense organs into eyes, the photoreceptive cells appearing among the hair cells, until finally in front the entire organ is enlarged and wholly visual in function. This observation has since been confirmed in a different species of leech by Hachloy (1910).

Many cœlenterates show no reactions to light, though most of the polyps and medusæ are photosensitive to some degree and some medusæ have well formed eyes arranged in series at the margin of the bell superficial to the nerve ring (p. 93). If these organs are removed, light reactions cease.

The skin as a photoreceptor. — In Protozoa, even in ameba where there are no differentiated organs, the general protoplasm is sensitive to light; and in some unicellular forms a special pigmented "eye-spot" is present, facilitating very precise orientation of the body with reference to the direction of illumination. Various unicellular forms, the earthworm, and some other invertebrates have been shown (Mast, 1915), to react in different ways to the several spectral colors. These forms cannot be said to possess color vision, for there is no evidence in the experiments cited that any individual can discriminate between the colors but only that the stimulating efficiency is very much higher in some regions of the spectrum than in others. The species differ greatly among themselves in their sensitivity, the stimulating efficiency being highest in the red in some and in the blue in others.

The skin of many invertebrates is sensitive to light. Even amongst the vertebrates there are many species possessing well developed eyes which also retain a considerable sensitivity to light in the skin (Parker and Burnett, 1900, Parker and Arkin, 1901, Parker, 1903, 1905).

The origin of vertebrate eyes. — Parker (1908) is of the opinion that the vertebrate eyes have not been derived from any form of eye known among the invertebrates, nor by elaboration of the general photic sensitivity of the skin, but that the vertebrate photoreceptors were first differentiated within the central nervous system itself in a transparent animal, an early stage in this process being preserved for us in the pigmented eye-spots found within the spinal cord of Amphioxus (Parker, 1908 a).

There is a pigment spot at the extreme anterior end of the central nervous system of Amphioxus which has been regarded as a light perceiving organ, but the experiments of Parker (1908) and Crozier (1917) have shown that this spot is insensitive to light. The only photoreceptors of Amphioxus are numerous minute pigmented "optic cups" imbedded within the spinal cord (Fig. 3). These are absent in the most rostral segments of the central nervous system and this part of the body is insensitive to light. The skin is insensitive to light throughout. There is, therefore, nothing in Amphioxus comparable with the vertebrate eyes, though Parker is of the opinion that the optic cups represent the organ from which these eyes have been developed.

Hesse (1896) has described in earthworms a transitional form of light receptor which is interesting in this connection. In these worms there are very simple photosensitive cells in the deeper layers of the epidermis. Other similar cells are found immediately under the epidermis and along the nerves as far inward as the brain, within which such cells are also imbedded. He believes that these cells were first differentiated in the epidermis and that some of them have migrated inward as far as the brain. It is not improbable that in the ancestors of Amphioxus a similar history was repeated and that in the living forms of Amphioxus the more superficial cells have disappeared.

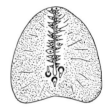

FIG. 3. — Transverse section of the central nervous system of Amphioxus, showing the positions of three pigmented optic cups embedded in the tissue of the spinal cord. Modified from Hesse.

Organs of hearing. —The senses of hearing and touch are physiologically and genetically related. Both are excited by mechanical or mass movements, hearing by vibrations of relatively high frequency and touch by relatively slow vibrations or single impacts. As shown by the table on page 24, the same stimulus may excite both sets of end-organs simultaneously, the analysis of the sensory quality (sound and touch respectively) being effected in the central nervous system.

All mammals have organs of hearing anatomically similar in a general way to those in the human cochlea, but experiments show that their ranges of hearing are in every case different. In fact, there is great variation in this respect among human beings. I well remember sitting at dusk one evening in a mountain cabin with my wife and daughter and three members of the family of Mr. Hall. Bats were flying overhead in and out of the room and one of the Hall children complained of the very disagreeable noise made by the bats. Inquiry revealed that the three members of the Hall family were all annoyed by the shrill piercing squeak of the bats and that the tone was quite inaudible to all of the three members of the Herrick family, though our hearing was regarded as normal and rather more than usually acute within our range.

That dogs have very acute hearing seems evident, and that their endowments in some respects are superior to our own was practically utilized in the late war, when they were employed in the listening posts to detect movements of the enemy before they were audible to their masters. But attempts to verify this conclusion under experimental laboratory conditions have given contradictory results and the matter requires further study.

Experiments made by Hunter (1915) have satisfied him that the white rat is practically insensitive to many tones in the lower region of the scale and that this apparently goes along with a sensitivity to noises of the same predominant pitch. The apparent reactions to tones are made, he believes, to accompanying noises and the rats are deficient in power to discriminate pure tones. The adult dancing mouse seems to be totally deaf (Yerkes, 1907).

Our knowledge of the sense of hearing in animals below mammals is still less precise. In none of these animals is there a spiral organ, or organ of Corti, of mammalian type and the differentiation of a true sense of hearing from tactile and allied forms of sensibility becomes increasingly difficult. Indeed, this distinction probably fades out completely in most, if not all, of the invertebrates.

In fishes, as in men, the ear contains two quite different sense organs — the organ of hearing and the organ of the sense of equilibrium. The latter lies in the semicircular canals, which in form and function are similar to those in the human body. Indeed, the semicircular canals probably play a larger part in the behavior of the fish, since maintaining perfect equilibrium is a more difficult matter for a fish suspended in water of about the same specific gravity as the body than for a man walking on solid ground. But when the man essays to fly, his semicircular canals again take a dominant place in his sensory equipment. In the practical testing of the fitness of men who are candidates for the Air Service of the Army the most important point to be determined is whether the semicircular canals are functioning normally.

Whether fishes hear at all has been hotly controverted. That they are very sensitive to mechanical jars and vibrations all agree, but it has been difficult to prove whether their responses to these vibrations are brought about through their ears or by refined cutaneous sensibility. The experiments of Parker (1918) have shown that both of these organs serve and that, in fact, fishes do hear true sound waves of rather low pitch with their ears. To tones of high pitch they are deaf and probably they have no power of tone analysis, that is, they can hear a noise but cannot tell one tone from another.

The fishes can boast no superiority over ourselves in being able to respond to low tones by both the ear and the skin. We can do the same, as can readily be shown by lightly touching the sounding board of a piano or organ when a low tone is struck. The same tone heard by the ear can be readily felt by the finger tips. But for perceiving still slower vibratory movements we, with all our boasted brain power, must admit ourselves inferior to the fishes. They possess an elaborate system of cutaneous and subcutaneous sense organs of which we have not a vestige. These so-called lateral line organs comprise a complex system of fine tubes under the skin, the lateral line canals and (in some species) ampullæ, and several kinds of sense organs in the skin, the pit organs. The canals ramify in various directions in the head and the main lateral canal extends along the side of the body back to the tail. They were formerly supposed to be for the secretion of mucus and are still often called mucous canals. But they are now known to contain numerous small sense organs which respond to slow vibratory movements of the water. The pit organs are scattered over the skin, the smaller ones each in a flask-shaped pit with a narrow mouth and the less numerous larger ones exposed on the surface.

The lateral line sense organs are all supplied by a single system of nerves related with the nerves of the ear and quite distinct from those for the general tactile and chemical senses of the skin and the cutaneous taste buds. That the lateral line organs respond to slow vibratory movements has been clearly shown by Parker, but the distinctive features of the ampullæ and pit organs are unknown and, in fact, our knowledge of the functions of the system as a whole is still very incomplete.

It is clear that cutaneous organs of touch, lateral line organs, and the organs of equilibrium and hearing in the internal ear form a graded series, and all have probably been derived in evolution from a primitive type of tactile organ. When therefore we both hear and feel a musical tone of the piano we are reminded of the long and dramatic evolutionary history of the very intricate human auditory organs, whose first and last stages both may function at the same time in our own bodies.[1]

The auditory organs of insects have recently been reëxamined by McIndoo (1922). The popular belief that insects can hear has been

[1] The preceding paragraphs are taken, with some modification, from " Natural History," Vol. 19 (Herrick, 1919).

received with much skepticism in scientific circles, for actual proof is very difficult. The evidence seems adequate that some species of insects do respond to vibrations which we can hear, but whether we should say that the insects hear them is perhaps a matter of definition. It should not be forgotten that we ourselves can sense sonorous vibrations with other organs than the ear.

McIndoo has examined all of the five organs of the honey-bee which have been alleged to serve as sound receptors and he finds that none of them seem structurally adapted to perform any function comparable with that of the human ear. He inclines to agree with Forel, who believes that insects do not hear as we do, but that their receptors for sonorous vibrations are more like our tactile organs than our ears. In the case of the supposed auditory organs of lower invertebrates this is still more probable.

Organs of smell. — The analysis of smell, taste and the general chemical senses is difficult even in human experience, and the problems relating to these senses become more and more perplexing the further we go from our own type of organization.

Man and primates generally are microsmatic, and the sense of smell evidently plays a relatively minor rôle in their behavior. Psychologists, however, have made much of the importance of this sense especially as a background of conscious attitudes and dispositions and as a significant component of mental complexes. The more primitive instinctive and impulsive reactions, and particularly those associated with sex, are especially sensitive to olfactory excitations, which seem to have a very strong affective quality. The sense of smell seems to be much more acute in young children and one experienced naturalist is of the opinion that his own experience justifies the statement "that the sense of smell, which seems to diminish as we grow older, until it becomes scarcely worthy to be called a sense, is nearly as keen in little children as in the inferior animals" (Hudson, 1918, p. 7). All of these things suggest a reverberation in human experience of ancestral conditions in which the sense of smell was a more potent factor than it is at the present time with most of us.

If the greatly reduced, almost vestigial, olfactory organs play so large a part in our own experience, we may well believe that the enormously larger apparatus of most other mammals gives them powers far beyond our comprehension. Indeed we have only to follow the course of a good hunting dog to satisfy ourselves that this is the case. With these macrosmatic animals there is not only greatly increased sensitivity to odors, but there are probably qualities of sense quite unrepresented in the human repertoire of olfactory experience.

The vomeronasal organ. — Most of the mammals possess an olfactory organ represented in the human nose only by a functionless rudiment, the vomeronasal organ, or organ of Jacobson. This is present also in reptiles and amphibians, but not in fishes. It is developed as a medial outpouching from the main olfactory chamber. In some cases it retains its connection with the primary chamber; in others it is cut off from it; and in many animals it is in free communication with the mouth cavity, either by a separate duct leading down to the roof of the mouth or by a communication with the posterior nasal aperture. There has been much speculation regarding the function of this peculiar accessory olfactory organ, a question which cannot be answered by appeal to our own sensory experience.

The recent observations of Broman (1920) and others seem to indicate that it serves primarily as a mouth-smelling organ, that is, it is adapted to smell the food after it has been taken into the mouth. This is supported by a number of interesting anatomical facts. In the first place, the apparatus is absent in fishes, where the posterior nasal aperture (choana) between nasal and buccal chambers is not present. It appears in the most primitive air breathers (tailed Amphibia) in very rudimentary condition and assumes its definitive form in the frog. Broman declares that its cavity is normally filled with liquid, not air like the main nasal chamber (though Parker, 1922, p. 100, says this is not the case in some mammals), and in many species there are various devices for pumping the fluids of the mouth cavity or nose into the vomeronasal chamber where their ordorous emanations are sensed. In some mammals fluids bathing the respiratory (non-olfactory) epithelium of the nasal cavity are pumped into the vomeronasal organ, the supposition being that odorous emanations brought in by the inspired air are taken up by this fluid, concentrated by evaporation during the passage of the respiratory air currents, and then forced into the vomeronasal organ, which is thus enabled to sense odors far too feeble to be adequate stimuli for the ordinary olfactory epithelium.

In serpents Broman finds that each vomeronasal cavity opens by a separate duct into the roof of the mouth and that the tips of the forked tongue enter these ducts. It is commonly believed that snakes use the tongue as a tactile organ as well as an organ of taste, and this observation suggests that they also use the tongue as an accessory olfactory organ. The protruded tongue, coming in contact with odorous substances or absorbing these from the air, is drawn in and inserted into the vomeronasal ducts, thus carrying the stimulus directly to the receptive organ. This interpretation offers a plausible explanation for the very large vomeronasal organs of serpents and also for their peculiar forked tongues.

There are other features of the vomeronasal organ which are of considerable interest from the standpoint of behavior. With it is connected a separate portion of the olfactory nerve, the vomeronasal nerve, which discharges centrally into a distinct part of the olfactory bulb, known for a long time as the accessory bulb. It has recently been shown (Herrick, 1921 a) that in the frog the tracts leading inward from the accessory bulb take a very different course from those derived from the remainder of the olfactory bulb. The latter are widely distributed throughout the cerebral hemispheres, but those from the accessory bulb transmit the excitations arising in the vomeronasal organ to a definite region in the ventro-lateral wall of the hemisphere which is regarded as the precursor of the mammalian amygdala lying under the temporal lobe of the cortex. Here the vomeronasal excitations are brought into physiological correlation with related gustatory, tactile and other systems and integrated into definite behavior patterns. The differentiation of the vomeronasal organ seems to have played a very significant rôle in the elaboration of the internal structural patterns of the cerebral hemispheres in air breathing vertebrates, but of the details of this history we have only very fragmentary knowledge.

In our own experience, in the absence of a vomeronasal organ, we are unable to distinguish subjectively the flavors of food sensed by the taste buds from odorous emanations passing from it through the posterior apertures into the nasal cavities where they are sensed by the organs of smell. In fact, we know from physiological experimentation that the true tastes are limited to the four qualities, sweet, sour, salty and bitter, and that the other so-called flavors are really odors. For this reason if the olfactory apparatus is out of commission, as when one is suffering from a severe head cold, we say, "all food tastes alike," simply because its olfactory qualities are shut out. An efficient vomeronasal apparatus probably eliminates this confusion and permits much more precise separation of the odors-from-a-distance from the mouth-smelling function.

Fishes, of course, receive their olfactory stimuli through the water.[1] In the transition to air breathing no fundamental change in the ol-

[1] On the olfactory organs of fishes, see page 182.

factory receptors is necessary, for in air breathers the olfactory medium is still liquid, since odorous substances must first be dissolved in the fluids of the nose before they can be sensed. There is little support for the idea of Broman that the vomeronasal organ is the direct survivor of the water-smelling apparatus of fishes. It seems, rather, to have been developed as a special adaptation for mouth-smelling in correlation with the opening of the posterior nasal aperture in land animals. In mammals, like the whales and seals, which have returned to life in the sea the olfactory apparatus does not return to the fish-like condition. Differentiation for air-smelling has gone too far in another direction and the olfactory organs simply atrophy, even to complete obliteration in the dolphin. The vomeronasal organ disappears with the rest of the system.

Organs of taste. — Taste in all animals is the sense to guard the entrance to the digestive tract, giving warning of inedible or noxious substances in the food and passing on with approval those which conform to the physiological requirements of the species. So far as this function is concerned, there is considerable uniformity among the different groups of vertebrates. Naturally in cases like the seed-eating birds, where tasteless food is swallowed without mastication, the selection of food must be made chiefly in terms of other senses and taste is accordingly reduced.

Conversely in certain fishes, especially bottom feeders like carp and catfish, taste is invoked to assist in the selection of food both within the mouth and before it has been apprehended (Herrick, 1903). The thread-like barbels around the mouth of the catfish and the filiform pectoral fins of the tomcod are trailed on the bottom, and both of these appendages are richly supplied with both tactile and gustatory nerve endings which coöperate in the selection of food. In the catfish and carp, moreover, there are taste buds freely distributed over the entire body surface. Unlike the allegation made of some people, their taste is not all in their mouths. In the carp the gustatory centers of the brain are larger than those of all other senses combined (p. 185).

General chemical sensibility. — The region of the nose is supplied by two other nerves in addition to those already mentioned, the trigeminus and the nervus terminalis. The terminal nerve is present in all types of vertebrates, though usually very small, and it is quite distinct from all of the others mentioned. Since its functions are unknown (even in man, where it is fairly well developed), it will not be further considered here. The trigeminus, or fifth cranial nerve, mediates general tactile and chemical sensitivity (especially to irritating substances) of the olfactory and respiratory epithelium of the nasal chamber.

There are three chemical senses, smell, taste, and general chemical sensitivity without specialized end-organs. The last is feebly represented in man, but very highly developed on the moist body surfaces of many lower animals. In the dogfish, for instance, Sheldon (1909) found that the skin where there are no taste buds is more sensitive to certain chemicals than are the taste buds themselves. In aquatic animals with moist skins this general chemical sensivity is widespread.

In some fishes the surface of the body is extremely sensitive to the slight electric currents set up when a metal object immersed in water is brought near. A catfish will react to the presence of rods of various metals several centimeters from the surface of the body. Parker and Van Heusen (1917) are of the opinion that these reactions are mediated by the cutaneous taste buds of this animal, a plausible conjecture though lacking experimental proof.

The three chemical senses have some features in common, but their differences are far more noteworthy. The olfactory end-organ is a very special epithelial cell in the mucous membrane of the nose whose inner end is directly extended without a break in protoplasmic continuity into the olfactory center of the brain. In the taste buds there are special epithelial receptive cells around which are wrapped the terminal filaments of the nerve fibers which lead the nervous impulses inward to the gustatory center of the brain. The apparatus involves two cells, a receptor and a conductor. The nerves of general chemical sensibility end in the deeper layers of the skin of fishes and mucous membranes of man, where there are no epithelial cells specially differentiated as receptors. These relations are shown diagrammatically in Fig. 4.

Centrally these three systems of nerves connect within the brain with wholly different types of correlation mechanisms far separated from each other. In the olfactory centers there are several different forms of apparatus for the intensification and summation of the excitations (p. 264) which are not represented in the centers of the other two chemical senses.

In view of these structural features it is not surprising to learn experimentally that the sensory threshold is high for general chemical sensibility, lower for taste, and still lower for smell. Ethyl alcohol is an adequate stimulus for all these organs in man and it has been found (Parker, 1922, p. 171) that if the dilution which will just stimulate the olfactory organ be expressed as unity, the concentration necessary to stimulate the organs of taste is 24,000 times as strong, and that to stimulate the general chemical nerve endings is 80,000 times as strong.

The chemical senses have recently been reviewed in a comprehensive way by Parker (1922). I have dwelt upon them here because they well illustrate some of the problems by which the student of behavior is confronted in his attempt to analyze the receptors of the

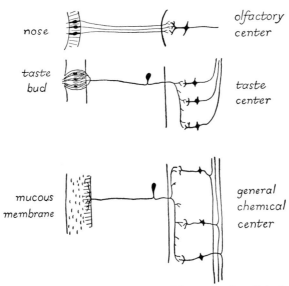

Fig. 4.—Diagram of the nervous connections of the organs of smell, taste and general chemical sensibility. The olfactory nerve fibers are direct continuations of the excited sensory cells; in taste buds the sensory cells do not give rise directly to the nerve fibers; in the mucous membrane there are no specialized receptive cells for the general chemical sense. These features are correlated with the extreme delicacy of smell as compared with taste and of taste as compared with general chemical sensibility.

animals under observation. Olfactory reactions prove to be especially difficult to study under laboratory conditions and our knowledge of the comparative physiology of this sense is still meager. The analysis of the peripheral receptors in the nose related with the trigeminus, the terminal nerve, the vomeronasal nerve and the olfactory nerve must be carried much further before an adequate study of the behavior related to these end-organs can be prosecuted. In this connection it must constantly be borne in mind that the olfactory organ is both a distance receptor of somatic or exteroceptive type and a visceral receptor of interoceptive type. The response naturally will be very different depending on whether one or both of these functions is acting.

Taste, as has just been pointed out, though typically interoceptive, may in some species of fishes also serve as an exteroceptor in the search for food. These cases illustrate the difficulty of applying rigid physiological or morphological criteria in the analysis of complex behavior and at the same time the advantage of such general schemata in the formulation of problems and the methods to be sought in their solution.

Kinesthetic and allied sensibility. — Study of the behavior of many animals whose eyes and ears are notably inferior to our own has revealed the importance, hitherto unsuspected, of a group of sensations which with us scarcely come into clear consciousness at all. Sensations of movement, posture and orientation of the body play a larger part than we formerly supposed in human life; but these are so intimately bound up with reflex adjustments of a very primitive sort as rarely to require attentive control by the focal consciousness. Their importance as components of the mental background and substratum, however, can hardly be overestimated.

In the experimental analysis of the behavior of the white rat it was found that the daily lives of these animals seem to be but little affected by the loss of all of the leading distance receptors — eyes, nose and ears. Watson, whose experiments most clearly brought to light this startling result, says (1914, p. 430): "If we made the statement that all of the work upon habit formation in all of the behavior laboratories (excepting the studies upon birds) points to the fact that the kinesthetic sense is the most important system of receptors, and yet that there was not one single thing that we could say about this sense in isolation, paradoxical as it might seem, it would not be far from the truth."

The visceral sensations, since the recognition by James and Lange of their importance in emotion, have received more and more attention, a consideration which is abundantly justified. These "intimate senses" (Starbuck, 1921) unquestionably share with the kinesthetic group in laying the basic organic foundation for the physiological superstructure and for many higher mental processes as well. But it should not be forgotten that, though fundamental, they do not themselves form the superstructure of either body or mind. Certain schools of physicians, in particular, have gone to so great extreme in their emphasis on "vegetative neurology" as almost to lead one to think that these faddists regard the brain, and indeed the entire central nervous system, as merely a sort of appendage to the gut and the ductless glands.

Sense organs as windows of the mind.— Attention has already been called to the fact that there is nothing in our experience, there are no mental powers, no skill in ratiocination or logical analysis, no capacity to forecast future events, no flights of imaginative fancy, which do not depend directly or indirectly upon sensory data. The mind of man is truly creative in the sense that new and hitherto unimagined ideas are fabricated, for the elements of experience can be recombined in new patterns. But the inventiveness of genius, whether dealing with material contrivances or with the less tangible whimsies of art and phantasy, can operate only with stuffs provided, in last analysis, through sense experience. We surpass the brutes in our capacity to use the data so provided and to supplement our limited and in some cases defective sense organs by artificial aids, such as spectacles and microscopes, but never can our thinking transcend the realm of sense experience. The most abstruse metaphysical speculation, in common with the highest flight of poetic fancy and the keenest esthetic appreciation, are earth-bound within the limits set by our physical sensory equipment.

The widening of experience by artificial aids to the senses, by travel and by discipline of the powers of observation, attention, reasoning and appreciation makes for fuller and richer life. This is education. What the result would be were our eyes like those of the eagle, our olfactory sense as keen as the dog's, our bodies sensitive to Hertzian waves, x-rays and the like and to other forms of energy manifestations perhaps as yet totally unknown to us — in what kind of a world we would live under these circumstances and what sort of minds we would have, it is beyond our power to imagine. And yet every infra-human organism differs from us in his sensory equipment more or less in these ways. The problems of human psychology are too difficult for us, even with the aid of the most refined and highly trained introspective analysis. The problems of animal psychology increase in difficulty in proportion as animals' sensori-motor organization differs from our own.

Even with the aid of language, facial expression, and gesture, we are able to communicate our ideas and feelings to our intimate friends only imperfectly, and this difficulty is multiplied many fold when we try to understand even the most intelligent of the brutes. The only recourse is to see how an animal behaves in a given situation and then in the light of what we know of human and animal bodily structure and function try to imagine how we would think in such a situation, taking into account the animal's limitations of nervous organization. Obviously this is a poor and uncertain method at best, and no wonder many psychologists have given up the problem in despair and decided that the only scientific procedure is to pay no attention to animals' minds and limit our inquiry to their objective behavior. Indeed, so impressed are some of them by the futility of scientific study of even the human mind by introspection that they advocate throwing overboard the whole science of introspective psychology. But this is too much like sinking the ship, cargo and all, to get rid of the rats.

No, if we wish to attain the heights of a true understanding of the significance of mind in evolution, we must keep to the steep trail and not yield to the temptation to take smoother paths leading to the rest shelters by the way. But we must watch our steps. By this I mean that, although we can interpret the animal mind only in terms of our own experience, yet we must not uncritically read our thoughts and feelings back into animals' minds. The only safe rule is to assume that an animal acts reflexly or unconsciously except when it can be shown that the unconscious mechanisms are inadequate to account for the behavior and intelligence alone is adequate. And these are very difficult things to prove in regard to animals so far removed from us in behavior type as are the fishes.

The popular dramatization of animal life and imputation to them of human thoughts and feelings may have a certain justification for literary or pedagogic purposes, the same as other fairy stories. But let it not be forgotten that this is fiction for children, not science nor the foundation for science; and there is a long, long road to travel before we shall be able to understand in any but the most shadowy outlines what a fish's mind is really like.

CHAPTER V

THE VITAL ENERGIES

Sources of vital energy — Intrinsic and integrative functions — Stimulus and response — Excitation and conduction — Dominance and subordination of parts — Mechanisms of growth and differentiation — Young, mature and senile tissues — Conclusion

Sources of vital energy. — The receptors, as we have seen, are the windows of the mind; they also serve the much more fundamental function of portals through which the manifold energies of surrounding nature penetrate within the body and are there transformed for its own uses. They are, in a manner of speaking, the push-buttons by which the vital circuits are activated.

The history of the further transformations of the energies of these excitations comprises the whole story of animal behavior. In reading this story it is important, not only to begin at the beginning of the individual reaction process, that is, the receptive end of the reflex arc, but also to turn back to the earliest recognizable stages of the historical development of the mechanisms of excitation and response. A brief survey of some recently formulated laws of behavior of protoplasm in its simpler forms, and presumably of primitive evolutionary type, will clarify the later discussion of the more complex neuromotor systems of higher animals.

The environmental adjustments within whose frame the vital processes are set are of two sorts. First, there is the material exchange, typified by food eaten and excretions eliminated; and, second, there is energy exchange, the energies coming in partly in latent form as chemical reserves of food consumed and partly as direct dynamic impact upon body surfaces. These two forms of energy intake are closely related, for even the ingestion of food, drink and respiratory gases is under closely guarded control of reflex mechanisms whose activities are released by triggers set in the sensory surfaces and whose driving force comes, in turn, from the latent energies of the substances assimilated.

Some of the energy released during bodily function is returned to the environment as heat and other forms of vegetative activity, but the part in which students of behavior have shown especial interest is returned as bodily movement. Energies derived from consumption of food taken and those resulting from the direct impinging of stimuli upon the receptive organs are converged into the organs of response and it is a fundamental problem of physiology to follow the courses of these two streams of energy, of so diverse origin and *modus operandi*, to their final conjoint expression in behavior.

On the energy flux in organisms see Lotka, 1922, 1922 a, and the works there cited.

The interesting discussion of the second law of thermodynamics by Johnstone (1921) leaves the biologist somewhat confused. The first of these laws states that the energy content of the universe is a constant quantity (law of conservation of energy). The second law recites, in effect, that "free" energy which is capable of doing useful work tends to change into "bound" energy without practical efficiency. Thus, if a hot body lies in contact with a cold body the energy as it passes from the first to the second is capable of doing work, but when the heat of the two bodies has been equalized the power to do work is lost, though the total amount of energy has not been changed. This passage of free energy into the more stable, or bound, condition is known as entropy.

In Johnstone's consideration of the relations of vital processes to the second law of thermodynamics one may readily accept the two main conclusions (p. 221): (1) "Our inorganic concept is, therefore, *the entropy of the universe tends toward a maximum value.*" (2) "*In living processes the increase of entropy is retarded* — this is our 'vital' concept." But that the retardation of the general process of levelling down of free or available energy into more stable forms (entropy) is characteristic of vital functions exclusively is obviously not true. If cold iron is struck repeatedly by a hammer, its temperature rises locally and its available free energy is increased. According to Chamberlin's planetesimal hypothesis the free radiant energy of the sun and other heavenly bodies has been increased by an analogous process — the impact of cold solid masses raises their temperature. The radiant energy of the sun falling upon the ocean lifts its water to the clouds, thereby giving it capacity to do additional work as falling rain and eroding streams.

These are local and transient retardations of entropy; so also are the vital functions. The plant body uses the energy of solar radiation to build starch out of carbon dioxid and water, thus transforming inert materials into a substance of high calorific value and obviously reversing locally and temporarily the process of entropy. The bodies of lower animals have less of this power of synthesizing unstable organic compounds capable of delivering large amounts of energy directly from inert inorganic materials than have those of plants; but they can fabricate from vegetable organic products still more complex and unstable substances of high energy value. And what is still more important, the available energy released within the animal body during the consumption of these complex substances is delivered in different patterns from those found in plant bodies — patterns that we call higher behavior (p. 15), such as locomotion, tropisms, adaptive reflexes, etc. The retardation of the entropy here, as elsewhere, involves a factor of pattern of energy change as well as the merely quantitative factors of the equations of energetics.

Furthermore, and this I take to be the main point of Johnstone's argument, each local and transient reversal of entropy of the inorganic type is self-limiting; it tends to run down, to wear out, and ultimately ceases to operate, with restoration of a lower level of equilibrium of available energy. The normal entropy again operates. But in organisms the machinery for reversal of entropy, that is for building up complexes of higher potential energy and making some part of this energy available for doing work, is self-propagating; the animal and plant kingdoms in the aggregate tend toward increased efficiency in the capture and utilization of low-level energies. These are first stepped up to higher levels (potential energies of complex protoplasmic organization and protoplasmic products) and then the energies released by the break-down of these organizations are utilized (in part) for the continuance and elaboration of the processes of life.

This progressive change in the amount of reversal of entropy and the consequent increment in the magnitude of the energy flux in the realm of living things is organic evolution in its energetic aspects (cf. Lotka, 1922). Bound up with this strictly quantitative aspect is the factor of pattern of the energy changes, and in this respect too there is evolutionary progress, for the quantitative increment is effected not merely by increase in the number or size of existing organisms, but chiefly by progressive diversification of their structural and functional patterns, that is, by the development of the higher life.

Now in man the reversal of entropy reaches its highest expression in intelligent behavior. In his body the patterns of energy discharge include, not only locomotion, reflex, instinct and other adaptive physiological reactions, but also a large measure of ability to modify behavior in terms of individual experience — habit, docility, intelligence, inventiveness, and the forecast of future events.

The human body has the capacity to synthesize very complex tissues from simpler organic and inorganic materials physiologically. The human chemist can in the laboratory synthesize a large number of highly unstable substances experimentally from inorganic materials. He can make certain kinds of sugar from carbon dioxid and water, utilizing the energy of ultraviolet light. He can fabricate explosives and many other compounds of high energy value which are unknown in inorganic nature. The engineer can design water wheels, engines, dynamos and countless other devices for increasing the available energy. All of these processes are local and temporary reversals of the universal process of entropy. And the measure of human control over nature (including his own self-control) may be expressed very largely in terms of his ability to reverse entropy and to determine the patterns in which the energy thus made available shall be expended. This is creative intelligence.

All this follows *naturally* from Johnstone's two laws as formulated above. But this author, like Bergson and many others, cannot see that it does follow naturally. They are constrained to invoke metaphysical principles — categories, intuitions, élan vital, entelechy, or whatever — which immediately carry the discussion into realms where the biologist cannot follow.

This is really quite unnecessary; in fact, it robs the biologist of a great wealth of factual knowledge — the entire fruits of introspective experience and the psychic life — which is legitimate material for his own use if only he will reach out and take it. Introspective psychology has much of value to offer to biology (*cf.* Herrick, 1915). If we recognize that consciousness (awareness) is a function of the body, as many physiologists do (*e. g.*, Bianchi, 1922), then the reversal of entropy, that is the local and transient increase in available energy, brought about by human artifice takes its place in the natural order along with other vital functions and the simpler inorganic processes mentioned at the beginning of this note. And there is no assignable limit to which this increase in the "free" or available energy of living bodies can go as long as life endures in our world.

We are dealing here with the *process* of living as we see it and no attempt is made to follow the process through to its final stages. These lie beyond the biologist's immediate horizon. It is clear that this process of reversal of the cosmic trend toward final degradation of all "free" or available energy has been growing progressively more efficient during the entire period of organic evolution, for animals and plants are in the aggregate to-day appropriating for their own use far more inorganic energy and they are utilizing this energy more effectively for their own advantage than were their ancestors whose fossil remains are preserved for us in the palæozoic rocks which were laid down upwards of 520,000,000 years ago. Living is on a higher plane in that organisms are subjugating and controlling natural forces in a larger and more diversified way. Organic evolution in the past has been on the whole progressive in this sense, and there are no indications of any change in this tendency in the immediate future. What the ultimate result may be some millions of years hence need not vex the spirit of the biologists of our generation.

Since this note was written, Eve (1923) has published a fascinating and stimulating survey of this field which points the way to a genuine understanding of the origins of the vital energies. He introduces two useful new terms. By *katergy* he means "the flow of energy to a lower potential or level," that is, entropy. By *anergy* he means "the flow of energy to a higher potential," that is, reversal of entropy. Emphasis is laid upon the presence of anergy in inorganic nature along lines somewhat similar to those developed above, and among organisms the green plants are cited as conspicuous mechanisms of anergic activity.

The argument then proceeds — "Animals, when fully grown, are mostly katergizers of food; whereas plants are simultaneously katergizers of sunlight and anergizers of food. Hence we estimate the vitality of an animal chiefly by its activities (katergy), and of a plant chiefly by its growth (anergy)." This statement may be accepted as true (broadly) of plants and lower animals, but the argument stops too near the beginning and falls far short of an adequate evaluation of the energy changes in higher animals. For the most distinctive feature of the animal kingdom (especially in its higher realms) is the ability to consume the materials elaborated by plants and to utilize the energy thus made available in part in the ordinary processes of living (katergy) and in part in the fabrication of protoplasmic tissues of still higher potentiality (anergy), whose ultimate expenditure expresses itself in living on higher planes than any plants can ever attain.

Animals utilize the energy reserves which have been built up by plants and stored away as food materials, and in their own activities they further extend the anergic process by the elaboration of nervous systems and the other apparatus of very complex behavior, whose potentialities when realized in the functioning of these highly differentiated tissues return the energy to a lower level as mass movement, heat, and other inorganic forms of activity. And in mankind this final katergic process, in turn, is adapted to step up lower energies to the plane of intelligent adjustment, setting them to work to invent and run machines, to maintain commerce and all of the other varied industries necessary to advance personal and social welfare, much as in a lower realm an electric transformer may take the energy supplied by the dynamo and step it up into a current of higher potential better adapted to do the work of some particular machine.

This progressive increase in anergic efficiency is "creative evolution," which in our time shows no signs of abatement.

Intrinsic and integrative functions. — In differentiated organisms the physical and chemical processes involved in the maintenance of the tissues, in muscular contraction and secretion are essentially local in their manifestations. These are the processes of growth, differentiation of the specific tissues, and the performance of the particular functions appropriate to these tissues. They are concerned largely with the up-keep of the bodily protoplasmic organization, including its nutrition, repair, elimination of waste products, and reproduction. Moreover, every living body shows more or less physiological division of labor, each part with a specific function (contraction, secretion, etc.) and a corresponding specific protoplasmic structure. The body is composed, as Ritter (1919) says, not of protoplasm, but of a large number of specific protoplasms; and the maintenance of the body involves an exceedingly complex interrelation of many systems of diverse chemical reactions, each kind of tissue characterized by chemical processes of building up of specific protoplasmic structure and consumption of this material in its normal functional activity in a different way from every other kind of tissue (Child, 1924, Chap. 2).

The most obvious feature of these specific functions is exchange of material between the organism as a whole and its environment or between the particular kinds of protoplasm of which it is composed and the body fluids in which they are immersed. This material exchange is almost always effected by means of chemical reactions. The chemical reactions in which protoplasm takes part in the aggregate are termed metabolism; accordingly, the intrinsic functions are conspicuously metabolic activities. Their most significant feature in the present connection is the specificity to which reference has been made;

that is, each kind of protoplasm has its own distinctive kind of metabolism. For instance, muscle and gland tissue each has a characteristic chemical composition and structural arrangement. Each assimilates different nutritive materials from the surrounding lymph, builds them up into its own appropriate protoplasmic structure, and during function eliminates particular kinds of waste products.

In addition to these intrinsic functions of the tissues there are those concerned with the maintenance of the integrity of the body as a whole and the unification of its multifarious activities. The mechanisms employed here are various, including transportation of materials from place to place (for discussion of the transportative functions see Child, 1924, Chap. 5) and especially the apparatus of excitation and conduction. It is to this last that our attention here will be especially directed, for the phenomena of excitation and conduction are basic in all behavior.[1]

The relation between the intrinsic functions and the integrative may be crudely illustrated by the plan of an electrically operated factory. The electric energy supplied may be transmitted to the operating machines directly as such or it may be first transformed into mechanical energy and transmitted by shafting, pulley belts or compressed air. The transmitting mechanisms in the aggregate, with the associated automatic regulators, governors, switch-boards, fuse-boxes, transformers, etc., knit the operations of the entire plant together so that the total available energy yields the desired manufactured product with minimum expenditure of energy and material. This phase of factory organization is comparable with the integrative functions of the living body.

In our analogy the processes of excitation and conduction may be compared with the generation and transmission of the electric current in the factory. The electric energy is the essential thing; the way in which it is generated is immaterial. Given electricity in sufficient amount from any source whatever, the plant will operate. And, again, what kind of work it will do is not determined by the kind of electric current supplied, but upon the construction of the conductors, transformers, motors, etc., and the kinds of machinery into which they deliver their energy. The electric currents transmitted over the feed wires are not necessarily identical, some may be strong, some

---

[1] Ritter (1919) has discussed the integrative functions under the caption, "The Organismal Conception of Life." Child (1921, 1924) draws a distinction between "protoplasmic" and "organismic" functions which differs in some respects from both Ritter's usage and the one here employed. See also Lillie (1923, Chap. 12).

weak, some of high voltage, some low; and the construction of the electric equipment is nicely adapted to the load to be carried and the purposes for which it is employed. Yet the electric energy is fundamentally the same throughout and is clearly different from all other forces employed in the factory.

So in the living body the processes of excitation and conduction are all of like fundamental type, regardless of the specific protoplasmic activities from which their energies are derived and maintained, of differences in the intensity of the process, rate of conduction and range of action, and of the nature of the responses by which they are externally manifested.

Stimulus and response. — The morning glory blossom opens in the sun and closes in the rain, an ameba approaches a food object and devours it but retreats from an injurious excitation, a child reaches out his hand toward the candle flame but withdraws it instantly when burned and thereafter may shrink away in terror at first sight of the pretty flame.[1] These and countless other instances of adaptive reactions show that all protoplasm is irritable; the response to irritation may be a seeking reaction or an avoiding reaction and in the broad view the organism will react in the way which best fits the situation from the standpoint of its own welfare, or if an error is once made it is less likely to be committed on repetition of the stimulus.

Given an adequate understanding of the reactions mentioned in the preceding paragraph and the foundation is laid for the entire program of this work. Unfortunately such an understanding is not yet within our grasp. The mechanism of the simplest protoplasmic reaction to excitation is to-day as profound a mystery as is that of any complex cortical association center — and the solution of the latter problem is likely to come by way of the former.

From this it should not be inferred that we know nothing about the mechanisms employed in these reactions. The fact is, we know a great deal about the cortical association centers as well as of the structure and functions of the ameba; and it is becoming increasingly probable that essentially similar biochemical and biophysical processes lie at the basis of all forms of excitation and response from the lowest to the highest. Our first inquiry is for these common proc-

---

[1] The most satisfactory experimental study of this reaction to the flame is given by Watson (1919, p. 278). In very young children (150 to 220 days) the avoiding reaction seems to be very slowly built up, as in lower animals. In older children it may appear after the first injurious stimulus.

esses and later, having brought some of them to view, we shall see how they are related among themselves and to other bodily processes in the fabrication of the life patterns of the higher animals.

First of all, it should be frankly recognized that much of fundamental importance for a true understanding of the nervous functions is quite out of our reach at present. The exact protoplasmic mechanisms by which the physical energies playing in the world about are transformed into vital processes of nervous or "neuroid" type remains obscure. Again, the problem of the mechanism of biological adaptation has not even been satisfactorily formulated; naturally the solution is not yet in sight. How the organism is able to respond at all, as indicated in the preceding paragraph, is not yet perfectly clear; and we are still further from an understanding of the way it can make the appropriate, that is the most beneficial or "adaptive," response to excitation and refrain from all other possible reactions. What constitutes the physiological difference between a seeking reaction and an avoiding reaction, why one and not the other is exhibited after a particular excitation, why and how "the burned child dreads the fire," what is the mechanism of inhibition — these and hosts of related problems are still far from solution.[1]

On the other hand, it is possible to present experimental evidence which points the way to the formulation of a few simple laws in accordance with which the processes of excitation and conduction are maintained within protoplasm. Some laws of protoplasmic transmission have been discovered; and since conduction is the basic function of the nervous system, even in its highest and most complex processes, the discovery of these laws in a first step of considerable importance in the direction of analysis of the activities of the nervous systems of higher animals.[2]

[1] Sumner (1919), Conklin (1921) and Child (1924, Chap. 13) have recently discussed the question of adaptation, and the latter author argues that all biological regulations are aspects of physiological equilibration. When the ordinary vital pattern is disturbed the vital energies tend to readjust to a condition of equilibrium, either by return to the original state or to some other. Those readjustments that favor survival and are therefore beneficial to the organism comprise the regulatory activities as these are ordinarily defined.

[2] For a critical review of this subject see Child (1924, Chap. 11). It may be stated here once for all that I regard the experimental evidence presented by Child and his co-workers for the mechanisms of organic integration and adjustment in non-nervous organisms and in non-synaptic nervous systems as adequate. The principles of protoplasmic transmission, of physiological gradients, of dominance and subordination of parts, and the like which these authors have formulated are here accepted as established in the realms of plants and the lower animals. The evidence from which these principles have been drawn is not here reviewed;

Excitation and conduction. — Herbert Spencer's definition of life in terms of correspondence of organism with environment is biologically sound, but it leaves open and wholly unexplored the question, what it is about the organism which maintains this correspondence and the mechanisms employed. Protoplasm acts under stimulation from without its own substance, that is, it reacts to impinging energies. So does a set of self-registering meteorological instruments. But protoplasm does more than this; it goes out to meet the assaulting energies, actively seizing upon them and appropriating them for its own advantage. It not only wages defensive warfare against the physical agents of disintegration, but it captures the attacking forces, appropriates their base of supplies, and compels the hostile phalanx actually to turn about and fight the battles of the triumphant organism.

The immediate response of living substance to irritation we call excitation. This is an active protoplasmic function — clearly a very special kind of physico-chemical process.[1] The regions most frequently excited in this way, the sense organs, are structurally adapted to appropriate each a particular kind of energy, and when excited they have more intense metabolism of this special sort. All protoplasm is capable of transmitting such excitations through its own substance — some with speed and facility and some less readily — and thus the activity irradiates for longer or shorter distances from the point of excitation. The total activity is an excitation-transmission process, the acts of excitation and transmission being mutually interdependent. In ordinary protoplasm the resistance to

---

the bibliographic references given will lead the interested reader to the original sources. In the later chapters of this book the attempt is made (a temerarious enterprise perhaps) to apply these same principles in an analysis of the apparatus of conduction and correlation of higher animals. This interpretation of synaptic types of nervous system (Chapters 18, 19) by no means rests upon so secure an experimental foundation as does that of the more primitive protoplasmic systems and our conclusions in this field must be regarded as tentative rather than as demonstrated. Though for clarity and conciseness of exposition dogmatic statements are sometimes made where adequate knowledge is still lacking, the critical reader will supply his own qualifying annotations.

[1] Child (1924, Chap. 11) suggests that excitation in primitive protoplasm is fundamentally nothing more than the acceleration directly or indirectly of the whole complex of processes involved in living, but that as soon as specialization of the reacting protoplasm begins (even of a temporary character as in ameba) this naturally involves specialization of the processes of excitation and conduction with corresponding differentiation of the tissues concerned. The present work is written from the point of view of the more highly differentiated animals in which this elaboration of the apparatus of excitation and conduction has been consummated.

transmission is great and the radius of action from an excited point is limited, that is there is a diminishing physiological gradient in rate and amount of metabolism from the excited point. In nerve fibers, however, no such decrement is readily demonstrable and their radius of action seems to be indefinitely great (Child, 1924, Chap. 11).

Behavior in its simpler forms is to a large extent, though by no means exclusively, direct response of the protoplasm to stimulation; and such behavior, even its most highly complex forms, is a manifestation of excitation-conduction phenomena. The compound form of this last expression implies that in nature excitation and conduction are always colligated, working together and playing into each other's hands in the maintenance of the vital adjustments. The excitation-conduction process has been extensively studied and some of its characteristics are now very well known.

It has been clearly shown (Child, 1921, 1924, Lillie, 1919, 1922, 1923) that excitation and conduction are different phases of a single type of process, the ultimate nature of which is as yet unknown. The facts at our disposal suggest that we are dealing here with a chemical process conjoined with a bioelectric (electrolytic) process in reciprocal interrelationship.

Experiments seem to show that an essential feature of excitation of living cells is a temporary increase in the permeability to negative ions of their membranous walls, thus permitting a more free passage of certain substances through them. The dissociated negative ions produced in the reactions of excitation can more readily pass through these membranous walls whose permeability has been increased by the excitation than through resting cell membranes, and this gives rise to the "action current" or "blaze current" which has long been known to be characteristic of excited protoplasm (Lillie, 1917, p. 184; 1919, p. 460; 1922; p. 22ff., Lillie and Johnston, 1919, p. 244). This negative charge is readily measurable and in the case of excited nerve fibers is known as the negative variation, which has been shown experimentally to be of sufficient strength to serve as an adequate stimulus to an unexcited fiber with which it is brought into contact.

Something of this sort seems to take place normally during all protoplasmic transmission. The action current developed at the point of initial excitation stimulates the adjacent unactivated protoplasm. The chemical reaction resulting is accompanied by an action current which in turn excites the protoplasmic zone next beyond. Thus the excitation is propagated in cycles of metabolism and electric ionization, the rate of transmission being dependent upon the speed of the chemical phase of the reaction and the whole process being comparable with an autocatalysis (Lillie, 1923, Chaps. 10–12).

Whether this or some other hypothesis of protoplasmic transmission be finally established, the experimental evidence clearly shows that excitation and conduction are indissociably related and that the conjoined process is the chief integrating agent in all living bodies and by far the most important factor in the apparatus of biological adjustment to environmental conditions.

Dominance and subordination of parts. — Regions of high excitability are regions of high metabolism and by reason of the conductivity of protoplasm these activated areas control the functions of all other parts within the range of their physiological influence (Child, 1924, Chap. 10). Thus arise "centers of physiological dominance," that is, centers of high metabolism which set the pace for other bodily processes, and the parts of the body are by this means bound together and their activities integrated by an internal mechanism which is nothing other than the dynamic control of the entire process of living by those centers in which the most essential processes of excitation are working with highest efficiency.

Mechanisms of growth and differentiation. — It has been shown that the vital processes of growth and differentiation resemble very strikingly the inorganic chemical reactions known as catalysis (chemical reactions which are accelerated and maintained by the presence of a substance which at the end of the reaction is not consumed or apparently modified), and in particular autocatalysis. Catalytic reactions are of frequent occurrence and various forms. Phosphorus, for example, will not burn in oxygen unless a trace of water is present, though the water is found unchanged at the end of the reaction. Very numerous chemical changes in the living body, notably those concerned in digestion, are dependent upon the presence of substances called enzymes which probably act as catalyzers. In an autocatalytic reaction the products of the reaction itself, or some of them, may serve to increase the rapidity of the reaction. If, now, in reacting protoplasm some products of the chemical change are retained as part of the structural organization of the protoplasm itself, they may on repetition of the excitation act like catalyzers and facilitate the recurrence of the former response. Though the reacting phase may be very short and though there is a tendency to return to the original inactive state, the return is not perfect and on repetition this particular response follows with greater ease, or, otherwise expressed, with less internal resistance.

In a very illuminating comparison of the chemistry of painting with some biological processes Mathews (1915, pp. 67–69) summarizes the resemblances between autocatalytic activities of mixtures containing linseed oil and certain forms of metabolism in these words:

"We do not usually speak of the long latent period of the oxidation as a period of teaching, but it is called in chemistry a period of 'inductance'; and we do not say that the oil is learning to oxidize itself, and doing it better and better, but we say that it shows phenomena of autocatalysis; nor do we say that it forgets again in the dark, but that the intermediary, autocatalytic agent has disappeared; but when organisms show the same kind of phenomena we speak of teaching, of latent periods, of stupidity, of good or bad memories. And it is not impossible by any means that the phenomena of memory, shown in greatest perfection by the mammalian cerebrum, may have at the bottom some such basis as this, and the persistence within certain cells of substances of an autocatalytic nature which have remained from a previous stimulation. Perhaps the brain cells remember longest because they most carefully maintain intact, or preserve, these labile autocatalytic substances. It may be mentioned that the whole of growth is an autocatalytic process. There are always left over in the cell, at the close of a period of feeding, substances, enzymes, derived from the metabolism of the foods, which hasten the metabolism of the next succeeding feeding and hasten growth. It is because of the presence of these autocatalytic substances that foods change into protoplasm so much more rapidly in cells than outside of them."

The process of differentiation of the tissues in general is carried out by the gradual transformation of generalized and relatively plastic protoplasm into a more special form structurally better adapted to do some particular thing (contraction, secretion, or what-not), and this at the expense of capacity for other types of function.[1]

Such a transformation is effected by and during the performance of a particular function, the activity in question resulting in the formation of two kinds of more stable products: (1) wastes which are eliminated, and (2) complex living substances which are retained as permanent components of the tissue by virtue of the fact that they facilitate the specific function in process. Nerve cells, for instance, are characterized by two specific protoplasmic materials of the second class just mentioned, chromophilic substance (Nissl bodies) and neurofibrils, which apparently have been produced in this way.

In a series of trial-and-error responses the successful reaction which has been followed through to its consummation will leave the organ-

[1] See Child (1915, p. 38, 1921, Chap. 5 and 1924, Chap. 8), Lillie (1918 a, p. 76, 1922 a), Lillie and Johnston (1919, p. 228), Reichert and Brown (1909) and Reichert (1913, 1914, p. 657). Reichert discusses the mechanism of differentiation from the standpoint of the stereochemistry of the reacting substance.

ism in a slightly more favorable attitude or "set" for the selection of this particular act when this situation arises again and the more frequent the repetition the greater the facilitation. The act has become habitual.

This change in the "set" or organization of the reacting substance probably involves a slight chemical readjustment of autocatalytic type such as to make a repetition of the discharge easier. It may be transitory or long enduring. This is organic memory. The same principle may work out in modified form in the cerebral cortex in connection with conscious memory, but of the details of this process we know nothing.

Young, mature and senile tissues. — The embryonic tissues are characterized by intense metabolic activity which is constructive in two senses, viz: (1) substance is added faster than it is removed as waste products (a quantitative factor of growth), and (2) the newly formed tissues are more complex than are those from which they were derived (a factor of pattern, *i. e.*, progressive differentiation). Autocatalysis, as we have seen, is probably involved in both cases; in the first case it is a circular type of activity, each cycle repeating the pattern of the preceding, but in the second case it is more like a spiral movement, each cycle leaving the tissue in slightly different form so that succeeding phases are progressively modified. The progressive factor in differentiation evidently must come from outside the protoplasm itself, that is, directly or indirectly from differences in environmental stimulation.

Regions of high metabolism in general have been shown (p. 55) to be centers of high physiological dominance. In lower organisms and in embryonic tissues the total metabolism is usually a reliable index of this dominance, but in higher animals with differentiated tissues it is metabolism of excitation which seems to play the chief rôle here. Highly sensitive and excitable tissues are dominant over others. Embryonic protoplasm is very susceptible to all sorts of external influences. It has, moreover, a generalized structure which is labile in the sense that it can readily be modified by external influences in adaptation to the performance of various functions as occasion may arise.

As embryonic protoplasm matures it tends to assume a more rigid or stable organization, structurally adapted for the performance of some particular function. This is what is meant by differentiation. The intrinsic metabolic activity of the matured tissue may in some cases be very high, especially under immediate excitation as in muscle, but its character is rigidly determined by the local organization; and in the physiological gradients this kind of local metabolism has not as great range of dominance as metabolism of excitation and conduction of the integrative or correlative type. This is due to the fact that excitation and conduction are interrelated phenomena and the range of dominance of an active region, other things being equal, is determined by the facility with which this activity can be transmitted away from this center. The metabolism of a large and active gland, for instance, does not dominate the functions of other parts of the body to the same extent as does an equal amount of metabolism in a nerve center — unless indeed the gland produces an important internal secretion, in which case it also becomes a center of integrative control of transportative type (p. 50. On muscle see also p. 252).

The reason why the activities of the muscle or gland do not exert so pronounced a direct regulatory control over the functions of remote parts is because these organs are not provided with ready-made conductors capable of dispersing this local or intrinsic activity. They are themselves the terminal members of the chief avenues of transmission of the integrating forces. This is more especially true of muscle, whose functions are typically under very direct nervous control.

The accumulation during the course of development of systems of protoplasm specialized for particular functions and characterized by a different sort of chemical process from that of the undifferentiated embryonic type occurs in two forms. There are, first, tissues of high metabolism (induced by excitation) like muscle and gland, and, second, relatively inert supporting elements like connective tissue, cartilage, bone. These latter retard metabolism locally and thus stabilize, localize and accentuate the diminishing gradients arising from the more active regions.

During development progressively more of the protoplasm of embryonic type is transformed into differentiated tissue systems and the more active centers of the fixed tissue systems of high internally excited metabolism like muscle also modify to some extent the primary embryonic gradients and those arising directly from external sensory excitation, resulting in great complexity of organization and dynamic pattern. These changes go on until *maturity* is reached.

With advancing age the accumulated fixed tissues, even those originally of high metabolic rate, lose their capacity for rapid function by the accumulation of more inert substances, all gradients are diminished and the vitality runs low. These changes constitute *senes-*

cence [1] and when carried to the extreme result in the death of the body. Death, after a normal span of life, is therefore in higher animals a strictly biological process.

It has been pointed out that the characteristics of the center of dominance are dependent primarily upon its higher rate of metabolism and the presence of open conduction pathways leading away to other organs. Now, high rate of metabolism may be effected by one of two types of mechanism, either (1) by relatively undifferentiated protoplasm, whose substance is relatively unstable and so capable of rapid chemical change (the "young" type of tissue), or (2) by organs whose tissues possess a large amount of highly differentiated and relatively stable substance of low metabolic rate (the "old" type of tissue) and in addition a more labile substance which can be rapidly mobilized in integrative activity of excitation and conduction without disturbing the pattern of the more stable framework. The first type is characteristic of embryos and of growing parts of mature plants and lowly animals without nervous systems. The second type culminates in the nervous systems of higher vertebrates, where there is (1) a very definite stable and heritable organization which expresses itself functionally in the reflex and instinctive life, and (2) pervading this organization the more labile substance which provides for the individual modifiability of behavior, including the capacity for learning by experience, education, and all higher conscious functions. The brain of man is, therefore, at the same time an organ of innumerable stereotyped actions of the most conservative sort and also the chief center of dominance by which these simpler units of behavior are controlled, modified, inhibited, reinforced and combined in new patterns as demanded by the varying exigencies of living on the human plane.

Conclusion. — All activities of living bodies are classified as intrinsic and integrative functions.

Organisms are composed, not of protoplasm, but of aggregates of

[1] Child would phrase this a little differently, for he maintains that the process of senescence begins with the first appearance of differentiation and is more or less continuous until its limit is reached in senile decay and death. The argument above is based on this conception, but to the present writer there seems to be a decided advantage in separating the progress of differentiation into two stages, of which the first, development, leads up to maturity and may continue for a long time in a condition of high metabolic efficiency before senile decay begins. During the progress of development there is a rapid decrease in rate of metabolism in the growing tissues and for the body as a whole, but particular tissues like muscle and gland may maintain high physiological activity under immediate stimulation.

numerous different protoplasms, each of which has its own specificity. This specific pattern is intrinsic. It is local and largely concerned with the transfer of material to and from the body and with the structural arrangement of this material in the specific protoplasms of the different tissues.

When we come to consider the correlating and integrating processes it is found that the most fundamental factor in all of the behavior patterns is not reducible to specific intrinsic physico-chemical substances or processes, but to the non-specific quantitative relations of excitation and conduction. These quantitative relations of amount of activity and of rate, distance and direction of transmission are not independent of the local chemical reactions of the protoplasm, for these are the sources of the energy; but the behavior value of these reactions for the organism as a whole is not determined by their own chemical specificity but, in higher animals, by the ways in which the separate elements of activity are combined in excitation-conduction systems.

The quantitatively measurable dynamic processes of excitation and conduction are, accordingly, basic phenomena in the study of the unified or integrative behavior of organisms in contrast with the physical changes and chemical reactions of the separate kinds of protoplasm concerned.

Irritability and capacity for the transmission of excitations through its substance seem to be characteristic of all protoplasm. This is regarded as a fundamental and primary factor in the establishment of bodily polarity and all structural and behavior patterns of the living body.

Physiologists of the keenest insight have long recognized that reproduction, growth, differentiation and normal function have certain features in common. So far as growth in size and the repetition of the familiar acts of daily life are concerned, these may be compared directly with inorganic types of autocatalysis. But differentiation, both of tissue and of function, and the acquisition of new biological patterns, such as we term learning by experience, inventiveness, etc., involve more than this, namely, a constructive or creative factor for which we have no inorganic analogies. We are reminded of Claude Bernard's, "*la vie, c'est la création*" (Lillie, 1922 a, p. 114).

Irritability, as a compound of excitation, conduction and response, is the key with which we shall seek to open the doors leading out from the domain of the general physiology of protoplasm and away into the higher levels of animal behavior and human conduct. This

key will not fit all locks nor admit us to every important field of biological exploration; but it will give access to many of the roads we
wish to travel in this inquiry.   We shall approach these problems
first from the general biological or natural history side, but cannot
hope to advance very far in this direction without calling in the aid
of some recently acquired biochemical and biophysical principles.
At best our progress will not be very fast nor can we hope to travel
very far; but if at the end of our reconnaissance we have truer ideas
of the field of human and animal behavior and the genetic factors
which bind these together, we may be able to look forward into the
still unknown territory with clearer vision and more discerning insight.

CHAPTER VI

EXCITATION–CONDUCTION GRADIENTS OF PROTOZOA

Irritability of the ameba — Neuroid and myoid functions in the ameba — Surface-interior polarity — Superficial differentiation — Polar axes and antero-posterior differentiation — Apico-basal polarity — The axial physiological gradient — Physiological gradients and head dominance — Methods for the study of physiological gradients — Illustrations of gradients in plants and protozoans — Conclusion

Irritability of the ameba. — If now we turn our attention to the apparatus of reaction in its most elementary form as seen, for example, in the ameba, we observe that all of the kinds of intake of material and energy and their internal conversion into the processes and machinery of living which were commented upon at the beginning of the preceding chapter are here present, though reduced to lowest terms. But there are no differentiated organs for any of these functions; the general protoplasm appears to be able to perform any of the vital functions and does, in fact, do so at one time or another.

If the surface of an ameba (Fig. 5) is pricked by a needle at any point (Fig. 6), the response as described by Hyman (1917) is as follows:

"When the amœba is subjected to such mechanical stimulation, the immediate response is invariable. The stimulated region contracts more or less depending upon its previous degree of activity but the most striking effect occurs at the advancing end of the amœba. This, whether it consist of one or more pseudopodia, contracts powerfully so that its surface is thrown into numerous short projections. The contraction of the anterior end, regardless of where the stimulus is applied, indicates that conduction through the protoplasm is extremely rapid and effective. As a result of this contraction, the protoplasm flows toward the middle of the body which bulges out. . . . After a little delay, new pseudopodia arise, and the animal moves away in evident haste. The place at which the new pseudopodia appear bears a direct relation to the place to which the stimulus was applied; it is opposite In this regard strong stimulation differs from moderate or weak stimulation."

This is a typical avoiding reaction. Obviously internal changes have been excited and these have been transmitted throughout the substance of the body so that the greatest activity may be manifested in the most remote part.

All protoplasmic activities concerned in these responses involve chemical reactions and liberation of energy. Excitation, conduction, and response are, therefore, forms of metabolism. In the cases here under consideration the metabolism is probably in part a series of processes of oxidation and reduction and the release of energy involved is effected much as in an internal combustion engine. In both cases the energy made available is immediately put to useful work because it is confined within a mechanism so arranged as to direct it into particular channels and set in motion other parts of the mechanism.

The initial stimulation by an external agent produces a local upset of the physico-chemical equilibrium with relatively great liberation of energy, which in turn excites the surrounding protoplasm with similar release of more energy. Thus the reaction once started is maintained, propagated, and on occasion even intensified by the internal apparatus. This propagation is not merely the passage of a wave of chemical change, like the burning of a fuse, nor is it merely

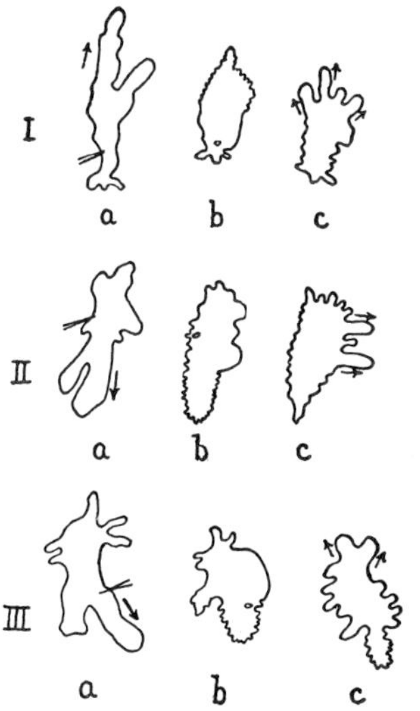

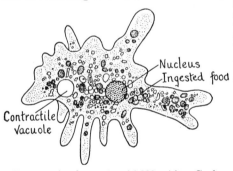

Fig. 6.—Drawings of three successive stages (a, b, c) of the avoiding reaction of three different amebas to strong mechanical stimulation by a prick of a needle. In ameba I the stimulus is applied to the posterior end of the body advancing in the direction indicated by the arrow. The anterior end contracts (b) and advances again (c). In ameba II the stimulus is applied to the side of the advancing body (a). The anterior end contracts (b). Locomotion then begins on the side opposite the application of the stimulus (c). In ameba III the stimulus is applied near the advancing end (a). The anterior end contracts (b). Locomotion begins at the posterior end (c). After Hyman (1917).

Nucleus
Ingested food
Contractile
Vacuole

Fig. 5.—Ameba proteus × 200. After Gruber. The projections of the body are pseudopodia. The ectoplasm is clear; the endoplasm is dotted.

the transmission of physical vibrations without permanent chemical alteration of the conductor, like the passage of the electric current over a copper wire. In reality it is probably a combination of chemical and electrical processes, each in a very special form and each reciprocally dependent upon the other (see page 54, Child, 1924, Chap. 11 and Lillie, 1923).

Neuroid and myoid functions in the ameba. — It was formerly the fashion to describe simple unicellular organisms like the ameba as composed of undifferentiated protoplasm; but this clearly is far from true, for even here there is a very definite and complex behavior with some visible structural differentiation. Structurally we find that the clear outer layer of the body (ectoplasm) is evidently composed of a different kind of protoplasm from the underlying more granular endoplasm, though the same material may occupy now one, now another of these different regions. In the interior of the body are many kinds of granules, an excretory organ (contractile vacuole), and the nucleus, circumscribed by a definite nuclear membrane and containing characteristic internal organization.

It has been shown by microdissections and otherwise that the ectoplasm is a semirigid solid or firm gel, while the endoplasm is much more fluid. A review of all the evidence suggests that the ectoplasm of the ameba is the part in which the neuroid and myoid functions are particularly evident. The excitations and resulting movements seem to be determined from this substance. This implies a local and transient differentiation and the beginning of the elaboration of specific tissues. Here the *pattern* of surface-interior differentiation is permanent, though the materials themselves are in constant flux.

The body of the ameba has no rigidly permanent form, though each species varies in shape within tolerably well defined limits and so can be said to possess a characteristic morphology. The protoplasm, however, is in a state of constant internal movement, thrusting out portions of its substance (pesudopodia) now in this direction, now in that, and crawling about in directions determined by the play of internal forces reacting with those of the environment. The visible internal structures are equally unstable, the nucleus and the ectoplasm alone persisting as permanent intracellular organs.

We are, therefore, not able in the ameba to designate any permanent excitomotor protoplasm, though any of the body substance which is at the moment in the ectoplasm phase seems to manifest excitomotor functions and so the ectoplasm (which is always present) may be said to be an excitomotor organ, though the material of which it is composed is not differentiated as permanent structure.

These animals are very sensitive to external stimuli and possess a high degree of motility, reacting to stimulation in ways that are not essentially different from the simpler human reflexes. Evidently these excitomotor functions reside in the same protoplasm which also serves the functions of nutrition, respiration and excretion.

When this labile material reaches the surface of the body and comes under the influence of the external medium it temporarily assumes the form of denser ectoplasm and reacts as substance in which the excitomotor function is predominant.

Some unpublished observations of Dr. S. O. Mast which he has kindly communicated to me indicate that in the locomotion of Ameba proteus the interior protoplasm (endoplasm) is streaming toward the advancing end, where it passes outward toward the surface and thus continually reconstitutes the ectoplasm at the advancing end. At the posterior end the reverse process takes place, the ectoplasm once more becomes endoplasm and reënters the interior stream.

Here the entire apparatus of reaction is represented by a single protoplasmic substance in which there is no obvious separation of receptive, conducting, adjusting and motor tissue. Though this apparatus contains neither nerves nor muscles regarded as tissues, it may be regarded as manifesting both neuriod and myoid structure and function, and at other times the general protoplasmic functions of nutrition, growth, etc. All protoplasm is sensitive, conducting and contractile, and irritation leads to response whose character depends on the pattern of the organization. The problem before us is, how did the differentiated nervous tissues arise from this relatively unspecialized protoplasm in which the neuroid functions are bound up with the others. Our first appeal is to the principle of functional polarity, which is a fundamental property of all living substance.

Surface-interior polarity. — The problem of the rise and nature of polarity in protoplasm has been discussed in detail by Child (1924, Chaps. 6, 9) and we need not review the argument. Here allusion may be made to only one phase of it. Since external stimuli are necessarily applied to the surface of the body, the initial protoplasmic reactions to these exciting agents are essentially surface phenomena. It is commonly believed that the ectoplasm of ameba is formed as a direct result of contact of the colloidal protoplasm with water. There are probably other factors present and the process as a whole may be regarded as a visible structural manifestation of the response of the protoplasm to environing influences (Child, 1924, Chap. 3, Lillie, 1923).

In the ameba we may assume a sustained movement of excitation-conduction currents from the surface inward, and the fluctuations in the strength of the peripheral excitation at different points and in the conductivity of different parts of the internal protoplasm may and do transform the theoretically uniformly distributed excitation gradient from surface to interior into constantly shifting local differences in dynamic polarity, leading to movements of locomotion or other activities, as illustrated on page 62.

The mechanisms involved in this reaction have been only partially analyzed, but what I want to emphasize here is merely that at this grade of organization we have a general surface-interior polarity which follows no structurally differentiated pathways and hence may change its pattern momentarily as the conditions of life are altered (Child, 1924, Chap. 6). The lack of permanently differentiated neuromotor tissue does not preclude the appearance of excitomotor responses which are coördinated with reference to the behavior of the body as a whole and therefore are of organismic type (p. 9).

From these considerations it has been argued by Child with great force that the integrating and correlating factors of the neuromotor type as represented by excitation and transmission phenomena and the patterns of their quantitative differences, or physiological gradients in rate and character of metabolism, antedated in evolution the appearance, not only of nervous tissue, but of all other tissues as well; they constitute, in fact, the fundamental basis of all organic response and adjustment.

Superficial differentiation. — In most one-celled organisms, as in all higher forms, the surface reaction to the environment takes the form of permanent structural modifications, such as ectoplasm or a protective cuticle or shell and locally differentiated sense organs. The cuticle raises the resistance to all kinds of excitations; the sense organs lower the resistance at each sensory area to some particular exciting agent, while perhaps raising it for all others.

Excitation involves a local acceleration of the physiological processes, that is, higher metabolism, which in turn (p. 57) is an essential condition for the differentiation of fixed or stable tissue patterns. Accordingly, we find in unicellular forms generally that the differentiation of both sensory or receptive organs and motor or responsive organs begins at the surface and for the most part is limited to it. Most protozoans have a definite body shape which is maintained by a relatively rigid cuticular layer, from which project the cilia or flagella, which are at the same time sensitive receptive organs and active motor apparatus.

Polar axes and antero-posterior differentiation. — In the simple flagellated monads the body is elongated and usually advances through the water with one structurally modified end in advance. At the anterior end are the principal sensori-motor organs, these usually taking the form of one or two stiff protoplasmic threads (flagella) by whose whip-like movements the body is propelled, together with some internal accessory structures. This structurally differentiated end is the region of highest excitability and highest metabolism. These unicellular organisms therefore possess, in addition to the surface-interior polarity already considered, an antero-posterior polarity and a principal or primary polar axis.

One of the most striking cases of this sort of differentiation is a soil ameba (Nægleria gruberi, Fig. 7) recently described by Miss Wilson (1916). This organism usually exhibits the ordinary protean form of a typical ameba, but under certain conditions it undergoes a metamorphosis into a stable phase with definite body shape which resembles in all respects a typical flagellate infusorian. The flagellate phase is temporary, lasting usually only a few hours, but while it lasts the body has a fixed form and intracellular organs and would certainly be classified with the biflagellate infusorians. In this phase the sensorimotor apparatus is partly external, the two flagella, and partly internal. Locomotion is effected by movements of the thread-like flagella, which probably also serve as receptive organs, and at the common base of these is the internal excitomotor apparatus, consisting of a granule (blepharoplast) connected by a dense protoplasmic thread (rhizoplast) with a large mass of chromatin (karyosome) within the nucleus.[1]

This organism ordinarily exhibits merely the transitory surface-interior polarity of the typical ameba as already described. In this phase there is a definite ectoplasm with

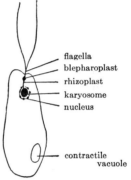

flagella
blepharoplast
rhizoplast
karyosome
nucleus

contractile
vacuole

FIG. 7.—The excitomotor apparatus of the soil ameba, Nægleria gruberi, in the flagellate stage. The body has a definite form and is provided at the anterior end with two motile flagella, at the base of which is a differentiated strand of protoplasm (blepharoplast and rhizoplast) which encircles the nucleus. Nervous and motor organs are not separately differentiated, the same excitomotor protoplasm performing both functions. The drawing is a combination of two figures from Wilson (1916), one drawn from life and one from a fixed and stained preparation.

the functional characteristics of high excitability, but the materials composing this superficial layer are constantly passing to and from the more fluid endoplasm. In the flagellate phase, however, the outer layer is much firmer and its material composition is. stable as long as this

[1] A still more striking case of the occurrence of ameboid and flagellate forms in the same life cycle has recently been described by Martha Bunting (1922).

phase endures. This more stable protoplasm forms the cuticle which keeps the body form more rigid, the mobile and sensitive flagella, and also the differentiated protoplasmic strand which extends inward from the flagella to the nucleus. That stable structural organization which appears temporarily in the flagellated phase of Nægleria is permanent in the true flagellates and this represents a further step in the direction of the formation of differentiated organs.

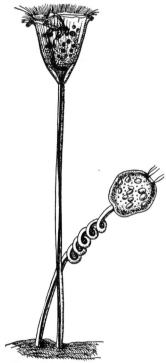

FIG. 8.—The bell animalcule, Vorticella, in the expanded and contracted condition.

The origin of this polarity of Nægleria is obscure. It is probable that in general those free-swimming unicellular organisms which have the habit of moving head first are derived from attached forms in which the apico-basal polarity was differentiated in the way to be suggested immediately. The differentiated apical end of the attached organism becomes the head end of the free form by reason of the greater sensitiveness of this part already established.

Some amebas, notably the "limax forms," maintain more or less permanently an elongated body form with tendency to move in the direction of the long axis of the body. The protoplasm, however, may flow freely from one end of the body to the other and there is no differentiation of a structurally fixed apico-basal axis, as in the forms next to be considered.

Apico-basal polarity. — Many of the unicellular animals are attached at one end of the body. The free apical end being exposed to more frequent stimulation develops greater sensitiveness and highly active motor organs, and here we find a permanent axial physiological gradient passing downward from high at the free end to low at the attached end. This is well shown in the familiar infusorians illustrated by the bell animalcule, Vorticella (Fig. 8), and the allied trumpet animalcule, Stentor (Fig. 9). Here the correlation of a physiological gradient with a definite structural pattern is very clearly evident. The body of Vorticella is shaped like a bell on a flexible cord. Around the margin of the bell (peristome) is a fringe of vibratile cilia and at one side of this are the mouth and esophagus, into which food particles are swept by the movements of the cilia. The body wall is rigid except at the peristome, which can be rolled inward carrying the cilia with it. This is an avoiding reaction to noxious stimuli. The body is attached by a slender stalk within which is a strand of contractile protoplasm so arranged that its contraction will coil the stalk spirally and withdraw the bell — also an avoiding reaction. The highest metabolism is evidently at the margin of the bell, where sense stimuli are received and strong motor responses are made. The contractile stalk is also a region of high metabolism, here typically motor.

Vorticella thus illustrates another important aspect of the axial gradients in their more differentiated forms, viz., the separation along the principal axis of the sensory or receptive apparatus (here mixed neuromotor at the peristome) from purely motor or effector organs (here the contractile stalk). Slight irritation at the mouth of the bell is followed by involution of the peristome, and more prolonged or stronger excitation is transmitted through the body protoplasm to the muscular stalk, resulting in its violent contraction. This behavior shows that the excitation-conduction gradient runs from the peristome downward toward the stalk and it suggests that there is a decrement in the body in the rate of metabolism along this axis. Experiment shows that this is in fact the case (see further on page 72).

Fig. 9.—The trumpet animalcule, Stentor roeselii. After Stein. The trumpet-shaped body is attached at the base. The body surface is ciliated and the margin of the free end (peristome) has stronger cilia which are in constant motion.

The axial physiological gradient. — In these forms there is clearly both structural and functional differentiation along the longitudinal axis of the body, with the most intense physiological activity centered at the anterior end in the region of the structurally visible excitomotor apparatus. This may be otherwise expressed by saying that there is an axial physiological gradient passing from a region of high activity at the anterior or apical end to a lower region at the posterior or basal end (Child, 1924, Chap. 6). And in cases like Stentor, where there is a separation of a more sensitive region (peristome) from a basal region of the body in which motor activities predominate, the physiological gradient passes downward from high at the sensitive pole to low at the motor pole. Such a gradient may be inferred from the body form and behavior of the animalcule, but we are not limited to this line of evidence, for in this and similar cases the differences in metabolic rate along the axial gradient have been demonstrated by a variety of methods to be mentioned immediately.

Physiological gradients and head dominance. — The case just described illustrates a law which applies to simple axial physiological gradients in general, viz., that regions of high excitability by virtue of their more active metabolism are physiologically dominant over regions of lower metabolism; that is, they exert a controlling or regulatory influence over the behavior, growth and differentiation of regions of lower metabolic rate.

These principles are well illustrated in the behavior of the infusorian Lacrymaria, as described by Mast (1911 a). This little creature, which swims actively through the water, is about 0.1 mm. long when at rest. At the anterior end is a little knob containing the mouth; this is bordered by a row of cilia. Behind this "head" is an extensible "neck" which may be stretched out to the amazing distance of eight times the length of the body and fifty times its own length (Fig. 10).

The head and mobile neck are thrust out in rapid exploratory movements, searching for food in every direction, darting, twisting and bending around obstructions to reach every nook and crevice within reach. In swimming, "it is the movement of the head that largely regulates the direction of movement of the body and the movements of the head are almost entirely controlled by the activity of the oral cilia" (p. 231).

This animal exhibits pronounced structural and functional polarity with strong head dominance. The reactions are of the trial-and-error type and the experiments show that the direction in which the head turns is regulated largely by internal factors other than tropisms in Loeb's sense. The action system of Lacrymaria is rather complex and the behavior is clearly well integrated. The mechanisms employed have not been so thoroughly studied as in some other species of Infusoria.

The extensive literature of the behavior of Protozoa furnishes many other illustrations of these principles, but these cannot be reviewed here. Some further references to these animals will be found in Chapter 20; see also Jennings (1906) and Mast (1911).

Methods for the study of physiological gradients. — Our knowledge of the nature of physiological gradients, excitation, conduction and polarity rests upon a large body of experimental work on lower organisms of which no adequate summary can be given here. Demonstrations of these factors have been made by Child and others by a considerable variety of methods, all of which give concordant results.

These observations include direct measurements of oxygen consumed and carbon dioxid given off at different levels of the gradients; differential susceptibility of different protoplasms to noxious influences — narcotics, poisons, heat, cold, lack of oxygen, etc. — employed as indices of metabolic rate; differences of electric potential along the gradients; graded differences in rate of penetration of vital dyes and precipitation of potassium permanganate by protoplasms in different metabolic states; evidence from rate of cell division, growth and differentiation; and evidence from adult structure and behavior (Child, 1924, Chap. 7).

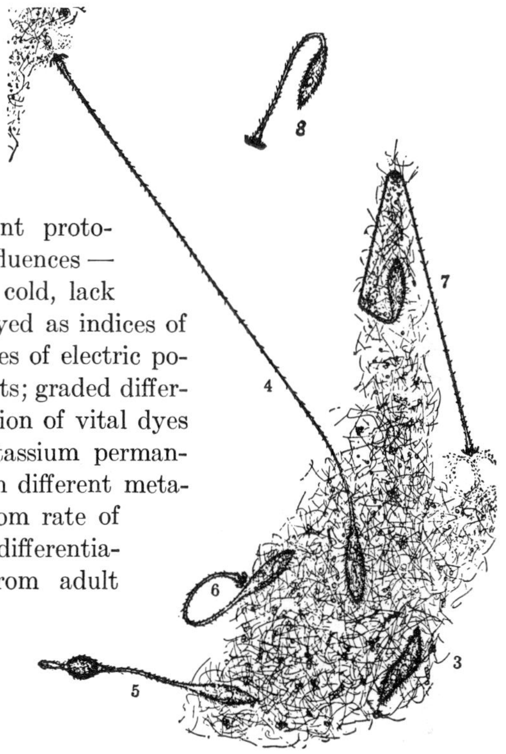

A few illustrations will serve to indicate the existence of gradients in susceptibility to noxious agents and their relations to the physiological and morphological axes of the body. There is independent evidence that these susceptibility gradients may serve as reliable indices of amount of metabolism

FIG. 10.—Behavior of Lacrymaria. The specimens drawn are entangled in filamentous and unicellular algæ, only part of which are shown. 3, at rest; the oral cilia are folded over the oral knob which contains the mouth, 4, with the neck fully extended; the dots in front of the head represent particles carried toward the mouth in a current produced by the oral cilia. 5, an individual shortly after having swallowed a small protozoan which is still lodged in the neck. 6, a sketch showing the neck bent on itself and the head in contact with the body over which it passes, apparently cleaning the surface. 7, showing the manner in which the neck is often bent so as to form sharp angles. 8, a free swimming specimen suddenly changing its direction of locomotion by turning the head and neck sharply to one side. After Mast (1911 a).

or physiological activity along these axes, the more susceptible regions having higher rates of metabolism and the activity or rate of living showing a decrement from apical to basal ends of the body.

Illustrations of gradients in plants and protozoans. — In some sixty or seventy species of marine algæ Child has demonstrated simple apico-basal physiological gradients in the younger growing parts, the susceptibility to certain ranges of concentration of potassium cyanide and many other agents being highest at the apical ends of the shoots and decreasing backwards. (For an account of some of these experiments see Child, 1916.) The death and disintegration of the protoplasm begins at the apex and proceeds from this point down the stem, the older and more differentiated tissues resisting the toxic agent longer than the younger and more rapidly growing apical tissues.

In the higher unicellular animals like Vorticella and Stentor, where there is well defined structural polarity with highly differentiated

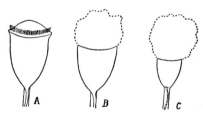

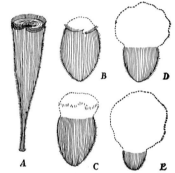

Fig. 11.—Three stages in the disintegration of the body after treatment with potassium cyanide in the case of Carchesium, a protozoan allied to Vorticella. First the peristome bulges outward (A); then the entire peristome region with its cilia disintegrates (B); this is followed by the disintegration of the muscular filament of the stalk and of the remainder of the body except the outer cuticle (C). After Child (1914).

Fig. 12.—Stentor cœruleus, illustrating the normal body form (A) and successive stages in disintegration under the influence of potassium cyanide (B–E). After Child (1915 a).

excitomotor apparatus at the free or apical pole, the protoplasm of this region of greatest sensitivity is the first to be affected and killed by solutions of potassium cyanide of proper strength (Child, 1914). Upon treating Vorticella with this chemical the body is killed and the protoplasm disintegrates, the region of the peristome first, then the muscular strand of the stalk, and later the general protoplasm lying between these points. The dense superficial ectoplasm shows a gradient in change of structure and contraction but retains its form to some extent after death (Fig. 11).

In Stentor there is similar evidence of differential susceptibility to potassium cyanide and many other agents. This protozoan has, in addition to the large cilia of the peristome, rows of smaller cilia over the entire body surface. Figure 12 illustrates the normal form of the body (A) and successive stages of its disintegration under the action of cyanide (B to E). According to Child (1915 a, p. 56) the process is as follows: In cyanide the body undergoes some contraction, death begins at the apical end (B) and is accompanied by the instantaneous loss of all movement and disintegration of structure in the part concerned, and the protoplasm swells and spreads out in the water, as indicated by the dotted outline. Other parts remain intact and the cilia continue to vibrate. From the apical region death and disintegration proceed along the body as shown in sketches C, D and E, the line of demarcation between the dead and disintegrated and the living portions remaining distinct at all times until the progress of death ends at the basal end of the body. The rate of progress of death over the whole body may vary from a few seconds to five or ten minutes, according to concentration of cyanide used, temperature, and other conditions.

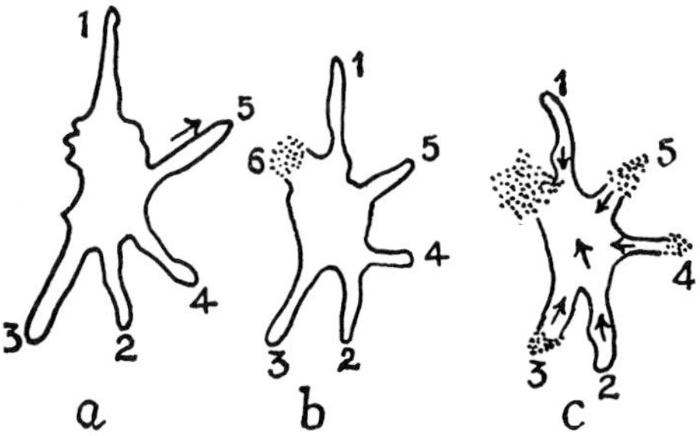

The relative susceptibility to injurious agents of the protoplasm of different regions is known to be an index of the excitation-conduction gradient and the physiological polarity of the body. This conclusion has been controlled by experiments upon so many different species of animals and plants and by so many independent methods that

FIG. 13.—Disintegration in potassium cyanide of an ameba with five slender pseudopodia, 1, the oldest, 5, the youngest. In a the animal is advancing along pseudopodium 5. In b it has been treated with potassium cyanide; there is a tendency to reverse the movement by formation of a new pseudopodium at 6, but before this can be formed the protoplasm here breaks down. In c pseudopodium 5 has almost completely broken down and disintegration of 4 and 3 has begun. Disintegration of 2 and 1 will follow. After Hyman (1917) slightly modified.

it can be used to discover physiological polarity even in cases like the ameba where there is no permanent body form or structural polar axis.

We have seen (p. 62) that the body of an ameba is constantly moving about in response to internal or external changes. There is a transient polarity or head-tail axis whose structural materials are changing from moment to moment as the advance is made first in one direction, then in another. Here Dr. Hyman (1917) has demonstrated the presence of metabolic gradients of the same type as in more highly organized bodies with structurally permanent form and antero-posterior axes. The tip of each pseudopod has higher susceptibility than its base, and the newer pseudopodia than the older ones. This is illustrated in Fig. 13, where the process of disintegration of the protoplasm under the action of potassium cyanide is shown.

The younger pseudopodia are those which at the moment are most actively stimulated by environmental contacts, and this excitation is apparently always characterized by high metabolism and by high physiological dominance. The higher dominance is manifested in the control exercised by the leading pseudopod over the rest of the body in locomotion.

The first orderly response to noxious stimulation is an attempt to reverse the direction of movement by the formation of a new pseudopod at the end of the body opposite the advancing tip. This youngest pseudopod immediately breaks down (Fig. 13 b at 6). Then the other pseudopodia gradually distintegrate from their distal toward the proximal ends, beginning with the one most recently formed (Fig. 13 c at 5) and ending with the oldest (Fig. 13, pseudopod 1). This type of gradient conforms in every essential respect with that found in worms and higher animals.

In all of these cases the free end of the attached organism, or in the case of locomotor species the anterior end, or in the ameba the portion of the mobile body which at the moment is advancing, will ordinarily be more exposed to contacts with surrounding forces, will receive more stimuli, and the character of these stimuli will determine the subsequent behavior. The reception of a stimulus is not a passive thing, but an active response by the protoplasm which involves chemical change, that is, metabolism. The act of response involves more metabolism, and the conduction through the protoplasm from the site of the stimulus to the apparatus of response also is a metabolic process with a certain expenditure of energy. The protoplasmic transmission last mentioned acts against a certain resistance or inertia and tends to diminish with the distance traversed; that is, it shows a decrement from the point of excitation. The more frequent stimulation at the apical or head end involves high metabolism at that point with a gradient of decreasing metabolism down the body toward the muscles or other organs of response.

Such gradients as have just been considered may have arisen in the egg or during the process of fission in consequence of fixation of the body at one pole with more direct action of environing forces on the exposed face of its protoplasm, and the presence of such a primary axial gradient may determine the whole sequence of subsequent responses to stimulation. These reaction patterns in their turn become factors in the maintenance, further development and modification of the primary gradients which were originally determined by the mere position of the body with reference to its oxygen supply and the sources of its excitation. (Child, 1924, Chaps. 8, 9.)

The transmission gradient, however, is not maintained wholly on the basis of rate of chemical change or amount of general metabolism. In Vorticella, as has been pointed out, the peristome is most susceptible to toxic agents, the contractile stalk next, and after these the general protoplasm of the intervening body substance. This means, as we know from independent evidence, that the chemical activity of the protoplasms in this animal is graded from high to low in the order given; nevertheless the transmission gradient passes from the region of highest rate at the peristome through the region of lowest rate in the body to a region of intermediate rate in the stalk. In 'other words, the maintenance of the transmission gradient is dependent not only upon the intensity of the metabolic process but also in the differentiated organism to some extent upon the pattern in which that metabolism is manifested. Contractile tissue occupies the lowest place in the transmission gradient, even though its own rate of metabolism (during contraction) is higher than that of intervening protoplasm.

This case is somewhat like that of a river which descends a cataract to spread out in a wide lake and then resume its course over rapids below the lake. From the standpoint of effective energy (say for waterpower) the cataract is highest and the rapids next in rank, yet the water flow passes downward through the intervening placid lake. The analogy, of course, is crude but here, as in the organism, the transmission gradient is dependent in part upon the structural configuration of the material substratum. The explanation in the case under consideration is that the energy of transmission through the body of the Vorticella is diffused in its passage through so large a mass of relatively inert protoplasm. Where the conducting substance is segregated, as in the neuromotor strands of Diplodinium and Euplotes (p. 78) and the nerve fibers of higher animals, the conducting pathways through which the gradients are maintained are structurally visible.

Conclusion. — Many different lines of physiological evidence indicate that polarity and symmetry rest primarily on physiological gradients of excitation and conduction, with which are correlated differences in rate or amount of metabolism. These can be measured and experimentally controlled and with them are associated differences in the structure of the various parts of the body.

In undifferentiated protoplasm regions of high excitability and of relatively rapid metabolism are physiologically dominant over centers in which this type of function is at a lower level. The range through which these dominant centers can exert their regulatory control is measured in part by the intensity of the metabolic processes which they exhibit and in part by the facility with which the excitation can be transmitted through the surrounding protoplasm.

Ordinary protoplasm is not a very good conductor of these excitations, and in the absence of nerves, which are good conductors, the size of the body which can be well integrated through the agency of the physiological gradients is necessarily limited. The Protozoa are small organisms. Plants, on the other hand, in which the body is not so well integrated (as illustrated by the ease with which they can be propagated by cuttings, buds, grafts, etc.) may grow to great size without nerves. In higher animals the presence of nerves extends the range of dominance of the centers of high excitability and so integrates a larger and more complex body, knitting its parts together effectively in coördinated activities of higher and more varied sorts than are possible in plants.

CHAPTER VII

THE PRECURSORS OF THE NERVOUS SYSTEM

Functional factors in differentiation — Intracellular excitomotor apparatus —
Early structural differentiation of the motor apparatus — Adjustments in
multicellular organisms — Integration in Gonium and Volvox — Excito-
motor adjustments in sponges — Summary

Functional factors in differentiation. — In even the simplest of the
unicellular organisms whose physiological mechanisms have been
adequately studied it is evident that the behavior pattern of each
species is the resultant of two factors or components: (1) the stable
protoplasmic organization of the species which is passed on from
generation to generation; (2) the reactions of this specific protoplasm
to the particular external influences which are present in the normal
habitat of the species and to which the organization of its protoplasm
permits physiological response. Or, otherwise expressed, we may say
that each species lives and thrives only in the environment to which
in the course of previous evolution its organization has become adjusted; and within this environment it responds only to those external
agents which are adequate stimuli for its own protoplasm, that is,
to which adjustment is essential to maintain its own welfare. Not
only the receptive apparatus, but the entire excitomotor machinery
will be attuned to respond to those particular stimuli which are significant factors in its correspondence with its specific environment
and to no others. If it normally lives in total darkness photoreceptors
and reactions to light may be wholly absent, while responses to other
stimuli may be proportionally elaborated.

In the simpler ameboid forms the differentiation of these specific
excitomotor systems is at the lowest possible level. The only visible
apparatus of excitomotor response is the separation of the clear denser
ectoplasm from the more fluid granular endoplasm. This separation,
as we have seen, is a permanent differentiation as regards the pattern
of organization, but the constituent materials are in constant flux,
the substances of the body (or some of them) passing freely from endoplasm to ectoplasm and conversely. It is the pattern only which is
stable, not the material, and this is a dynamic pattern, and immediate response of the material to external agencies. Thus arise the

separation of neuromotor protoplasm from the rest, surface-interior and longitudinal polarity, and those gradients in the transmission of excitations from the surface to the depths of the body or from functionally apical to functionally basal or posterior ends to which reference was made in the preceding chapter.

It is a very significant thing that this polarity and the physiological gradients which maintain the integrity of the body and its effective contacts with its environment may appear in the absence of permanent bodily organs serving these functions. It has been shown that in the development of bodies of higher animals polarities and axial gradients of similar type but different patterns appear in advance of the differentiation of the tissues, and it is probable that in the earliest stages of organic evolution dynamic patterns of excitation and response preceded the structural differentiation of permanent receptive organs, conductors and effectors. In short, neuromotor organs were differentiated within preëxisting functional patterns which are direct physiological responses of the living substance to external agents. We shall next pass in review some lower organisms which illustrate different steps in the fabrication of definite neuromotor organs.

Intracellular excitomotor apparatus. — The intracellular excitomotor apparatus is most clearly manifested in a number of unicellular forms recently described from the Zoölogical Laboratory of the University of California. Some of these are free swimming animals and some are internal parasites. The interesting peculiarities of the soil ameba described by Miss Wilson (1916) have already been mentioned. Beginning with this simple and transitory excitomotor apparatus, and extensive series of increasingly complex forms has been described in various unicellular species, culminating in the extraordinarily complex systems of Euplotes (Yocom, 1918, Taylor, 1920), Trichonympha (Kofoid and Swezy, 1919, p. 41) and Diplodinium (Sharp, 1914).

Diplodinium is an actively swimming animalcule which lives in the stomach of cattle and feeds on small solid particles, probably chiefly bacteria. The body is elongated with an antero-posterior polar axis, the anterior end containing the mouth and a very complex sensori-motor apparatus for feeding and locomotion. There are bands of tufted cilia (membranelles) around the mouth which are sensitive receptors and also actively motile; connected with the bases of these are "neuromotor" strands which converge into a central mass of protoplasm, the neuromotor mass or "motorium." From the neuromotor mass other neuromotor strands encircle the esophagus and extend downward into the interior of the body. Here they accom-

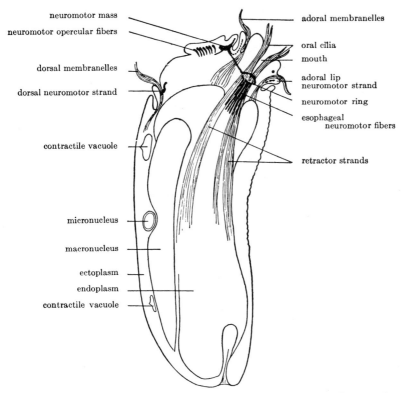

neuromotor mass

neuromotor opercular fibers

dorsal membranelles

dorsal neuromotor strand

contractile vacuole

micronucleus

macronucleus

ectoplasm

endoplasm

contractile vacuole

adoral membranelles

oral cilia

mouth

adoral lip
neuromotor strand

neuromotor ring

esophageal
neuromotor fibers

retractor strands

Fig. 14.—Diagrammatic longitudinal section of the body of Diplodinium ecaudatum. This drawing is simplified from one given by Sharp (1914) by omission of many details. The mouth is surrounded by a row of oral cilia and at the anterior end of the body are several series of vibrating plates or membranelles. At the bases of the membranelles are neuromotor strands of denser protoplasm. These are connected by strands not visible in the plane of this figure with the neuromotor mass which seems to serve as a center of correlation for the entire neuromotor apparatus. The esophagus is surrounded by a ring of neuromotor protoplasm which is connected with the neuromotor mass and sends esophageal neuromotor fibers downward along the retractor strands. The latter are primarily contractile in function. The entire neuromotor apparatus seems to be both nervous and contractile, with nervous functions predominant in the neuromotor strands, esophageal neuromotor fibers, circum-esophageal ring and neuromotor mass; but the retractor strands seem to be more nearly purely muscular in functional type. Here is exhibited the first step in the separation of nervous from muscular apparatus in a common neuromotor mechanism.

pany other and larger protoplasmic bands termed retractor strands which are highly contractile. A noxious stimulus causes contraction of the whole body and involution of the membranelles through the action of the neuromotor strands and the retractile strands. Figure 14 illustrates some of these features as seen in median section of the body.

It is clear that we have here a well differentiated excitomotor apparatus, but without complete separation of the nervous and muscular components. The retractor strands appear to be almost purely muscular in type and Sharp is of the opinion that in the motor mass and neuromotor strands the nervous or neuroid functions predominate.

Euplotes is a free-swimming fresh water ciliate infusorian somewhat more simply organized than Diplodinium, in which Yocom described a system of neuromotor strands converging into a "motorium." The anatomical arrangements suggest that these protoplasmic strands are neither supporting nor contractile in function, but that they are primarily conductors by means of which the activities of motor organs are coördinated from the "motorium." This hypothesis was subjected to experimental test by Taylor (1920), who performed various surgical operations upon the living animalcules under the microscope. He finds that "destroying the motorium or cutting its attached fibers interrupts coördination in the movements of the adoral membranelles and the anal cirri" (the chief locomotor organs), and that any incision which does not sever these fibrils does not impair normal swimming or creeping movements. The function of the neuromotor strands is thus shown to be conduction and that of the motorium coördination, that is, these are "neuroid" organs.

Still more recently Rees (1922) has demonstrated a similar neuromotor center and similar neuromotor fibrils in the familiar ciliate, Paramecium. Microdissections in this case also prove the coördinating and conduction functions of this intracellular organ system.

To recapitulate, in the simpler Protozoa like the common ameba there is no permanent body form and little evidence of structurally defined polar axes and very little differentiation of visible intracellular organs. Nevertheless we find definite physiological gradients which are transient and correlated with the direction and time sequence of movement. In Protozoa with definite structural cell walls and morphologically differentiated antero-posterior polar axes the physiological gradient is a permanent feature of the organization. And in some of these forms, as in Diplodinium, there is a very clear structural indication of the segregation of two types of protoplasm, namely, the differentiated excitomotor organs on one hand and the general unmodified endoplasm on the other hand, and this differentiation is much more stable than in the ameba.

The definitely organized excitomotor apparatus of Diplodinium is the morphological expression of an action system characterized by great precision and speed of response; it is well integrated and stable. The physiological gradients of this organism have not been studied experimentally, but the work of Child on other similarly organized forms indicates the probability of a strong dominance of the anterior end of the body, and the general behavior of the animal shows that this is in fact the case.

Early structural differentiation of the motor apparatus. — In the differentiation of these protozoan organs the contractile organs of response are among the first to assume definite form and they are the only elements of the excitomotor apparatus hitherto recognized in many of these animals. The contractile stalk of the bell animalcule, Vorticella (Fig. 8, p. 68), illustrates this very well. In Diplodinium and some other species there is in addition a suggestion of a further differentiation of a nervous or neuroid mechanism in the neuromotor mass and the strands connected with it, and the partial separation of this from the motor strands.

This precocious structural differentiation of the effector apparatus in Protozoa is of more than passing interest. We shall find as we pass up to the many-celled forms that cells of characteristic structure appear earlier on the motor side than on the sensory side of the reacting apparatus; in brief, muscles as differentiated tissue seem to be more primitive than nerves and sense organs (p. 86).

Adjustments in multicellular organisms. — Wherever many cells are united to form a single body some provision must be made for correlating the activities of the single cells; otherwise the body would not be able to act as a single organism but the conflicting activities of the several cells would result only in interference and destructive incoördination. The correlation may be effected by an internal adjusting mechanism or by a differential mode of response of different cells of the group to external stimulation. Of course, the matter cannot be allowed to rest with this teleological form of statement. What we want to know is how these two factors actually operate and the apparatus with which they work. An illustration taken from the lives of higher animals may help us in the formulation of the problem.

A crude analogy may be drawn from animal societies. In an ant colony each of the various castes which make up the household is structurally adapted to react in a predetermined way to particular situations — the soldier, the various worker castes, the male, the fertile female (p. 147). Each, by reason of its innate structure, can do certain duties and no others, and this organization is such that all of their activities in the aggregate are adapted to conserve the colony. By virtue of the intrinsically determined differential modes of response which characterize the several castes a very efficient coördination of the labors of all of the individuals is effected without any external machinery of social control.

Contrast with this the organization of civilized human societies where the greater freedom of action of the individuals necessitates complex systems of external control by social convention, economic pressure, legal enactments, etc., in order to maintain efficient team-work.

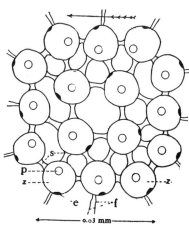

FIG. 15.—Sketch of a colony of Gonium seen from the posterior surface. The 16 cells (z) of which the colony is composed are connected by protoplasmic strands (s) and each is provided, on the face opposite to that here shown, with two flagella (f). Each cell also has an eye-spot (e) and a chlorophyl-bearing organ (p). The flagellated face of the colony is directed forward in locomotion and the colony rotates, usually in the direction of the arrow at the top. After Mast (1916).

In the simplest cellular aggregates a very successful integration of limited range may be effected in a way analogous with that of the ant colony — by differential modes of response of individual cells — and this method of differentiation (speaking broadly) holds its own throughout the plant kingdom, with far less elaborate intercellular adjusting apparatus than in animals. The nervous system is *par excellence* the intercellular adjusting mechanism, without which the complex of local activities of higher animal bodies cannot be effectively correlated and integrated.

We are interested in the steps by which these master tissues have attained their position of dominance.

Integration in Gonium and Volvox. — The method of adjustment by differential response of the separate cells is illustrated by some simple colonial plant forms like the water nets. Gonium is such a colony, composed of a flat sheet about 0.1 mm. wide containing 16 individual cells connected by strands of protoplasm (Fig. 15). Each cell (Fig. 16) is ovoid in shape and is provided with two motor threads (flagella), which by their vibratory movements propel the colony through the water. These cells in structure and behavior are similar to some of the simpler one-celled forms known as flagellated monads (Fig. 7, p. 67).

Mast (1916) has studied the reactions of these colonies to light. He finds that the colony orients very directly, swimming with the flat surface bearing the flagella perpendicular to the rays of light. "If the position of the source of light is changed after the colony is oriented so that the rays strike the anterior surface obliquely, it turns at once until the rays are again approximately perpendicular to this surface." This orientation is effected by differential movements of the flagella of the separate cells in different parts of the colony. "The turning of the colony in the process of orientation is due to an increase in the activity of the flagella of the zooids farthest from the source of light." Those cells in which the photosensitive substance

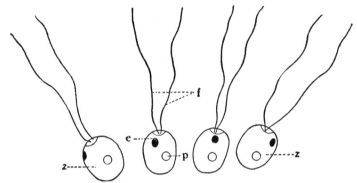

Fig. 16.—Four separate cells from a colony of Gonium seen from the side. Significance of the letters the same as in figure 15. After Mast.

is more strongly illuminated react differently from those in which they are less strongly illuminated, and the orientation of the colony is brought about by these differences in the reactions of the separate cells and not by any central correlating mechanism.

The individual zooids of the colony of Gonium are directly connected by intercellular protoplasmic bridges and it is not improbable that there is under some circumstances a measure of correlation of the activities of the several zooids by internal transmission of excitations from cell to cell, as is known to be the case in the similar but more highly organized Volvox, even through the experiments cited do not reveal this internal factor.

Volvox is in many respects similar to Gonium but considerably more elaborately organized. It is a small spherical body composed of from 200 to 20,000 cells arranged in a single layer around a central cavity. The cells are of two sorts, distinguished as somatic and reproductive, the former being more numerous and resembling those of Gonium (Fig. 17). All of the somatic cells of the body are almost, though not exactly, identical in form and functions. There is so little evidence of differentiation among these that the body is frequently called a colony of cells rather than a single organism. Nevertheless there is some difference of structure among the cells, so that anterior and posterior poles can be recognized, and the group reacts as a whole, it has individuality, and there is evidently some apparatus for integrating and correlating the functions of the cells of which it is composed.

The reactions of Volvox to light have also been studied by Mast (1907), who finds that the organism orients with reference to the

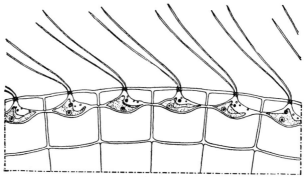

Fig. 17.—Section through a portion of the body wall of Volvox, illustrating the internal structure and protoplasmic connections of the somatic cells. Redrawn from Janet (1912).

direction and intensity of light. In his more recent work (1923 and personal communication) he describes the eye-spots as provided with a well developed lens, beneath which is a pigmented cup of photosensitive protoplasm, more sensitive to blue and green rays than to red and yellow. These eye-spots function as direction eyes. Those at the anterior pole of the body are much larger than those at the posterior pole and these appear to determine the orientation.

The cells of Volvox are not anatomically separate but they are all connected by strands of protoplasm which pass through apertures in the dividing cell walls, forming a true syncytium or protoplasmic network. The reactions as described by Mast and by Janet (1912) make it clear that in Volvox there is an internal apparatus for integrating and coördinating the activities of the body as a whole and both the reactions and the structure suggest the presence of an apico-basal physiological gradient, but data on this point are not yet available.

The anterior pole of the body is directed forward in locomotion, the flagella over the entire surface beat harmoniously, that is, in such a way that the effect of the beat of each zooid supports that of the others in orderly fashion, and there are other reactions which indicate that there is some degree of internal correlation. We may, therefore, accept the conclusion of Janet that Volvox is an organism and not a colonial aggregate of unicellular individuals.

We have in Gonium and Volvox the very lowest possible types of many-celled body as distinguished from a colonial group of separate individuals. The machinery of protoplasmic conduction from part to part is present, comparable with the nervous system of higher animals, but in so imperfectly developed a form as to play a relatively small part in the economy of the body.

The distinction between a colony of individual cells joined together and a multicellular individual is hard to draw and no sharp definition is possible. The criterion just mentioned is of value but cannot be applied rigorously. That is, it is a question of degree of integration of the group as a whole in comparison with that of the several cells of which it is composed. The same applies to larger bodies composed of many cells. The single polyp is regarded as an individual even in cases where many are united by cellular tissue to a common stem, for each polyp is well integrated with a clearly defined center of chief dominance and the individuals are well isolated physiologically. In most hydroid colonies and in the stag-horn corals there is also a physiological gradient in the colony as a whole, one of the persons exhibiting marked physiological dominance over the others. In compound sponges, on the other hand, the physiological individuality of the parts is much less marked and the differentiation of the separate persons is far less evident. The group as a whole, moreover, lacks a single center of highest dominance, so that the compound sponge is regarded as a colony of poorly integrated individuals.

Excitomotor adjustments in sponges. — The jellyfishes, polyps and their allies (cœlenterates are the lowest forms known to possess true nerves and here the first steps in the evolution of the nervous system have been sought. But recent studies of the sponges by Parker have shown that these still simpler animals give us the first stage in the cellular differentiation of the reflex apparatus in many celled organisms and that this is represented by well formed muscles without any special nerves or sense organs whatsoever. These facts have been so clearly and fully presented in Parker's recent book (1919) that a brief reference only will here be necessary.

The structure of a simple sponge is illustrated in Fig. 18. The body is shaped like a vase with thick porous walls. Water enters the central cavity by numerous superficial pores and leaves it by a single aperture at the tip, the osculum. In the fingered form of sponge, Stylotella, with which Parker worked, the osculum may be opened and closed. The oscula tend to close in still water, after mechanical injury to the sponge, and in some other situations.

The osculum is encircled by a ring of primitive muscular tissue whose contraction closes the aperture. There are no nerve cells, nerve fibers, or special sense organs, the stimulus apparently being applied directly to the muscle or transmitted to it by simple protoplasmic conduction. There is very slight coördination of reaction in different parts of the body of the sponge. From his experiments Parker concludes: "Sponges, then, represent that stage in evolution in which a primitive type of muscle tissue has made its appearance unaccompanied with nervous elements. To state this conclusion in the terms used in the earlier part of this discussion, sponges may be said to have among their cell combinations effectors, but no receptors or adjustors. They mark the beginnings of the neuromuscular mechanism in that they possess the original and most ancient of its constituents, muscle, around which the remainder of the system is supposed subsequently to have been evolved." This last conclusion is reinforced by citing a number of cases in the higher animals where muscles may act independently of nerves, as in the human iris.

Fig. 18.—Diagram of the canal system of a calcareous sponge. The cavities are drawn in black. The innumerable superficial pores receive water from the exterior, as shown by the arrows on the sides; the osculum at the apex discharges water to the exterior. After Parker.

In Parker's studies of sponges and other lowly organisms it seems to be assumed that where there are differentiated muscles or effector organs but no differentiated receptive organs or nerves we have an isolated "effector system" in contrast with the "receptor-effector systems" of higher animals. But, of course, an isolated pure effector would be as useless as an isolated sense organ. The apparatus of response implies of necessity a sensitive mechanism as well as a motor organ.

The experiments of Parker really show that the so-called constrictor muscles which close the exhalent apertures of sponges are not isolated effectors, but that each is a system combining receptive and motor functions. Though there is some response to powerful stimuli applied a short distance from the aperture, this conductivity is limited to what ordinary undifferentiated protoplasm may be expected to perform, such as is exhibited by unicellular species and primitive multicellular types like Volvox. In sponges the experiments show (Parker, 1919, pp. 40–41) that the most rapid and positive responses result from local stimulation applied directly to the so-called effectors, *i. e.*, the tissues in the immediate vicinity of the aperture to be closed. These supposed muscles are, therefore, really neuromotor organs from the start. The same is doubtless true of excitomotor tissues of higher animals, like the muscles of the iris in the human eye. (See further discussion of this matter by Child, 1921, Chap. 13.) The bodies of simple sponges exhibit physiological gradients similar to those of polyps, the metabolism being higher at the oscular end (Hyman and Bellamy, 1922, Child, 1924, Chap. 7).

The differentiation of receptor and effector apparatus in the sponge is really not so far advanced as in some one-celled forms, *e. g.*, the Diplodinium figured on page 79. In the latter case there are within a single cell differentiated strands of neuromotor protoplasm and of these there are two systems, the retractor strands and the neuromotor strands. Both of these systems combine motor and nervous functions, but in the first the motor (effector) factor predominates and in the second the sensory (receptor) and conducting factors predominate. In a neuromotor apparatus of the most primitive type like that found in protozoans and sponges the receptor aspect is at least as important a factor in determining the high dominance of the apical regions as is the motor aspect of the complex, and probably more so.

It remains true, however, as Parker maintains, that as soon as the neuromotor apparatus reaches the stage of differentiation represented by typical reflex arcs with separate receptor, effector and adjusting mechanisms the motor elements of the complex exhibit a high degree of tissue differentiation earlier than do the sensory. This applies in the embryologic development of vertebrates and probably also in phylogeny. The organs of contraction are "mature" tissue types, but despite their high structural differentiation and high metabolic rate under excitation, they remain always subordinate in the physiological gradients to the receptive and adjusting apparatus; muscle is the servant of nerve.

Summary. — In Protozoa physiological gradients and polarity may be functionally manifest as immediate response to excitation without accompanying permanent structural differentiation of the reacting substance. With the development of permanent organs — cuticle, receptors, motile flagella, etc., — structural polarity also appears, usually of the apico-basal type. Within these bodies a very elaborate intracellular excitomotor apparatus may be differentiated with incomplete separation of protoplasm which is predominantly neuroid from that which is clearly myoid.

A number of cells may be combined to form a body in two ways: either (1) by the formation of an aggregate in which the positions of the separate cells with reference to one another and to the sources of external stimulation lead to differential responses in the various parts of the body such as result in appropriate or adaptive behavior of the aggregate, or (2) by the development of an internal adjusting mechanism (primordial or definitive nervous system as the case may be) which effects correlation and integration of the diversified activities of the parts. In the first case each cell acts as an independent organism and we have a colony of cells comparable with colonies of social insects where, though there is no anatomical connection between the persons, yet each by virtue of its innate organization adjusts its behavior to that of the group as a whole. In the second case we have a multicellular organism whose individual cells and organs are subordinated to a single center of physiological dominance. All grades and combinations of these two types of aggregation are found.

Sponges possess a very loosely organized multicellular body, often of large size. They multiply by budding through physiological isolation of parts, thus forming colonies of multicellular persons in which the limits of the separate individuals are hard to define. Each person or separate lobe of the aggregate has a dominant apical region possessing differentiated excitomotor cells which morphologically have been characterized as muscle cells, though they probably are excitomotor elements.

CHAPTER VIII

THE DAWN OF THE NERVOUS SYSTEM

Neuromotor cells of polyps — Receptor-effector systems — Nerve net of polyps and jellyfishes — Nerve ring of medusæ — Physiological gradients and dominance in cœlenterates — Summary of nervous system of medusæ — Nervous system of the starfish — Cephalization — Theories of the origin of the nervous system

Neuromotor cells of polyps. — A true nervous system first appears in the cœlenterates (polyps, sea anemones and jellyfishes). This has long been known, but it has been very difficult to discover the exact facts regarding the structure of these primitive elements and our knowledge is still very fragmentary; see the summaries by Parker (1919) and Havet (1922).

Kleinenberg (1872) taught that in the freshwater hydra (Fig. 19) certain cells of the outer layer of the body wall (Fig. 20) combine the functions of a neuromotor apparatus, the external part of the cell being receptive and the basal prolongations being motor; and on the basis of this there was formulated an elaborate theory of the evolution of the nervous system which has given rise to much controversy. Child, who has devoted a great deal of attention to the behavior of polyps, is of the opinion (1921, p. 240) that

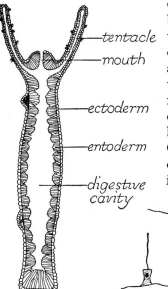

tentacle

mouth

ectoderm

entoderm

digestive cavity

supporting cell

sensory cell

A **B**

Fig. 19. — Diagrammatic longitudinal section through the body of the fresh water Hydra. Modified from Shipley and MacBride's Zoölogy.

Fig. 20.—Various types of neuromuscular cells in cœlenterates. A, after Pütter. B, after Hertwig (modified).

89

such neuromotor elements occur essentially as described by Kleinen-berg. In some polyps these superficial neuromotor cells may be present in addition to special sensory cells and a rudimentary nervous system in the deeper layers of the body.

Receptor-effector systems. — In some polyps and in the tentacles of the sea anemone certain superficial cells are especially modified so as to increase their sensitiveness to stimulation and their central ends are prolonged into filaments which reach down into contact with underlying muscle cells (Fig. 21 A).

Here we have a neuromotor unit of two cells, one of which combines the function of sense organ (receptor) and nerve fiber (conductor) and the other represents the effector. This two-celled unit is called a receptor-effector system. The receptor element is a true nerve cell and the animal possessing it has numerous advantages over the sponge: (1) The sensory cell is structurally adapted to respond to weaker stimuli than is the surrounding protoplasm; that is, the threshold of excitation has been lowered. (2) Different sensory cells may be differently organized so as to be responsive to different kinds of stimuli; for example, the threshold of one may be lowered for pressures and of another for stimulation by chemicals. Here is the beginning of the differentiation of the separate sense organs. (3) The protoplasmic filament is structurally modified to facilitate rapid conduction, giving truly nervous as contrasted with the "neuroid" type of transmission and making possible much more rapid responses. There is, however, no special mechanism for connecting this activity with that of other parts of the body except the immediate vicinity of the spot stimulated, and the correlation of the actions of distant parts of the body remains on a plane scarcely removed from the "neuroid" type of conduction seen in Volvox and sponges.

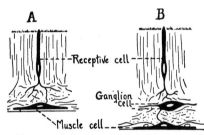

FIG. 21.—Diagrams of primitive nervous systems. A, a simple "receptor-effector system," where the receptive cell is directly connected with the effector cell; B, a more complex system in which a conducting element is interpolated between receptor and effector cells. After Parker.

Nerve net of polyps and jellyfishes. — The next step in the fabrication of the nervous system was taken when special cells were set apart to serve as conductors only and thus to facilitate free intercommunication of part with part (Fig. 21 B). We know by experiment that the receptive parts of the body (tentacles and parts about the mouth) are in general physiologically dominant over other parts and that

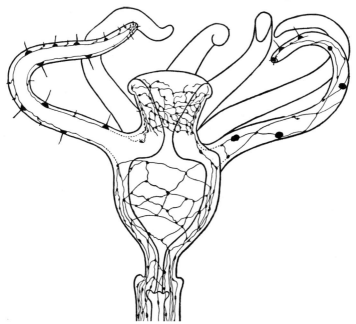

FIG. 22.—Diagram of the arrangement of the nerve net in a polyp.
After Max Wolf (1904).

increase in the range of this dominance is a big factor in the enlarge-ment of the individuality of the organism.   This is accomplished by the more efficient conducting apparatus.

The simplest form of this ap-paratus is found in some polyps and in the jellyfishes, where nerve cells scattered between the sense cells and the muscle cells have numerous branching processes which unite into a net which connects with the fibrous processes of the sensory cells on one side and with the muscle cells on the other side (Figs. 22, 23, 24).   Thus the excitation of

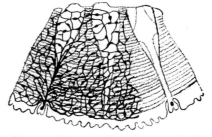

FIG. 23.—Nerve net from the subumbrellar surface of a medusa.   The muscle fibers are indicated by gray shading, the nerve fibers by the black network.   After Bethe.

a single group of sensory cells may be diffused and result in the con-traction of many muscle cells, perhaps all of the muscles of the body

(Hertwig, 1918, p. 396).   The excitation of many sensory cells may reinforce each other and so strengthen the response, or on the other hand two excitations which tend to produce opposite effects may act on the same muscle cells with resulting blocking of the response.

The presence of the nerve net, accordingly, introduces the following improvements in the neuromuscular apparatus: (1) the excitation has a greater range of application and total responses to stimulation and integration of larger and more complex bodies are possible;

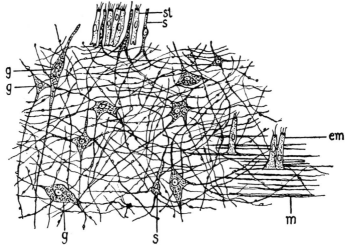

Fig. 24.—Schematic picture of the ectodermal nervous, sensory and muscular systems of the cœlenterates.   A portion of the ectoderm (epidermis) is shown at the top of the figure. This epithelium consists of supporting cells (*st.*), among which are scattered sensory cells (*s*).   The basal ends of the latter are extended to form fine nerve fibers which spread out in a subepithelial nervous plexus.   The epithelium also contains muscle cells (*em*), whose basal ends are extended to form contractile filaments. There are muscle fibers (*m*) which lie wholly below the epidermis.   The nervous plexus which extends between the epithelial sensory cells and the muscle cells contains nerve cells of several kinds. After Hertwig (1918).

(2) reinforcement and (3) inhibition of response are facilitated.   The last two points are of the greatest signficance in the elaboration of more complex types of behavior.

But the nerve net is at best a rather indifferent conductor as compared with the nerves of higher animals (see p. 103), so that the integrating power of this type of nervous system is not great, and no well organized central adjustor is provided.   In the bodies of these animals, therefore, there is a large measure of local autonomous control and the unifying or integrating influence has advanced very little beyond the level seen in Protozoa and the simple polyps.

In these animals local reactions to stimulation can be made promptly and efficiently, but the control is chiefly local, not central. If a piece of meat is put on the tentacle of an anemone it will bend toward the mouth, this being a part of the normal feeding reaction. And if the tentacle is cut off and similarly stimulated, it will bend in the direction which would take it toward the mouth if it were still attached to the body, showing that the movement is locally not centrally directed.

The bodies of jellyfishes are so much larger than those of unicellular forms that the neuroid type of protoplasmic conduction as exemplified in the Protozoa would be quite inadequate to traverse the longer distances, and the more widely separated parts would be more or less completely isolated physiologically from one another, as indeed is the case in sponges. The nerve net is able to diminish this physiological resistance to transmission, and so to maintain the integrity of the organization; but its conductivity is not sufficiently good to provide a much higher type of integration than that shown by the protozoans. The physiological characteristics of the nerve net of the large medusæ have been much studied and some of this work is summarized on page 104.

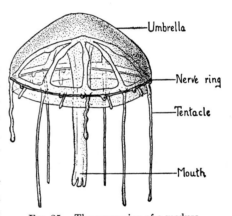

FIG. 25.—The nerve ring of a medusa.

Nerve ring of medusæ. — In some jellyfishes, as in the umbrella-shaped medusæ (Fig. 25), a series of tentacles hangs pendant from the margin of the umbrella, and on these tentacles are the chief receptive organs by whose stimulation the activities of the body as a whole are largely directed. The tentacles are movable and are very sensitive. There is also an elaborate system of sense organs at the margin of the umbrella along the line of attachment of the tentacles. Locomotion is effected by pulsations of the whole body which force water out of the cavity inclosed by the umbrella and thus drive the body onward. This movement may be excited by a stimulus applied to a single tentacle.

The portion of the nerve net which borders the margin of the umbrella at the base of the fringe of tentacles is concentrated into a denser ring of nerve cells and fibers (Fig. 25). This nerve ring is so

connected with the more diffuse nerve net that a local stimulus anywhere may rapidly be transmitted to all of the muscles of the body
and so start locomotor movements.

The local condensation of the nerve net in the nerve ring at the
margin of the umbrella is the first step in the development of a center
of correlation or adjustment in many-celled animals. The nerves
coming in from the tentacles enter the nerve ring, as do also those
from the sense organs at the margin of the umbrella. The nerve
ring is similar in principle to the neuromotor mass and its connecting neuromotor strands as described in the protozoan Diplodinium
(p. 78), and it is functionally scarcely more efficient save that the
many cells of which it is composed are able to reach a wider extent
and so to correlate the activities of a large body.

Physiological gradients and dominance in cœlenterates. — The
nerve net has a functional polarization. A strong excitation applied to
it anywhere will be irradiated in every direction and any part of it can
conduct in one direction at one time and in the reverse direction at
another time. This is in sharp contrast with the reflex apparatus of
higher animals, whose elements (neurons) are structurally polarized
and so articulated with each other that nerve impulses can pass
from one element to another in one direction only. For reasons
which will appear (p. 105) the nerve net is called a non-synaptic
nervous system in opposition to the structural polarized (synaptic)
systems of higher animals.

There is, however, a certain measure of permanent structural polarization in the cœlenterate body, as appears clearly in the body form of
polyps (Fig. 19) and in the arrangement of their nerve nets (Fig. 22).
This polarization is expressed physiologically as an axial gradient of
high metabolism at the apical end running down to lower metabolism
at the attached end. Similar conditions prevail in medusæ.

Yerkes' experiments on the medusa, Gonionemus (1902), show that
the tentacles and the mouth region (manubrium) are the most sensitive parts of the body. Responses are most often excited by stimulation of these regions in the normal life of the animal. In a sense they
give physiological direction to its activities. If, however, a single
tentacle or the mouth region is cut off, the detached part will respond
to stimulation in ways similar to those of the normal feeding reaction.
The movements of these parts are, therefore, under local control and
are not wholly dependent upon connection with the nerve ring.
Yerkes concludes that there is no single center of coördination in the
medusa which physiologically controls the body as a whole as does

the brain of higher animals. The coördinating power of the nerve ring seems to be due chiefly to the fact that it is a better conductor than surrounding parts. The nerve ring is, accordingly, only a first step toward the central nervous system of higher forms. Its integrating power is very slight and this can apparently be reduced largely to the simple quantitative factor of greater conductivity.

These conclusions were reached from the behavioristic study of the medusæ. On the physiological side Child and Hyman have found that the regions of highest sensitiveness in both medusæ and polyps are also centers of highest metabolic rate and of physiological dominance, as shown by experiments on susceptibility to toxic substances and by other methods. The tips of the tentacles and the mouth region are the first to show the effect of the drugs. They also show the highest chemical activity, as indicated by power to reduce potassium permanganate, by difference in oxygen consumption and carbon dioxid production, and the highest galvanometric electronegativity. The hydranth (body) of polyps occupies a higher position in the physiological gradients than does the stem, and apical pieces of stem regenerate hydranths more rapidly than do basal pieces. The physiological gradients of these forms as demonstrated experimentally conform fully to the polarities observed in general behavior (Child and Hyman, 1919; Hyman, 1920; Child, 1919, 1921 a, 1924, Chap. 7, Hyman and Bellamy, 1922).

That the sense organs and associated nerve ring of medusæ are centers of higher metabolism and do exert a control over other activities of the body in regeneration after injuries and otherwise has been shown by Carey (1916, 1917) in a series of ingenious experiments.

The individual parts of the body also show local gradients both in structure and in function. In the tentacles of the sea anemone the nerve fibers arising from the sensory cells grow for the most part downward toward the attached base of the tentacle (Grošelj, 1909), and when one of these tentacles is stimulated midway of its length it shortens more vigorously from the point stimulated toward the base than toward the distal end (Rand, 1915, p. 185).

The activities of cœlenterates show a small measure of that individual modifiability resulting from personal experience which is found in Protozoa. For illustrations of this capacity for "learning by experience" and its limitations see Jennings (1905 a) and Parker (1917, 1919, pp. 163–174).

Summary of nervous system of medusæ. — In these animals we have a structural differentiation of a true nervous system whose functional pattern can be expressed quantitatively in several ways: (1) increased sensitiveness (lowered threshold) of the receptors; (2) differentiation of the receptors into qualitatively specific sense organs with lowered thresholds permitting more effective analysis of the diverse environing energies — a process which has barely begun in polyps is in medusæ far advanced; (3) lowered resistance to physiological conduction of the nerve net and greater range and rate of transmission; (4) condensation of the nerve net in the nerve ring and a limited measure of localized physiological control through its better conducting power; (5) higher metabolic activity in the more sensitive regions; (6) increased physiological dominance in the same regions and capacity for more complete integration of the body as a whole; (7) correlated with the last a limited measure of permanent structural and physiological polarization, that is, a short step in the direction of the process of cephalization.

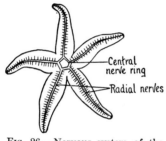

FIG. 26.—Nervous system of the starfish.

Nervous system of the starfish. — The starfishes and their allies elaborate this plan. The chief central apparatus is a circumoral ring from which nervous cords extend out into the rays (Fig. 26). But this pattern appears to be incapable of very high development. In these so-called radiate animals the principal polar axis is relatively unimportant; they have no heads and no center of great physiological dominance. They are poorly unified and in general lowly organized.

Cephalization. — Worm-like forms, on the other hand, have a definite habit of moving head-first, the head and tail ends are clearly separate, and the leading segments are highly dominant over the rest of the body. This is the beginning of a process which carries through all the higher ranks of the animal kingdom and is known as cephalization. This progressive elaboration of the head is an expression of the increasing importance of the chief center of dominance in animal evolution.

Theories of the origin of the nervous system. — It has been pointed out that theories regarding the early phylogenetic stages in the evolution of the nervous system have centered chiefly in the cœlenterate animals considered in this chapter. This history has been reviewed by Parker (1919) and by Child (1921, Chap. 13) and need not again be summarized here.

In the consideration of this topic it is essential that we take our departure from the fact brought out in strong relief in the preceding chapters that those functions which especially characterize the nervous system — excitability, conduction, integration — are well developed in lowly forms which totally lack differentiated nervous elements. These non-nervous bodies in most cases show obvious anatomical and physiological polarization and in almost all cases there are excitation-conduction gradients correlated with apical or head dominance of some sort and general integration of the organismic type.

From this it follows that when the first differentiated nervous apparatus appeared it was laid down in a physiological matrix which shaped the course of its development from the start. This conception has been elaborated by Child (1921, 1924) and we can proceed at once to follow out his argument further. The earliest differentiated cells of the neuromotor arcs, whether we consider the so-called muscle fibers of sponges, the neuromotor cells of polyps, or the sense organs, nerve nets and muscles of medusæ, are differentiated *in situ* within an excitation-transmission gradient in which all of the physiological factors of reflex arcs as these are known in higher forms are actually present — receptors, conductors, effectors, and something more than the mere potentiality of correlating or integrating factors. Furthermore, these most primitive types of response are in general adaptive; they tend, when all is said, toward the conservation of the individual or the species.

At the time, then, when a hypothetical primitive nerve net was first laid down, it was not an equipotential system conducting indifferently in all directions, but its elements arose from undifferentiated cells whose functional polarities were already established by virtue of the excitations by which they were habitually activated. The unknown ancestors of our present-day polyps and medusæ undoubtedly possessed apico-basal polarity before they possessed nerves, just as do the still more primitive unicellular forms. It is significant also that the early developmental stages of many multicellular forms also exhibit it, even from the first appearance of the egg in some cœlenterates (Child, 1921, p. 54, 1924). Within such a gradient sense cell, nerve cell and muscle fiber may have arisen from a single neuromotor cell, as Kleinenberg supposed, or from separate cells, as the Hertwigs believed; but in any case their polarities were predetermined by the general gradients within which they were developed.

When, however, the improved conductors were laid down in definite circumscribed pathways and these were connected into a nerve net pervading the entire body, a strong stimulus at any point could irradiate through these conductors in any direction, for such an excitation can overcome the permanent primary axial gradients. The result is that the whole body is intimately knit together and so the apparatus is at hand for vastly greater complexity of response than before.

So long as the nervous fabric is in the form of such a loosely woven network, as seen for instance in the polyps (Fig. 22), the integrating power is small, indeed perhaps inferior to that of some protozoans. The greater ease of communication from part to part permits local and transitory excitations to run counter to the primary axial gradients and no part gains undisputed control; there is no single center of very high dominance which keeps the rest of the body in subordination. The primary axial gradients, however, are not lost and the organism retains its individuality.

With the further concentration of the nerve net in the more highly excitable regions the course of evolution is set in a new direction and from this point forward a local center of highest dominance takes a larger part in shaping the destiny of the individual and establishing the pattern in accordance with which future differentiation must take place. An orthogenetic factor has entered which is nothing other then the establishment of limits within which further evolutionary progress must be confined (Herrick, 1920). This center of highest dominance may or may not coincide with the high point of the primary axial gradient, depending on various physiological, morphological and embryological factors. Henceforth in evolution the principle of head dominance plays an increasingly important rôle.

Some of the physiological factors operative in the earlier phases of this process have already been outlined. High functional activity, especially that directly evoked by external excitation, has been shown experimentally to be correlated with a high rate of metabolism. The constituents of the activated protoplasm are kept in unstable chemical equilibrium and regulatory activity tending toward a return to the unexcited condition is transmitted from the focus of the excitation, thus giving rise to the physiological gradients.

In forms possessing relatively unspecialized tissues without nerves, the conduction from the primary center of dominance is slow and limited in range. But with the development of nerves the control of the dominant center is greatly widened; excitations are rapidly transmitted to relatively great distances and, by reason of the readier conductivity of the nerves as contrasted with non-nervous tissues and of some nervous pathways over others, the dominant center exerts its influence in a differential way, some parts of the body responding only to one kind of excitation, others to a different kind. Thus the structural pattern of the body has been laid down in the course of the elaboration of diversity in the modes of response; and, conversely, the behavior pattern of the animal, or its action system, comes to be an expression of the structural pattern of the centers of excitation and conduction. The steps by which this stable pattern came to be developed will be examined shortly.

The nervous system, accordingly, is the chief apparatus of excitation, conduction, and integration, by which environmental forces acting on the body are transmitted to the particular organs of response whose activity produces the appropriate reaction. Some of these neuromotor connections may be so made as to produce tropisms in the sense of Loeb, that is, orientation of the body with reference to the source of the stimulus which is directly forced by the specific action of the excitation on a neuromuscular apparatus so connected up as to necessitate the response in question and no other; but many of them are undoubtedly more complex than this with variable types of interaction, in the centers of adjustment, of numerous simultaneous or successive excitations leading to one of several possible responses depending upon the internal physiological condition of the reacting mechanism at the time. The identical stimulus applied to an earthworm may at one time be followed by forward crawling and at another time by an avoiding reaction in the form of a quick jerk backward which brings into play an entirely different set of nervous elements (p. 133), the difference in response depending on the physiological state of the worm at the time.

This conception of the analysis in the correlation centers of an excitation-conduction complex so that the discharge may eventuate in diverse ways at different times on account of varying internal states is by no means a vague generalization or a meaningless play upon words, for many of the factors involved have been definitely analyzed and quantitatively expressed in terms of physiological gradients, bio-electric changes, accumulation of toxic products of metabolism in fatigue, and more important still "competing" conduction paths. Some of these factors have been most clearly analyzed in simple non-nervous protoplasm (which exhibits the same phenomenon of modifiability of reaction), others in nervous tissue, and the evidence is clear that the phenomena do not differ in principle in these two cases.

One of the greatest steps in advance in evolution, accordingly, was the acquisition of the simple habit of moving head-first. The resultant process of cephalization carries with it not only the development of the sense organs and their related ganglia in the leading segments separate from the locomotor mechanisms, but also the elaboration of the more complex feeding mechanisms in association with them. The history of the course of the evolution of the nervous system from worms upward is to a large extent bound up with the process of cephalization and the habit of looking ahead in the world. Man owes his preëminent position to the fact that his higher brain centers enable him to see even beyond the data of present experience and to shape his conduct in view of probable future events.

CHAPTER IX

TISSUE DIFFERENTIATION IN THE NERVOUS SYSTEM

Differentiation of tissues — Embryologic differentiation — Differentiation of nerve cells — Synaptic and non-synaptic nervous systems — Origin of the synaptic nervous system — The neuron concept — Polarization of the neuron — The synapse — Rhythms of nervous discharge — Conclusion

Differentiation of tissues. — One of the first steps in the differentiation of protoplasm is manifested on the behavior side by the elaboration of fixed and stable action systems and the separation of these from the more transient, labile and readily modifiable phases of activity. An ameba can "learn" to avoid noxious substances and irritants (p. 289) and other one-celled animals have some ability to form "habits." Though a much slower biological process, some lines of conduct are more permanently woven into the complex organic fabric and appear as fixed tropisms, reflexes and instincts common to all members of the species.

Parallel with these processes there is on the anatomical side a gradual change in the structure of the protoplasm — the plan of the building is transformed to fit the growing business housed therein. Some of these changes are temporary readjustments related to evanescent functional phases, a mere rearrangement of the office furniture; but others are much more permanent alterations formed by setting apart special chemical substances which serve particular functions — nuclei, intracellular mechanisms of contraction, conduction, excretion, and the like, and rigid supporting cell walls and cellular frameworks. Later in evolution there is a further differentiation of entire groups of cells for particular duties, that is, tissue formation, illustrated by connective tissue, glands, muscles, and so on, each with a characteristic and permanent hereditary structure.[1]

These stable structural differentiations are in all cases correlated with the mode of life of the organism, but it is not to be inferred

[1] The mechanism of this process of tissue differentiation need not be considered here. Child (1924, Chaps. 5, 8) argues with cogency that the same fundamental physiological factors lie at the basis of tissue differentiation and the formation of behavior patterns, namely, the physiological gradients as responses of protoplasm to external stimulation. Somewhat similar views have been expressed by Lillie (1918 a, 1923) and Bok (1917).

from this that they are formed by inheritance of acquired characters in the Lamarkian sense. This may or may not be true, for natural selection, organic selection and other biological factors are adequate, as Child (1921, pp. 66, 270, 1924, Chap. 3) has made clear.

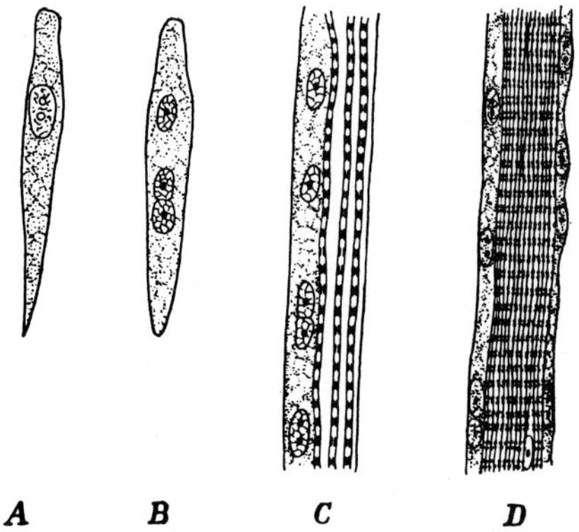

Embryologic differentiation. — The fertilized egg is really a very highly organized affair, but in the cleavage stages the several cells show little evidence of the diverse patterns of the adult body. These cells pass through a succession of changes, some leading up to one type of differentiated or "mature" tissue and some to another. In the development of the striated or voluntary type of muscle, for instance, the muscle fibers pass through the stages diagrammatically shown in Fig. 27. There is first a single embryonic cell with one nucleus; then a cell with several nuclei; next a portion of the protoplasm shows longitudinal and cross striation; later the whole fiber elongates, the number of nuclei greatly increases, and more of the protoplasm assumes the striations characteristic of specialized muscle fiber; finally nearly all of the greatly increased protoplasm is thus transformed into contractile substance and the muscle fiber is complete.

A   B   C   D

Fig. 27.—Diagrams of successive stages in the embryonic development of muscle fibers. A, embryonic cell with one nucleus; B, the same cell with several nuclei; C, further increase in number of nuclei and appearance at one side of differentiated contractile protoplasmic fibrils; D, the mature muscle fiber with most of the protoplasm differentiated and a small residue of undifferentiated protoplasm surrounding the nuclei. The sketches are based on Dahlgren and Kepner's illustrations of the development of striated muscle of the fish, Catostomus.

In various adult animals we find matured muscle fibers in which differentiation has advanced to permanent forms corresponding approximately with these transitory stages of differentiation of muscle in higher species. The neuromuscular cell of Hydra (Fig. 20, p. 89), is an epithelial cell but little modified from the generalized form. In the nematode worms

Fig. 28.—Muscle cell of a nematode worm. From Claus and Grobben's Lehrbuch der Zoologie, 2 ed., Marburg, 1910.

(Fig. 28) there are muscle cells in which a large part of the cell protoplasm has been transformed into specific contractile substance; and in other animal species there are still different degrees of differentiation of the specific contractile elements.

Differentiation of nerve cells. — The cells which compose the nervous system of cœlenterates are woven together into a continuous protoplasmic network whose strands are structurally adapted to transmit excitations with more or less facility, thus promoting the integration and correlation of bodily activities. The structural principle is similar to that which finds still simpler expression in the protoplasmic bridges which connect the cells of Gonium and Volvox (p. 82). This type of nervous system is known as a nerve net; its organization is not far removed from that of the general protoplasmic apparatus of transmission in non-nervous organisms.

In most types of animals above the jellyfish grade of organization the nervous system is elaborated on a different and much more efficient plan, the definitive nervous elements (neurons) having emerged from the more generalized nerve net in a way analogous with that by which striated muscle fibers arise from simpler and less efficient contractile substance, as just outlined. The origin and significance of the neurons will, accordingly, next be considered.

Synaptic and non-synaptic nervous systems. — In the nerve net conductivity is more efficient than in multicellular forms like sponges where there is no nervous system at all, but it is scarcely better than that of ordinary protoplasm and very far from that of the nerve fibers of higher animals. The rate of nervous transmission in sea anemones varies from 0.146 to 0.211 meter per second (Parker, 1918 a), in jellyfish it is about 0.5 meter per second (Harvey, 1922), that of the sciatic nerve of the frog is about 25 meters per second, and of some human nerves is 125 meters.

The nervous system of jellyfishes appears to be a true syncytium, that is, there are no visible cell boundaries. The nuclei of the constituent protoplasm lie at the nodes of the network. There are, therefore, no neurons and no synapses. This nervous system can transmit nervous impulses indifferently in any direction. It doubtless participates in the general polarization of the body to which reference has already been made (pp. 78, 94), and quite possibly (though this has not been experimentally proved) its protoplasm in the resting state shares in the physiological gradients of the body axis with a decrement in rate of metabolism from highly excitable surfaces to the deep muscular masses. But these permanent gradients are easily overcome by strong local stimulation anywhere and the excitation is transmitted in every direction from the point stimulated.

The nerve net does, however, possess some of the distinctive nervous properties, notably that upon sufficient stimulation the excitation is self-propagative and the transmission can continue indefinitely with no obvious decrement in rate or vigor. This has been graphically illustrated by Mayer (1906, 1908) and Harvey (1912, 1922), who cut rings of tissue shaped like a doughnut from the disk of the jellyfish, Cassiopea, and upon excitation the nervous impulse was entrapped and passed round-and-round the ring. Its course can be observed because the underlying muscles are stimulated to contraction with each revolution. In one of Harvey's experiments the nervous impulse continued to move in such a ring for eleven days continuously with no change in rate, traveling 737 kilometers, or 457 miles, at the rate of 0.4647 meter per second, or about 67 kilometers per day. It stopped after eleven days only because regenerating tissue gave rise to impulses which counteracted the entrapped impulse. This result can be secured only if the ring of tissue is large enough to allow a short interval of rest between successive passages of the nervous impulse. In these experiments the muscle showed fatigue earlier than the nerve net.

In summary, the nerve net by reason of the protoplasmic continuity of its strands is a better conductor of protoplasmic excitations than is found, for instance, in sponges, where no such avenues of discharge are present. It is more efficient than the protoplasmic intercellular bridges seen in Volvox because, first, its protoplasm is specially differentiated for conduction, and, second, it does not connect all cells of the body indifferently, but it passes between specific receptors to specific effectors without direct physiological connection with tissues other than those of the reacting system. These improved conductors increase the range of the physiological gradients and so permit the more perfect correlation of the parts and their more unified action in larger bodies than would otherwise be possible. The nerve net is, however, merely a conductor; there is no evidence of well developed centers of correlation in cœlenterates (p. 95).

In most groups of animals above the cœlenterates the cells of which the nervous system is composed (or some of them) are related to each other quite differently from those seen in the meshwork of continuous protoplasmic strands which compose the nerve net. In these higher animals the immature nervous elements, which are known as *neuroblasts*, are in early embryonic stages quite separate cells. Throughout life they retain more or less of this anatomic separateness and also a measure of physiologic individuality. When the neuroblasts are functionally mature they become the *neurons*. In these animals the nervous conductors are chains of neurons and the junctions where nervous impulses are transferred from one neuron to another are the *synapses*. A nervous system composed of neurons separated by synaptic junctions is a synaptic nervous system, in contrast with the non-synaptic systems within whose nerve nets there are no such junctions.

Origin of the synaptic nervous system. — It is probable that the synaptic systems of all higher animals were derived from the non-synaptic prototype, though the precise steps by which this transformation was effected are unknown (Parker, 1919, pp. 199–214). The flatworms, as we shall see (p. 121), are in many respects transitional between the non-synaptic cœlenterates and higher forms with synaptic nervous systems. But the study of the minute structure of the flatworm's nervous system is beset with so many difficulties that no one has succeeded in getting clear pictures of the arrangement of the cells of which it is composed.

The nervous system of the simple marine mollusk, Chromodoris, has recently been studied by a physiological method (Crozier and Arey, 1919) with results of interest in this connection. This species, which has no shell, is provided with a crown of twelve plume-like gills and with tentacles around the mouth, which latter receive their innervation from central ganglia.

It has been shown (Moore, 1917) that small doses of strychnine of definite concentration disturb the functions of synaptic nervous systems, while the same concentration does not affect a non-synaptic nerve net. The functions of the latter, however, are abolished by definite doses of magnesium sulphate. Experiments with these drugs and by other methods show that in this mollusk the gill plumes and other peripheral parts of the body are innervated by a non-synaptic nerve net, but that the nerves and ganglia which supply the tentacles are of synaptic type.

Chromodoris is, therefore, in an interesting transitional state, with the body pervaded with a non-synaptic nerve net of primitive form, from which, however, synaptic ganglia and nerves for the tentacles have been differentiated. In still higher animals (mollusks and others) a progressively larger proportion of the entire nervous system is transformed into the synaptic type, but usually with some remnants of the non-synaptic type remaining. Even in the human body there are said to be such nerve nets in parts of the peripheral sympathetic ganglionic plexuses.

The neuron concept. — A method of impregnation of nervous tissues with salts of silver devised by Golgi of Pavia gave the first clear and complete pictures of the forms and arrangements of the nervous elements. Parallel with these observations the same elements were shown by His of Leipzig to be derived embryologically from undifferentiated cells, as are the other tissues of the body. In short, the nervous system is a cellular fabric in the same sense and with the same limitations as the other organs, and the neuron is first and last simply a nerve cell in its entirety. [1]

The storms of controversy which have surged around the so-called neuron theory are not different in principle from those evoked by the cell theory itself, of which the neuron doctrine is only a particular phase. The cells of higher animal bodies are not individual organisms and they can be understood only in their relations with the whole body (*cf.* Ritter, 1919); so the nerve cells, while real units of embryological development and adult structure, cannot be interpreted, either as regards their functions or the forms which they assume, apart from their anatomic and physiologic relations to one another and to the body as a whole.

The primary function of neurons is conduction. Their forms and internal structures are specifically adapted to perform this duty, and in fact a neuron may be considered as an elongated conducting cell with nucleus and some surrounding protoplasm or cytoplasm (these two together being called the cell body or perikaryon) and one or more elongated strands of protoplasm extending away from the cell body (nerve fibers). The fibrous processes are of two sorts, dendrites conducting toward the cell body and axons conducting away from it. Neurons are classified as sensory, motor, or correlation neurons depending on whether they conduct from a sense organ, toward a motor organ, or lie wholly within a nerve center for connecting its various parts.

The shapes of neurons are infinitely diverse depending chiefly on the space relations of the parts which they connect. Some are

---

[1] A great variety of special and often very complex methods have been discovered for revealing the structure and combinations of the nervous elements. It is only by the use of all of these methods that the organization of the nervous system can be brought to light. The literature of the neuron is very extensive; for good summaries see the following works: Meyer (1898); Barker (1901); Nissl (1903); Golgi (1907); Parker (1918 b); Child (1921, Chap. 10); Herrick (1922, Chap. 3); and the numerous other textbooks on the nervous system.

very long. Fig. 29 illustrates the course of the voluntary motor pathway in the human body. The first neuron extends from the

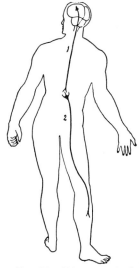

cerebral cortex to the lower end of the spinal cord. Here there is a synaptic junction and the second neuron takes up the nervous impulse and transmits it through the sciatic nerve to the appropriate muscle of the leg. The chief conductor in each of these cases is a very long nerve fiber; it may be a meter long, yet each neuron is a single cell.

At about the time when the developing nerve cell begins to function as a conductor of nervous impulses there appear within its protoplasm delicate threads of more dense material, the *neurofibrils*. In the mature neuron these spread throughout the cytoplasm of the cell body and converge in densely crowded formation into the out-

FIG. 29.—Diagram of the voluntary motor pathway, consisting of two systems of neurons: (1) the upper motor neurons of the pyramidal tract, and (2) the lower or peripheral motor neurons.

growths which form the nerve fibers (Fig. 30). These are found in both in-vertebrate and ver-tebrate nerve cells; but whether they occur in life or are coagulation artefacts produced during the preparation of the protoplasm for microscopic examination is still in controversy.

The neurofibrils can be stained in living nerve cells and fibers by vital dyes, but there is doubt in the minds of some histologists whether the stainable substance in these cases is not a coagulation product marking the beginning of the death of the protoplasm, for the vital dyes are toxic substances. In the

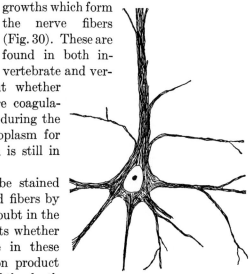

FIG. 30.—Arrangement of neurofibrils in pyramidal cells of the human cerebral cortex. After Ramón y Cajal.

retinal cells of the slug, Limax, Grant Smith (1906) observed the presence of neurofibrils in stained preparations and in the living cells he demonstrated a fibrillar structure by the use of polarized light. Similar observations upon the retinal elements and axis cylinders of nerve fibers of vertebrates have been recorded by Howard (1908). It is, therefore, probable that neurofibrils do occur in the living nerve cells. They are commonly regarded as the essential conductors of the nervous impulse, but of this there is no direct evidence.

At a stage of growth subsequent to the development of the neurofibrils there appears in the cytoplasm of the neuron a special readily

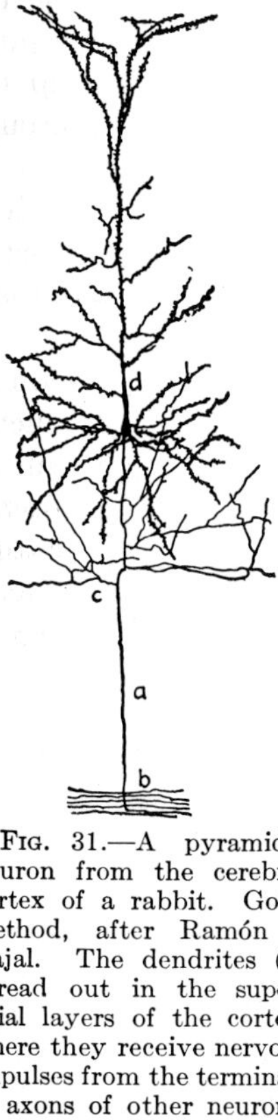

Fig. 31.—A pyramidal neuron from the cerebral cortex of a rabbit. Golgi method, after Ramón y Cajal. The dendrites (*d*) spread out in the superficial layers of the cortex, where they receive nervous impulses from the terminals of axons of other neurons. The axon (*a*) gives off numerous collateral branches (*c*) close to the cell body and then enters the white substance (*b*), within which it extends for a long distance. Only a small part of the axon is included in the drawing. The upper motor neuron of the voluntary motor path (fig. 29, 1) is of similar form.

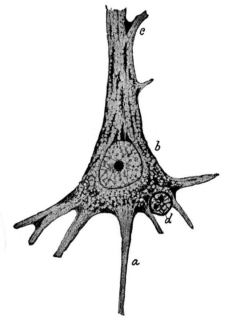

Fig. 32.—The cell body of a pyramidal neuron of the human cerebral cortex stained by the method of Nissl, showing the arrangement of the Nissl bodies. After Ramón y Cajal. This is a cell of the same general type as illustrated in figure 31: *a*, axon; *b*, cell body; *c*, a mass of chromophilic substance in the angle formed by the branching of a dendrite; *d*, nucleus of a neuroglia cell (not a part of the neuron).

stainable material, the *chromophilic substance*. This usually takes the form in stained neurons of flaky masses of considerable size known as Nissl bodies (Figs. 32, 34). They are found in the cytoplasm of the cell bodies and larger dendrites, but never in the axon or the conical axon hillock at the point of origin of axon from cell body. These bodies are apparently artefacts, the result of coagulation of the protoplasm by reagents, but the chromophilic substance itself is doubtless present in life more evenly distributed throughout the protoplasm. This substance is a nucleoprotein containing iron and it appears to play an important part in the metabolism of the cell. It is consumed during intense activity of the neuron and in certain pathological conditions. It is restored to the normal fatigued cell during rest.[1]

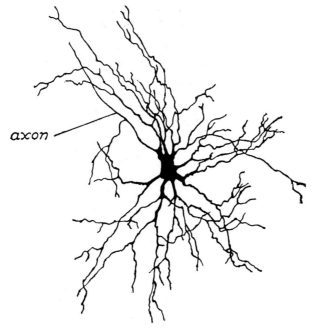

axon

FIG. 33.—Motor neuron from the spinal cord of the human fetus. The axon, only a small part of which is shown, extends outward to form a motor fiber of a peripheral nerve (fig. 29, 2). After von Lenhossék.

The arrangement of the Nissl bodies in stained neurons is quite variable, but cells of like function tend to resemble each other clearly in size, shape and internal structure. The result is that in micro-

[1] For summaries of the rôle of the chromophilic substance see Barker (1901, Chaps. 19–25), Herrick (1922, pp. 107–110) and Heidenhain (1911). The oxidation of the chromophilic substance is an important source of energy in nervous function (p. 256), but this material seems also to play a more fundamental part in the life of the neuron, as has been clearly brought out in chemical studies of the behavior of its contained iron (see Nicholson, 1923, and the literature there cited).

scopic preparations of the brain the various centers, each of which has a characteristic function to perform as determined by its fibrous connections with other centers or end-organs, exhibit structural differences in their neurons. Such collections of nerve cell bodies of like structural and functional character are known as nuclei.[1] Each such aggregate of cell bodies is the terminal nucleus of the fiber tracts which end within it and the nucleus of origin of the fiber tracts which arise from its own cells. Nuclei are usually named after their functions, positions or other distinguishing characters, as the vestibular nucleus, the interpeduncular nucleus, the red nucleus.

Jacobsohn long ago pointed out a striking difference between sensory and motor nerve cells in that the former exhibit finely granu-

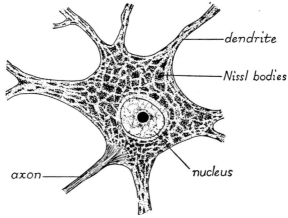

FIG. 34.—Motor neuron of the human spinal cord to illustrate the arrangement of Nissl bodies.

lar evenly distributed Nissl bodies while in cells of motor type the chromophilic substance is arranged in coarser masses. Malone (1913, 1913 a) has carried this analysis further and shown that visceral motor neurons discharging through the sympathetic nervous system have smaller and less deeply staining Nissl bodies than do motor neurons which discharge upon striated muscle. These structural differences are doubtless correlated with the obvious functional peculiarities of these classes of nerve cells. As an illustration of these

---

[1] This use of the term nucleus is unfortunate, though deeply intrenched in our nomenclature. The nucleus in the neurologic sense must not be confused with the nuclei of the individual neurons which constitute the center in question. Some careful writers apply the term nidulus to the cell cluster commonly called a nucleus and thus evade the ambiguity (C. L. Herrick, Jour. Comp. Neur., Vol. 1, 1891, p. 17).

functional differences, it has been shown (Baglioni, 1900, 1905) that phenol is an excitant of motor nerve cells, while strychnine stimulates sensory nerve cells but not motor.

Any severe injury to the neuron which impairs its metabolic activity — extreme fatigue, effects of toxic substances and other diseased conditions, or injury to its axon — may cause a disappearance of the chromophilic substance. This is known as *chromatolysis* and may be permanent in case the neuron is irreparably injured or transient in case restoration to normal conditions is effected.

Polarization of the neuron. — Some recent discussions of the polarization of the neuron have led to confusion because of failure to take separate account of structural and functional criteria. Our concept of polarization and its basic factors must be clearly defined if fruitless controversy about words is to be avoided.

It has already been pointed out that the neuron is fundamentally a conductor and that the differentiation of the nervous system, both phylogenetically and ontogenetically, begins and is consummated within a field which is already functionally polarized by preëxisting axial gradients (p. 97). Since the neuron develops within these primary organismic gradients and develops its own polarity and associated structural peculiarities through the further working of the same type of physiological agencies as operate in the establishment of the primary axial gradients, it is evident that our interest centers chiefly in the physiological aspects of the question.

The neuron is a cell, and as such the maintenance of its functions is contingent upon the physiological integrity of the nucleus of the cell and the protoplasm surrounding it (cytoplasm). If a portion of this cytoplasm is isolated from its nucleus, as by cutting a peripheral nerve, the detached part will die, though the remainder of the cell may survive and even regenerate the lost portion of the nerve fiber. This is a feature common to all cells which has nothing to do with polarity.

But the directions taken and forms assumed by the fibrous outgrowths of the developing neuroblasts are determined chiefly by factors of a different sort — by the primary axial gradients of the growing field (Kappers, 1917, 1922, Child, 1921, Chaps. 10 and 11), by the dynamic influence of excitations traversing neighboring nervous pathways which are already functionally active (stimulogenous fibrillation of Bok, 1915), by bioelectric currents produced by both of the preceding activities and by other means (*cf.* Ingvar, 1920), by the process of neurobiotaxis described by Kappers to be referred to beyond (p. 195), and finally during the course of functional development of the neuron by the trophic stimulus of its own physiological activity, the amount and direction of growth of the fibrous processes of the cell and their collateral branches being determined (in part) by the selection, from among all possible functional connections, of particular ones which are more frequently activated (Ramón y Cajal, 1911, p. 887). The last item includes a mnemonic factor (Bok, 1917) or, briefly, habit formation and is probably of incalculable importance in all higher animals, though of the details of the process we know but little.

The cell body is the trophic center of the neuron and the physiological importance of this can hardly be overestimated — in growth, regeneration of injuries and normal function. Dendrites in general appear to share in this trophic function, while axons (and greatly elongated dentrites) do not (Kappers, 1922). The protoplasm of the cell body is very specially modified in adaptation to the peculiar and intense metabolism of nervous excitation (explosive type of function, p. 256). The chromophilic substance is the chief visible expression of this characteristic. The protoplasm of the fibrous processes, on the other hand, is more or less modified in adaptation to the function of conduction, the longer fibers usually consisting of an axis cylinder, composed chiefly of neurofibrils imbedded in a small amount of more fluid neuroplasm, with or without enclosing sheaths. The shorter dendrites do not exhibit this special structure, but their protoplasm resembles more the cytoplasm of the cell body, often containing chromophilic substance.

The cell body may be placed anywhere in the course of the length of the fibrous conductors of the neuron. Usually it is near the receptive end (Figs. 29, 31, 33); it may be midway of the length of the neuron, as in the elements of the spinal and cranial ganglia (Figs. 4, 75); or it may be at the emissive end of the neuron, as illustrated by the neurons of the mesencephalic root of the fifth cranial nerve.

The typical neurons illustrated in Figures 31 to 34 have short processes conducting toward the cell body and long specially modified processes conducting away from it. By common consent the former are called dendrites and the latter axons (neuraxons or neurites). But the distinction between dendrites and axons is drawn differently by various neurologists and the matter is in some confusion. To define axon on the basis of its structure, as a long process with the special modifications usually associated with this elongation as just described, is only to obscure the really significant features. The neuron is certainly polarized, that is, it has a receptive and an emissive end, and the trophic center (nucleated cell body) always lies somewhere between these poles. It is by far the simplest practice to adhere consistently to the strictly physiological definition: dendrites conduct toward the cell body, axons conduct away from it.

This is very far from saying, as Parker intimates in his critique (1918 b, p. 154), that this usage "involves the assumption that the cell body of the neuron is the center of nervous activity," but it is quite consonant with the statement which he makes further along in his argument, "the polarity of the neuron is best described in the statement that nerve impulses are received at one end of it and discharged at the other." Nor is the polarity of the neuron determined entirely by the arrangement of the related synapses. There are in reality two strictly functional factors in the polarization of the neuron, one extrinsic and one intrinsic.

The intrinsic polarity is manifested in the adult resting neuron by differences in metabolic rate along its course. This is a typical physiological gradient similar to that found in lower organisms and it is demonstrated by the same methods. It seems to be a matter of permanent organization of the neuron rather than a direct result of stimulation. Whether it has arisen through use under the influence of extrinsic factors of excitation, etc., is not known.

Tashiro (1917) has shown that resting nerve fibers give off measurable amounts of carbon dioxid and that during the transmission of a nervous impulse the amount of carbon dioxid given off is approximately doubled. He finds also that each neuron, and indeed the reflex arc as a whole, has a gradient in the sense that the metabolism is highest at the receptive end of the system and lower as the point of discharge into the muscle is approached. That this is a true physiological gradient has been confirmed by Child (1914 a) by the independent method of differential susceptibility. As one passes from sense organ toward motor endings in a nervous pathway the nerve fiber is more resistant to the destructive action of the poisonous drugs employed, the diminished susceptibility being a sign of lower metabolism. Tashiro's conclusions have been controverted by some other physiologists (e. g., Moore, 1919), but the experimental controls seem adequate (Tashiro, 1922).

The extrinsic polarization of the neuron is determined by the environment and functional connections of the cell. In early developmental stages, as already pointed out, the neuroblast is oriented (probably through differential growth of its parts) with reference to the primary physiological gradients of the body within which it grows. In functional stages the receptive end of the cell and its dendritic outgrowths are under the constant physiological influence of the nervous excitations transmitted to it, while the emissive end of the cell and the axon are discharging nervous impulses to the next neuron of the series or, in the case of peripheral motor neurons, directly into the effector.

The functional polarization of the mature neuron during excitation is not consequent wholly or chiefly upon its inner constitution, for in fact it may run counter to the intrinsic polarization described above and overcome it. An adequate stimulus applied anywhere along the length of a nerve fiber will be transmitted in both directions from the point of application to the limits of the particular neuron excited. Beyond these limits the excitation can be transmitted freely in the direction of normal discharge, that is, toward the effector, but not in the reverse direction toward the receptor. This implies that at the junction between two neurons there is a barrier which acts like a valve in that it can be traversed by the nervous impulse in only one direction (toward the effector). This junction is the synapse.

The synapse. — There has been much controversy as to the exact nature of the bond between the neurons at these synaptic junctions. Some claim that there is actual fusion of the protoplasms of the two neurons and passage of neurofibrils across the junction; others maintain that there is a membrane separating the neurons. This represents the walls of the participating cells, which are therefore related by contact merely.

In some cases it seems well established that such membranous walls exist and are structurally visible. A remarkable instance is presented by the so-called Mauthner cells of the medulla oblongata of some fishes and amphibians which have been studied by Bartelmez (1915, 1920). There is a single pair of these enormous cells in the medulla oblongata opposite the entrance of the eighth cranial nerves. No less than twelve different kinds of sensory fibers end by synaptic junctions upon the dendrites or bodies of these neurons, chief of which are peripheral fibers from the vestibular nerves. The axons cross the mid-plane and descend as two giant fibers throughout the whole length of the spinal cord, probably serving an important function in the coördination of swimming movements and maintenance of equilibrium. In this case there is clearly a membranous barrier between some of the afferent fibers and the neuron with which they are functionally connected. In some other synapses which have been described there is a structurally visible difference between the protoplasms of the two neurons where they are in contact, even though no membranous wall is obvious.

The presence of such a barrier at the synaptic junction does not imply that the neurons are not in protoplasmic continuity, for the separating membrane itself is living substance. What it does indicate is that there is a change in the physico-chemical nature of the conducting substance at the synaptic barrier. Langley has termed this barrier junctional tissue and of its great physiological importance there can be no doubt. It is regarded by most physiologists as a semipermeable membrane, through which the ions dissociated during the excitation-conduction process (p. 54), or some other substances, can pass in one direction and not in the reverse direction. There are inorganic analogies of such a situation. It may, therefore, be regarded as established that at the synapse there is a contact of two dissimilar protoplasms, with resulting profound modification of the conduction at the apposed surface (Lillie, 1923, p. 272).

Whatever the anatomical structure of the synapse, it is clear that the physiological barrier here interposed between the neurons is real and functionally significant. At the synapse there is a reversal of cellular polarity of extrinsic origin in the sense defined above (p. 113); there is delay in transmission; there is greater susceptibility to fatigue and to certain toxins than elsewhere in the nervous system; degenerations resulting from destruction of neurons or parts of them do not ordinarily cross this barrier; and finally nervous impulses can cross the synapse in one direction only and not in the reverse direction.

Neurons are thus linked together in chains whose patterns are functionally defined; that is, open conductors are provided for all of the customary reactions to stimulation that fall within the normal action system of the species, facilitating the discharge from each receptive organ to the muscular systems appropriate to execute the reflex response in question. This is largely a matter of innate organization. But this is not all. Besides the main trunk lines of through traffic thus laid down and numerous interconnecting paths which permit the various reflex arcs to coöperate in a great variety of ways in complex innate patterns, there are in the nerve centers collateral connections of less frequent use and other devices which make possible a great variety of new nervous connections and hitherto unused types of response which are not represented in the innate structural pattern.

The great number and flexibility of these individually acquired nervous connections and the ease with which they may be established and strengthened by repeated use give the special characteristics of the correlation centers of the brain and particularly the cerebral cortex of higher vertebrates. On the functional side this appears as modifiability of behavior through experience, associative memory and intelligence. On the structural side we note that many different kinds of fibers may make synaptic junctions with a single neuron and, further, that the axon of a single neuron may divide so as to distribute its excitation to neurons of two or more very different functional types in centers far removed from each other. These arrangements provide the anatomical mechanism for correlations and coördinations of the most intricate patterns, and for modifications of the directions taken by nervous impulses arising from transient fluctuations in the relative permeability of the different synaptic junctions which are anatomically present. Such adjustments are quite impossible in nonsynaptic systems and also in synaptic systems in which the neurons are connected in more simple ways.

Rhythms of nervous discharge. — In some quarters the opinion has long been held that the nervous current excited by a momentary stimulus is not a single pulse of energy, but that each nervous impulse has a characteristic rhythm of its own. These conjectures are now receiving experimental support which is briefly summarized by Lillie (1923, Chap. 13).

Forbes and Gregg (1913) showed that a single stimulus may cause a series of nervous impulses in rapid succession in the nerve fiber. Gasser and Erlanger (1922) state: "It is now a well-known fact that muscle and nerve respond with rhythmical currents to stimulation by the make or break of strong constant currents," and it has been shown (Gasser and Newcomer, 1921) that in the case of the dog's diaphragm the electromotor rhythm of the phrenic nerve corresponds exactly with that of the muscle which it innervates. Foà (1911) has demonstrated that both of these rhythms are centrally determined, presumably by the rhythmical discharge of the motor nerve cells, and that they are very regular and uniform (*cf.* Hill, 1921).

From these experiments it seems probable that the nerve fiber has an intrinsic rhythm of discharge, whether it is artificially excited by a stimulus applied directly to it or naturally excited in the intact condition by the activity of some other neuron with which it is in functional connection. These nervous rhythms are different for different neuromotor systems, the rate varying between 40 and several hundred vibrations per second. They may play a large part in the central ordering of incoming nervous impulses and their distribution in the correlation centers to appropriate motor paths so as to activate only the muscles which normally coöperate in the performance of the several movements involved in the execution of particular acts. That is, a given system of synergic muscles may have the same rhythm throughout with a vibratory rate which is different from that of other synergic systems.

The experiments of Lucas (1917) and others cited by him suggest that the "junctional tissue" at the motor end-plates and synapses may play a significant part in reinforcement, inhibition, and other forms of modification of the ordinary course of nervous conduction. Each nerve fiber has a refractory period following excitation during which it is inexcitable, and again following this there may be a very brief period of supernormal sensitivity, and these periods differ in different nerves and in the same nerve in various functional states. The "junctional tissue" is regarded as a region of decrement in transmission. A detailed consideration of the durations of the refractory periods of the nerve fibers under different physiological conditions and of the relations of these periods to the decrement at neuronic junctions leads him to say (p. 50):

"According as we time impulses in the nervous system to follow one another at a shorter or longer interval, we can make them less or more capable of being conducted through any regions of decrement which the system may contain. If there is a region of decrement such that a normal impulse just cannot pass, then impulses of moderate frequency may pass it successfully, while impulses of a high frequency may not only fail to pass it, but may by their frequency prevent any other impulses finding their way through." And again on page 102: "On the basis of this analysis we have pictured the central nervous system as a network of conductors having different refractory periods, communicating through regions of decrement, easily fatigued and capable of setting up a train of impulses in answer to a single stimulus."

Lucas is not here discussing rhythms of discharge which are intrinsic to the fibers in question, but those effected by repeated stimulation, and it seems not improbable that the intrinsic rhythms of normal nervous conduction to which reference was made above may be related to those of various other systems of neurons with which they are in synaptic junction in much the same way. That is, certain rates of vibration can pass a given synaptic junction, others cannot and of those which do pass some which are in attunement with the intrinsic rhythm of the second neuron may excite the latter to activity, while others of different rate do not affect it.

M. and Mme. Lapicque (1907–1912), after experimental study of the chronological factors of excitation on the two sides of the synaptic junctions, reach an interpretation somewhat different from that of Lucas. They hold that ordinary nervous impulses pass the synaptic junctions in cases where the two nervous elements involved are in "attunement" (homochronous) and that they do not pass other junctions where the time intervals are not in accord (heterochronous). But with stronger stimulation the conditions are so changed that the nervous impulses may spread through the heterochronous junctions and the activity may irradiate beyond the usual pathway through various collateral connections.

They picture the activities at the synaptic junctions in this way: Let us suppose that an afferent nerve, A, divides before ending in its central terminal nucleus into three equal branches, each of which makes synaptic junction with one of the three neurons, B, C, D. Let it be further assumed that the normal time factor of excitation (chronaxie) of B is identical (synchronous) with that of A, while C and D are heterochronous, the normal time factor of one being less and of the other greater than that of A. If now, while B, C, and D are in the resting state, an excitation reaches them from A which is just powerful enough to pass the synaptic threshold it will be able to excite only the element B whose natural chronaxie is synchronous with its own, while the heterochronous elements, being out of attunement with A, will not be activated, giving a localized reaction of a single system of synergic muscles. Stronger excitation of A may, however, change its chronaxie so that its nervous impulse may be transmitted also to C and D, resulting in irradiation of the nervous current and a more extensive or different reaction.[1]

These theories of interneuronic attunement are far from final demonstration, but they rest on sufficient factual basis to justify further experimentation and the hope that the analysis of the phenomena of central adjustment, correlation, reinforcement and inhibition in terms of demonstrable physiological laws (probably in the domain of bioelectric phenomena) may be realized.

If this or some similar interpretation of the observed facts can be substantiated, clearly there is provided a physical basis for the sorts

---

[1] The Lapicques' idea seems to be out of harmony with the current statements of the all-or-none law (p. 263), but if restated in terms of intrinsic neural rhythms and of decrement at the synaptic junctions their observations may prove to be not out of harmony with a modified form of the law. It should be added that the field of this discussion has been very recently reviewed by Forbes and others (Am Jour. Physiol., vol. 66, Nov., 1923, pp. 553–617) with extensive new observations which seem to alter former conceptions of the mechanism of the refractory period of nerve and muscle.

of central analysis to which reference was made on page 21. It is a matter of central attunement of the afferent neurons with particular functional systems of efferent neurons with which they are in physiological connection and of the chronological factors in the transmission across the synaptic barriers. These natural rhythms and the chronological relations at the synapse are not inflexible, but their periods may be altered in various ways, and changes of this sort may lie at the basis of that individual modifiability of reactions which is so characteristic of all higher types of nervous systems.

The synaptic junctions are probably the critical points in such functional modifications of reaction patterns, for the junctional region is known to be especially susceptible to such functional factors. There is always delay or a refractory period at the synapse and this varies in different synapses and in the same synapse under varying functional conditions.

These facts and many others that might be cited suggest that in synaptic nervous systems the ordinary course of behavior, that is, the innate action system, is structurally determined by preëstablished systems of neuronic connections of low synaptic resistance or of like natural rhythms. These form the great highways of reflex and instinctive nervous transmission. But these trunk lines of traffic are interrelated by countless subsidiary collateral connections, the refractory periods of whose synaptic junctions and the natural rhythms of whose neurons may be different from those of the primary trunk lines. Under varying functional conditions these subsidiary connections may be activated with consequent modification of the innate behavior patterns, and through facilitation by use they may in time acquire a functional value not inferior to that of the primary systems. In terms of behavior we say, the animal has acquired a habit.

Conclusion. — The marvelous history of the growth of the nerve fibers and the adaptive and apparently purposeful precision with which they finally reach the exact spots necessary to effect synaptic connections with the end-organs or with other neurons required to complete the various functional circuits have led one recent writer to ascribe to each cell an intelligence of its own which would really transcend that of the man of which it forms a part. No, the problem of the soul of man is not brought nearer to a solution by the postulation of millions of other similar souls within his body.

It is possible, however, to take some short steps forward in the direction of a solution of the problems of human individuality and personality by a study of some of the dynamic factors which create and maintain the unity in multiplicity of his body. Some of these integrating factors are seen to be the interaction in bioelectric fields of equilibrated systems of chemical processes, each of which develops its own bioelectric field. Thus arise successive hierarchies of physiological gradients, local differentiation taking place under the influence of local centers of dominance and the organism as a whole developing and functioning under the control of a center of highest physiological dominance. Each reflex circuit, which is our unit of structure and of behavior (p. 12), is a system of such gradients, the correlation centers are regions of higher dominance combining and integrating the reflex activities in old and new patterns, and in man the cerebral cortex is the center of highest dominance, reinforcing, inhibiting or redirecting the nervous currents of the lower centers. Individual neurons and functional systems of neurons grow and act in accordance with biological laws different from those of polyps and protozoans but of common origin and common fundamental type. These are the organismic forces which hold the body together and direct its activities into ever more varied and progressively more efficient modes of behavior as we pass from lower to higher animals.

CHAPTER X

THE NERVOUS SYSTEM OF WORMS

Nervous system of flatworms — Ladder type of nervous system — Brain of the earthworm — Locomotor reflexes of the earthworm — Giant fibers and avoiding reactions — Physiological gradients and head dominance in worms — Physiological isolation and fission in worms — Behavior of the earthworm — Summary.

Nervous system of flatworms. — In the most primitive worms (flatworms, planarians) the nervous system is scarcely more highly organized than in the jellyfishes, but its pattern is very different, with cephalic ganglia, longitudinally arranged nervous strands connected by commissural fibers, and bilateral symmetry (Fig. 35). This pattern is capable of indefinite development, for here we have the most fundamental features of the nervous systems of the higher animals, though reduced to lowest terms.

Some phases of the planarian physiological patterns are more fully known than are those of any other animals, for much of Child's work on physiological gradients has been done on these forms. The details of these studies we need not review, for the conclusions derived from them have recently been reformulated with a summary of the evidence by Child himself (1924). It should be emphasized, however, that because of the fundamental similarity of pattern of these worms and all higher forms, generalizations based upon them can be applied with a high degree of probability even up to the human body, with such modifications, of course, as result from increasing complexity.

This is brought out in a very striking way by the discovery that by the use of narcotics, poisons and other depressing agents under appropriate conditions almost identical malformations may be produced at will in planarian worms and vertebrate embryos. A not very rare type of human monstrosity is the cyclops, or the fusion of the two eyes in the middle of the face (Fig. 36). All grades of cyclopean monsters, from a slight approximation of the two eyes to their complete fusion and even their total disappearance, are found in the descriptions of human teratology and these have been produced experimentally in a variety of animal species.

Various degrees of inhibition of head development by external

121

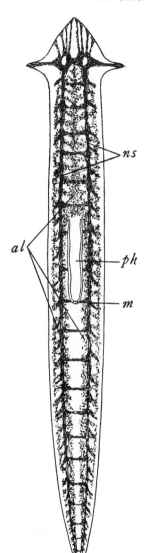

physical and chemical agents, as well as by physiological factors, controlled by stage of development, concentration of agent employed and period of exposure, yield in planarians a series of cyclopean forms which parallel the human series with remarkable fidelity [1] and Bellamy (1919, 1922) has accomplished the same thing in the developing frog (Fig. 37). Almost any desired modification of this type of defect can be produced in embryonic development at the will of the experimenter by applying the depressing agent at the appropriate stage of development, the result obtained being an expression of the depressing effect of the agent applied upon a differentially susceptible protoplasm, that is, a developmental arrest. The susceptibility differs at different stages of development, with resulting change in the nature and magnitude of the defect. Stockard had previously obtained

[1] On experimental production of cyclops in planarians see Behre (1918), Buchanan (1922), Child (1911 a, 1916 a, 1920, 1921 b, 1924, Chap. 8), Child and McKie (1911).

Fig. 35.—A planarian worm, Planaria dorotocephala, seen from the dorsal side, enlarged. The nervous system (ns) is drawn (somewhat diagrammatically) in solid lines, the alimentary tract (al) in stipple, and the positions of the mouth (m) and pharynx (ph) are shown. After Child (1915), by permission of the publishers, The University of Chicago Press.

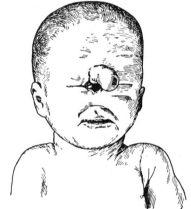

Fig. 36.—A human cyclops. The figure illustrates a new-born babe described by Dr. Carmalt (1901). The two eyes are fused in the middle of the face and above them is a fleshy proboscis.

similar malformations in embryonic fish, which he at first (1909) ascribed to the specific action of the drugs employed, applying the term "magnesium embryo" to the malformations produced by this depressing agent. Later (1921) he corrected this error, adopting a principle of differential susceptibility to the toxic agent which is

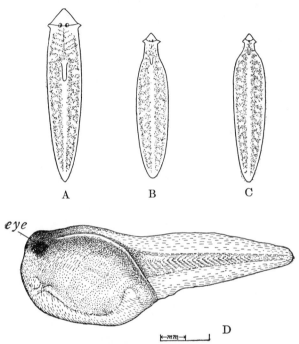

FIG. 37.—A, B, and C are illustrations (after Child) of planarian worms in process of regeneration after transverse section. The posterior pieces, without heads, regenerate heads of various forms under different conditions. A shows an approach to the normal form (as in figure 35) under standard laboratory conditions; B and C illustrate different degrees of retardation of head development under conditions which depress or inhibit growth. In B the two eyes are closer together than normal, and in C they have fused in typical cyclopean form.

D illustrates a cyclopean frog tadpole (after Bellamy, 1919). This egg was treated with lithium chloride for three hours in the early gastrula stage. The development of the eyes was partially inhibited and the two eyes are fused in the median plane and reduced to a small vestige.

essentially similar to that previously demonstrated by Child, though without comment upon this similarity.

The general structure of the nervous system of planarians is well known (Sabussow, 1904, has given a good description); but the details of the arrangement and functional connections of the component cellular elements have hitherto baffled all students of the question, for these tissues are peculiarly refractory to the ordinary neurological methods. It may therefore be said of these paradoxical creatures that we know more about the general physiological foundations of their behavior than of any other invertebrates and less about the actual structures which mediate this behavior.

Child has investigated particularly the organismic behavior of the planarian worms, that is, the reactions of the body as a whole to external agents and the physiological processes by which the bodily activities are integrated and correlated among themselves. The methods employed are for the most part studies of rates of metabolism of various parts under different conditions, the distribution of physiological gradients of excitation and conduction and their modifications consequent upon changes in external conditions and internal state, centers of physiological dominance and the method of their control of subsidiary parts, the effects of natural or artificially produced physiological isolation of parts upon the organismic processes, and like matters of fundamental physiological import.

The validity of the physiological methods employed does not depend upon a detailed knowledge of the correlated anatomical structures, and in fact we are still in the dark regarding so fundamental a question as the relative parts played in these reactions by nervous and non-nervous tissue. It has already been pointed out that the fundamental organismic processes of correlation and integration lie at the basis of protoplasmic responses to the action of external agents and that these processes can be demonstrated in primitive organisms which lack differentiated fixed tissue systems of nervous or any other special organs of excitation, conduction and response. The physiological gradients were doubtless laid down in the organization of the ancestors of worms before any specific nervous organs were differentiated, and the nervous system was developed within these gradients. How far the nervous system of flatworms has taken over these specific functions of excitation and conduction and how far the protoplasm of other parts of the body mediates them has not been determined. That the nervous system does play the dominant rôle in these processes has, however, been suggested by the experiments of Child (1910) and Olmsted (1922, 1922 a).

In the parasitic round worm, Ascaris, the nervous system is somewhat better developed than in planarians, but far simpler than in the earthworm. There is a nervous ring around the pharynx, from which several ganglionated nervous strands pass backward and forward within the skin. These strands are very simply organized, the total number of ganglion cells directly related with the nerve ring not exceeding 160. These nerve cells are connected by protoplasmic fibers into a very simple nerve net (a non-synaptic nervous system). A much-branched nervous feltwork (neuropil) is practically absent — in contrast with the annelids, insects and all higher forms (Bütschli, 1912, p. 481). This is important in view of the fact that these nervous feltworks of more highly elaborated nervous systems contain the complex synaptic junctions between the nervous elements which give to these animals their capacity for complex and rapidly modifiable behavior.

Ladder type of nervous system. — The annelids, or segmented worms like the common earthworm, are much more highly organized than are the flatworms. The body tissues of the latter in general are poorly differentiated, but in the earthworm most of the tissue types found in higher animals are well developed. The nervous system, unlike that of jellyfishes, is (for the most part at least) of the synaptic type rather than a nerve net, and its nerve cells (neurons) form a fully "matured" tissue in the sense in which this term is defined on page 58. These nerve cells are related to one another physiologically in very complex patterns of conduction.

Most of the nerve cells of these worms are concentrated in a double chain of ganglia on the ventral body wall, one pair of ganglia in each segment of the body. The two ganglia of each segment are connected with each other by a fibrous commissural strand across the mid-plane and with the corresponding ganglia of the adjoining segments by longitudinal fibrous connectives, so that the whole central nervous system resembles somewhat a rope ladder with most of the nerve cell bodies accumulated in the ganglia at the nodal points where the ropes of the ladder are tied (Fig. 38).

Fig. 38. — The ladder type of nervous system of a simple crustacean, Branchippus venalis. After Hilton (1917).

Not all of the nerve cells of the worm are concentrated in the central nervous system just described, for there is an extensive peripheral plexus containing ganglion cells, especially under the skin and between the muscular layers of the body wall. This is regarded by Dawson (1920) as a survival of the diffuse type of nervous system seen in the cœlenterates. Moreover, there are in the skin receptive cells (Fig. 39) which are very similar to those of the simple receptor-effector systems of polyps (p. 90), save for the presence of a long nervous process

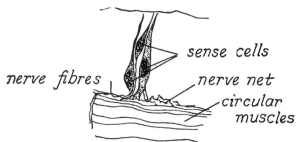

Fig. 39.—Epidermal sense cells from the skin of the earthworm. From the base of each cell a nerve fiber extends toward the central nervous system and collateral branches are given off which enter the subepithelial nerve net. Redrawn from Dawson (1920).

which reaches the central nervous system. Other similar cells (Fig. 40) have sunk below the skin surface, with which they keep contact by one process, while other short processes are in contact with the muscles. This type of cell may combine the functions of skin sen-

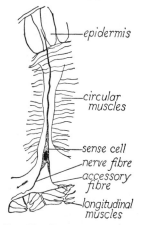

sibility and muscle sense and serve as one link in the chain of reflex arcs involved in ordinary vermiculate locomotion (p. 132). That these cells do actually serve the muscle sense is indicated by the physiological experiments of Moore (1923). Similar neurons have been described in amphibian embryos (Herrick and Coghill, 1915).

Fig. 40.—Deep sensory cell from the ventral side of the body wall of the earthworm. From the base of the cell a main nerve fiber extends toward the central nervous system and an accessory fiber enters the longitudinal muscles. Redrawn from Dawson (1920).

The ladder type of nervous system is found in all segmented worms (annelids), crustaceans, spiders and insects. A typical form from a simple crustacean is shown in Figure 38. In most of these cases, as in the earthworm (Figs. 42, 43) and insects (Fig. 53), the ganglia of the two sides are closer together than in the simple case shown in Figure 38, so that in a dissection there may appear to be but one ganglion in each segment. In many cases also a number of segmental ganglia may be partially or completely fused to form a compound ganglion, as in the flies shown in Figure 53.

This ladder type of nervous system is very different from the vertebrate type both in mode of embryological development and in adult structure. It arises in the embryo by splitting off of cells from the

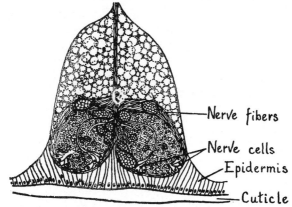

Fig. 41.—Ventral nerve cord of Segalion (Hatschek).

outer epithelium of the ventral body wall in the form of a neural plate. In some worms it persists throughout life as a ganglionic nervous plate within the epidermis (Fig. 41), but in the earthworm the ganglionated nerve cord is separated from the skin by masses of circular and longitudinal muscle and other tissues (Fig. 42).

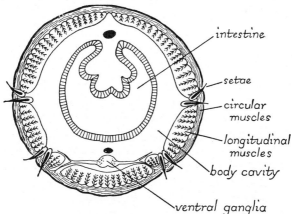

Fig. 42.—Diagrammatic cross section through the body of the earthworm.

One step in the transition from the primitive uniformly diffused nerve net to the concentration of nerve cells to form a central nervous system has been cited (p. 93) in the case of the nerve ring of the jellyfishes. The integrating power of this arrangement is, however, very slight. It has been suggested that in the process of further condensation of the diffuse nervous system the centers of adjustment tend to accumulate adjacent to the most important receptive surfaces. In primitive worms which crawl on the ground and hence receive their chief excitations from contacts on the ventral surface, it follows that the central nervous ganglia are found in or near the ventral body wall (Herrick, 1910 a). But, in accordance with the same principle, the dominant ganglia of the leading segments in the annelid worms are lifted away from the ventral segments and encircle the mouth (Figs. 44, 45) which is in these animals the most important receptive surface.

Each ganglion is connected with the organs of its own segment by peripheral nerves and the two ganglia of a segment are so connected by nerve fibers of the cross commissure as to enable them to work in unison for the regulation of movements involving muscles of both sides of the body. Each pair of ganglia thus serves as the center of regulatory adjustment for the activities of its own segment.

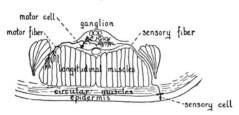

Fig. 43.—Transverse section through the ventral body wall and a ganglion of the central nervous system of the earthworm. Modified from Retzius.

Figure 43 illustrates a diagrammatic cross section through a pair of segmental ganglia and the associated peripheral nerves of the earthworm. Only two of the very numerous neurons are indicated. In each ganglion there are many other nerve cells of the same and different sorts. On the right of the figure is a sensory nerve cell whose cell body lies in the skin and serves as receptive organ. The base of this cell is prolonged as a sensory nerve fiber which ends in a terminal arborization within the ganglion. Inside the ganglion is another nerve cell, one of whose processes interlaces with the terminal arborization of the first element and whose other process is prolonged as a peripheral motor nerve fiber which ends on the organ of response, a muscle. This is the simplest possible reflex apparatus, consisting of only two nervous elements, sensory and motor, and a center of adjustment in the ganglion. In terms of modern physiological parlance we have a neuromotor system of three elements arranged as follows: (1) a receptor in the skin and sensory conductor, (2) an adjustor in the ganglion and a motor conductor, (3) an effector, the muscle.

But so far as shown in this diagram we have advanced but little over the simple receptor-effector apparatus of two cellular elements found in the most primitive polyps (p. 90), save for longer and more clearly defined nervous pathways and better conducting apparatus. This, however, is only part of the story of the adjusting mechanism, for many other sensory fibers discharge into this ganglion and many other motor fibers leave it, making possible diversified responses to several different kinds of stimulation, for many of the sensory neurons may discharge into a single motor neuron, each receptive cell may connect with many motor neurons and there are other forms of central connection permitting recombination of the reflex units. There are numerous connections between sensory and motor neurons which lie wholly within the central nervous system. These latter

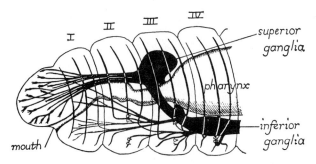

Fig. 44.—The brain and anterior nerves of the earthworm seen from the side. Modified from Shipley and MacBride's Zoölogy.

are correlating nerve cells which connect the sensory and motor organs of the same and different segments in various ways, thus permitting the different combinations of sensori-motor connection required for the performance of the complex reflexes of the worm's daily life. This apparatus of reflex adjustment is similar in principle to that of all higher animals.

Brain of the earthworm. — Near the anterior end of the worm the double ventral nerve chain separates into its lateral components and these pass forward to encircle the esophagus and again unite dorsally of the mouth to form the superior or supra-esophageal ganglion (Fig. 44). There is also an enlarged inferior or infra-esophageal ganglion just below the mouth formed by the fusion of the first two ganglia of the ventral segmental chain. These two ganglionic masses and the connecting circum-esophageal ring constitute the brain of the worm.

Some of the free swimming marine worms have more complex sensory equipment of the head than the earthworm, the brain and its associated nerves here being enlarged in corresponding measure (Fig. 45). In leeches the ganglia of several of the anterior segments are fused to form a larger inferior ganglion and so increase the size of the brain (Whitman, 1892).

Even in these lowly forms the nerves of the most anterior segments are very different from those in the midbody region, with a great proportional increase in the number of sensory nerve fibers relative to the motor fibers. This is incidental to c e p h a l i z a t i o n and runs through the entire series of higher animals and in increasing measure is an expression of the important rôle played by the receptive apparatus in establishing head dominance.

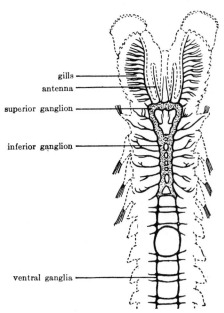

gills
antenna
superior ganglion
inferior ganglion
ventral ganglia

FIG. 45.—Anterior part of the nervous system of a polychaete annelid, Sabella, showing a more complex arrangement than in the earthworm (E. Meyer and Bütschli).

Locomotor reflexes of the earthworm. — The structure and function of the nervous system of the earthworm have been studied many times, the papers of Krawany (1905), A s h w o r t h (1909), and Bovard (1918, 1918 a) being of especial value for our purpose. The ganglia of each segment in general control the activities of that segment, but the movements of the worm as a whole are in part controlled directly from the brain and in larger part by general physiological gradients, extending throughout the body with a center of highest dominance in the head region and a separate center of dominance near the tail end of the body.

The analysis of the neuromuscular mechanism of the usual crawling movements has been variously described by different physiologists. Simple observation shows that in this locomotor movement a wave of elongation of a few segments of the body passes down the length of the worm, followed by a wave of shortening of a few segments.

The two phases which thus coöperate follow downward through the body and are succeeded by others of like character.

During the phase of elongation the longitudinal muscles of the body wall (see Fig. 42) are relaxed and the circular muscles are contracted. During the phase of shortening the converse relations prevail, viz., the contraction of the longitudinal muscles and the relaxation of the circular. Since the body wall is provided with several series of stiff bristles (setæ, Fig. 42) which project backward and act as holdfasts preventing backward movement, the muscular contractions described result in forward progression.

The rate of conduction of these waves of locomotor activity is slow, being ordinarily about 25 millimeters per second.[1] This rate is exceedingly variable and when the worm is in an excited condition it may rise as high as 100 millimeters per second. The rate is dependent upon many variable factors within the ganglia through which the impulses pass, where it may be reinforced by stimuli applied to the segments or by muscular activity within them.

The locomotor movement is probably normally a typical chain reflex, the activity of one segment serving as the stimulus for reaction of the adjacent ones. Nevertheless it has been shown experimentally by Bovard and others that the locomotor nervous impulses may be transmitted through a number of segments of the central nervous system quite independently of any peripheral activity in those segments. The neurons involved, however, are short and probably few of their fibers extend farther than from one segmental ganglion to the next, or at most through a very few segments. In each ganglion the nervous impulse of the longitudinal conductors is interrupted by passage over from one neuron to another through synaptic junctions.

The nervous mechanisms involved in these two types of transmission are diagrammatically indicated in Figs. 46 and 47. The apparatus of simple longitudinal conduction through the central nervous system is shown in Fig. 46. The nervous impulse descending from higher levels is passed onward from segment to segment through a chain of short neurons. In each segmental ganglion the path may divide, one branch passing the impulse downward to the next segment and the other connecting with a peripheral motor element, as illustrated in segment B (neuron 3′).

---

[1] This, of course, is not the rate of nervous transmission in these worms, but the rate of propagation of a very complex neuromuscular reaction, each cycle of which must be completed before serving as a stimulus for the next (a chain reflex).

The ordinary locomotor movements involve a much more intricate chain of nervous and muscular activities. From this complex, selection may be made for purposes of illustration of one series of neuro-muscular reactions only out of the total number. We choose for this illustration three segments in the midregion of the body desig-

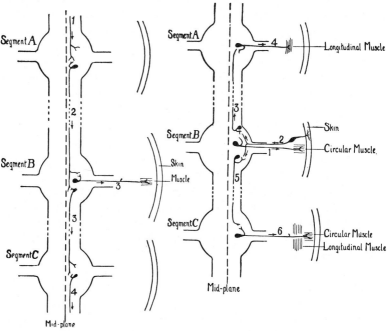

FIG. 46.—Diagram of the chains of nervous elements within the central nervous system of the earthworm, which are concerned in the longitudinal conduction of nervous impulses. The nerve cells successively activated are numbered 1 to 4. At each segmental ganglion these connect with peripheral nerve cells, one of which is indicated (3′). See the text.

FIG. 47.—Diagram of the nervous elements concerned in ordinary locomotor movements of the earthworm in three segments of the midbody region in successive phases of the locomotor process. For description see the text.

nated on Figure 47, A, B and C, which are in successive phases of the locomotor movement. At A the body is shortening, at B it is elongating, and at C it is shortening. Each of the segments figured is to be regarded as representative of the entire group of segments in like phase. For simplicity the intervening segments are omitted from the diagram.

Assuming that segment B is in the phase of contraction of the circular muscles which have been excited by motor neuron 1, with the longitudinal series of muscles relaxed, the resulting elongation of the body in this region exerts traction in the skin and underlying tissues which serves as a stimulus for a sensory neuron (2) which passes inward from the skin to end in the ganglion.   Here the nervous impulse is passed on to two other neurons, one of which (3) transmits it upward, and the other (5) downward.   The ascending impulse is taken over in segment A by a peripheral motor neuron (4) with resulting contraction of the longitudinal muscles of this segment and shortening of the body in this region.   The descending nervous impulse is taken over in segment C by a peripheral motor neuron (6) which excites contraction of the circular muscles of this segment, thus propagating downward the phase of body elongation now in progress in segment B.   In this way the successive phases of the locomotor movements pass downward along the length of the body.

This account, however, includes only a part of the process.   As each of the muscles is excited to contraction there is probably relaxation of its antagonist (reciprocal innervation).   Moreover the nerves and muscles of both sides of the body are acting synchronously. The nervous apparatus involved in these aspects of the total movement do not differ in principle from those here pictured and it will be unnecessary to consider them in detail.

It is probable that in ordinary locomotion the mechanisms just described alone are employed, but local excitations may modify this movement by intercurrent nervous impulses passing through the chains of central nerve fibers (Fig. 46) in either the descending or ascending direction.

Giant fibers and avoiding reactions. — In addition to the locomotor neuromuscular apparatus already described, there is another motor system of very different character served by a few very large nerve fibers known as giant fibers.   These are differently arranged in the various species of segmented worms.   Each fiber of the earthworm and some other annelids is formed by a fusion of processes of several large nerve cells.   In the large marine annelid, Halla parthenopeia, which may attain a length of nearly a meter, the giant fibers and the giant cells from which they arise have been fully described by Ashworth (1909), who finds a simpler arrangement than in the earthworm.   Here there is a considerable number of giant cells and fibers, each fiber arising from a single cell located in one of the segments near the head end of the worm.   Some of these nerve fibers extend backward without interruption to the extreme caudal end of the nervous system. In each segmental ganglion they give off branches which connect with the peripheral motor neurons of that segment, as diagrammatically indicated in Figure 48. In this worm there are also smaller giant cells in the posterior segments, whose fibers are directed forward.

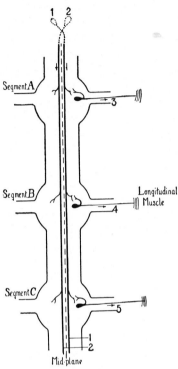

Nervous impulses are transmitted down the giant fibers very rapidly as compared with the slow rate of the ordinary locomotor impulses, this rate being about 1500 millimeters per second in typical cases. The response in this case is never a coördinated locomotor movement, but a rapid contraction of the longitudinal muscles only, resulting in a quick jerk of the body backward — an avoiding reaction.

The giant fibers are clearly the most important longitudinal conductors and serve to maintain the neuromotor gradients in a greatly elongated body. Those arising in the region of highest dominance near the anterior end of the worm are larger and longer than those arising from the secondary center of dominance near the tail end.

FIG. 48.—Diagram of the relations of the giant fibers in the central nervous system of the annelid worms. The giant cells and fibers are numbered 1 and 2 and a peripheral motor nerve cell in each of three successive segments is indicated (3, 4 and 5). These are activated from collateral branches of the giant fibers. This diagram is based on the marine annelid, Halla. The earthworm is similar in principle but somewhat more complex. See the text.

We have now described in these worms four general kinds of neuromuscular mechanisms: (1) Local segmental reflex systems such as diagrammed in artificially simplified form in Figure 43. (2) Locomotor apparatus in the form of chain reflexes employing reflex arcs similar to the last so connected intersegmentally as to synchronize the contraction of circular and longitudinal muscles in vermiculate movement (Fig. 47). (3) Longitudinally arranged chains of nervous elements for fore-and-aft conduction (Fig. 46), probably acting in diverse ways, among which is the modification of the ordinary locomotor movements after local stimulation.   Through these systems the entire central nervous system may be under control by the dominant ganglia (brain) in the head.   The links in these chains are short neurons, extending only from one segmental ganglion to the next, and the rate of transmission is slow.   (4) A few giant fibers arising near the head end and running the entire length of the body (Fig. 48). Their rate of conduction is rapid and their excitation causes very quick avoiding reactions.   These uninterrupted pathways of high conducting capacity permit the dominant head ganglia to exercise more direct and immediate control over the body segments, a control which is apparently exercised only under strong stimulation or in dangerous or unfamiliar situations.   A similar pair of giant nerve fibers (so-called Mauthner's fibers) is present in the spinal cords of fishes, serving for the regulation of locomotor reflexes, chiefly under the influence of the vestibular apparatus of the ear (p. 195).

The preceding analysis of nervous mechanisms is, of course, very schematic and no attempt has been made to fill in the details of the picture.   The four types chosen for illustration might be multiplied many times, and the cross connections by which different reflexes are bound together into the complex behavior patterns actually observed are left out of account.   But these crude illustrations may serve to give a true, though very incomplete, view of the ways in which the cellular elements of the nervous system are connected up in working reflex patterns.

Physiological gradients and head dominance in worms. — The concentration of the nerve cells to form a central nervous system, with enlarged brain in the leading segments of the body, together with variously developed longitudinally conducting pathways thus reducing the physiological resistance to conduction and so reducing the steepness of the physiological gradients between the dominant center and the organs of response, marks a great structural advance over the nerve net of the jellyfishes and its nerve ring.

The gradients of a number of worms have been carefully studied by the same methods used with lower forms, and with results which bring into clear relief the part played by the nervous system.   In various annelid worms related to the earthworm it has been experimentally established (Hyman, 1916; Hyman and Galigher, 1921; Hyman and Bellamy, 1922) that there is a center of greatest dominance at the head end, another center of dominance at the tail end (an expression of physiological isolation), with diminishing gradients extending in opposite directions from these two places.

In the little naid worm, Dero limosa, the accompanying Figure 49 illustrates the susceptibility of the body to potassium cyanide at three successive stages of the action of the poison. Beginning at the head end, the tissues of the body disintegrate progressively under the action of an appropriate concentration of the drug. After several segments of the head end have been involved disintegration of the tail begins, as shown in the first figure. The second figure shows some further disintegration at both ends and the third figure a later stage, the two processes of disintegration meeting at a point behind the middle of the worm. This susceptibility to the poison is a reliable index of metabolic activity in the normal tissues, the regions of higher metabolism breaking down earlier than those of lower metabolism. This demonstrates an axial physiological gradient highest at the head, next higher at the tail, and diminishing away from these two points.

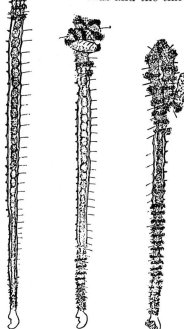

FIG. 49.—Three stages in the disintegration of Dero limosa under the action of potassium cyanide. After Hyman (1916).

Physiological isolation and fission in worms. — Various observations have been made to learn how far the behavior of the worm is actually under the dominance of the head and how far the more posterior segments are able to function independently of this control.[1] Child's observations (1915 a, pp. 93, 94) on flatworms (Planaria) may be summarized here. The species in question normally reproduces asexually by fission, or splitting the body in two in the plane marked *f — f* on Figure 50.

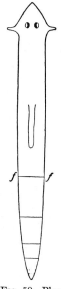

FIG. 50.—Planaria in fission. After Child (1915 a).

[1] For a general discussion of physiological isolation see Child (1924, Chap. 10).

"The separated posterior portion becomes a new animal, while the anterior portion develops a new posterior end, and fission is sooner or later repeated. There is no morphological indication of a second individual or zoöid in the posterior region of the body, but one or more such individuals are indicated by the metabolic gradient of the major axis and by various other physiological differences. The apical region of this gradient is the head of the animal, and from the head the metabolic rate decreases to the level where separation occurs in fission; there a sudden rise in rate occurs, and then again a downward gradient toward the posterior end. The region where the rate rises suddenly represents the apical end of the second individual and the downward gradient following is the gradient of the major axis of this zoöid. In the shorter animals only one of these zoöids is present, but as the length increases the basal body region may show two, three, or more of these distinct gradients. Represented graphically the metabolic gradient in such an animal is like the curve in Fig. 45 [here reproduced as Figure 51]; *a* is the head region, the long slope the body of the anterior chief zoöid, which forms most of the body of the worm, *b* represents the apical end of the second zoöid, *c* that of a third, etc. These zoöids are the result of successive physiological isolations of the basal region as the animal grows in length. First a single zoöid is formed at the basal end, but the range of dominance is short in this undeveloped individual, and as growth proceeds its basal region soon becomes physiologically isolated, and a second zoöid arises, and

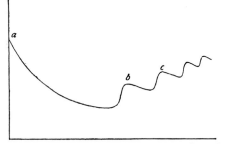

FIG. 51. — Diagrammatic representation of the major axial gradients of Planaria in fission After Child (1915 a). This and the preceding figure are copied by permission of the publishers, The University of Chicago Press.

so on. While the degree of physiological isolation is not sufficient to permit the development of the new individual to proceed very far, some degree of rejuvenescence in the part does occur and its metabolic rate rises slightly, and with each successive isolation there is a further increase in rate, so that in each successive zoöid the gradient is at a level somewhat higher than that of the preceding."

The waving respiratory movements of the posterior regions of some aquatic oligochete worms allied to the earthworm are initiated from the posterior end and occur only when the head is not excited. Excitation of the anterior end inhibits them. They also occur in headless animals. Dr. Child calls my attention to this case as a beautiful example of physiological isolation occurring only when the chief center of dominance is not excited and the integration of bodily activities is therefore incomplete.

The physiological gradients of the earthworm have not been experimentally studied, but in related annelids the experiments cited above show that in the primary longitudinal axis of the body these gradients indicate to some extent the degree of integration of the segments, that is, the unity of the body as a whole. Where the gradients are steep and the body is elongated, the parts remote from the primary center of dominance in the head may be physiologically isolated and the unity of the body thereby impaired. When this is carried to the extreme the physiological isolation of the posterior part of the body may be followed by structural transverse division, and reproduction by fission results, as in Planaria and some species of annelids, but not in the earthworm.

In the earthworm, with better conducting apparatus in the nervous system, so great physiological isolation of the parts is not possible and this mode of propagation does not occur, though the body segmentation is an expression of a similar type of physiological isolation of parts during embryological development. Each segment is an incomplete zoöid which is never set free but is retained under the dominance of the body as a whole. The more highly developed nervous system probably prevents the completion of the physiological isolation of the segments; their anatomical separation is thereby inhibited, and they are reorganized as integral parts of the body as a whole. The integration of the earthworm's body is, however, not so great as to prevent the very extensive regeneration of lost parts if the worm is cut in two, a form of biological regulation which is impossible in higher animals with still more highly developed nervous conductors.

Behavior of the earthworm. — The annelid worms offer ideal objects for the study of the general physiology of the nervous system. In flatworms the pattern of bodily organization of higher animals is forecast, with, however, so little differentiation of either nervous or other tissues as to make the study of the nervous functions as such very difficult and to give the impression that the physiological gradients and other fundamental dynamic factors are matters of quantitative relations of the total metabolism of different parts of the body rather than specific functions of the nervous apparatus. In the annelids, on the other hand, differentiation has advanced so far as to give a clear indication of the patterns characteristic of all higher animal bodies, including: (1) a nervous system fabricated from separate neurons in contrast with the nerve net of coelenterates (synaptic as opposed to non-synaptic type of nervous system); (2) a well developed central nervous system; (3) pronounced segmentation of the body as a whole and of the nervous system, with segmental ganglia acting as local centers of physiological dominance within each segment; (4) a chief longitudinal polar axis; (5) pronounced cephalization, with a center of chief physiological dominance in the head, to which are subordinated centers of secondary dominance near the tail end of the body and in smaller measure in each segment; (6) bilateral symmetry. These features are clearly defined, and yet they are so simply developed and withal in a body so large as to permit analysis of the particular parts of the nervous system concerned in the diverse functional factors just enumerated.

There are few animal bodies so favorably organized for the study of the separate fundamental factors of behavior and the correlated nervous structures as the annelid worms, and no field of investigation offers greater promise of large returns from carefully conducted physiological experimentation. Much has already been done (see, for instance Darwin, 1883, Loeb, 1894, Friedländer, 1894, Hesse, 1896, Maxwell, 1897, Harper, 1905, Jennings, 1906 a, Gross, 1921), but numerous problems of primary importance still await investigation.

To what extent the behavior of the earthworm can be reduced to stable inherited patterns of action of the tropism type and how far this behavior is of the individually modifiable type requires further study. A very interesting method of approach to this problem was opened by Yerkes (1912), who devised a simple modification of the maze, consisting of a T-shaped passage with entrance at the stem of the T, and exit at the right hand turn and at the left turn a piece of rough sandpaper, beyond which was a device for giving the worm a painful electric shock. After from 20 to 100 experiences the worms learned to avoid the left turn and go directly to the right and so escape (Fig. 52). After this habit was acquired the brain was removed by cutting off the anterior five segments. Forty hours after this operation the worm was tested in the maze and made the correct turn after considerable hesitation at the dividing of the ways, and a few minutes later it made the correct turn promptly, reacting about as before the operation. This was repeated many times, showing that the effects of training persist, at least to some extent, after removal of the brain. During the following two months while a new brain was being regenerated the habit completely disappeared, the worm having been given no training during the second month. Systematic training during the next two weeks resulted in the partial re-acquisition of the original direction habit.

The latter part of this experiment was based on a single worm, but the whole procedure has since been repeated under the direction of Dr. Elizabeth Crosby (unpublished), using several specimens, with substantially similar results. A much more extensive investigation has recently been published by Heck (1919–20) in which many earthworms were carried through courses of training in a similar maze with the following results: (1) Normal worms perfectly learned to make the correct turn to the right, thus avoiding contact with the electrodes on the left, after 200 trials. If now the electrodes were changed to the right side of the maze and the exit to the left, these worms after 65 additional trials learned to reverse the former turn to the right and invariably turned to the left. (2) After the worms had learned to make the correct turn invariably, removal of the brain (supra-esophageal ganglion) did not destroy the habit; the worms reacted as before. (3) Removal of the brain, or indeed of several of the anterior segments, from untrained worms, did not incapacitate them from learning to make the correct turn.

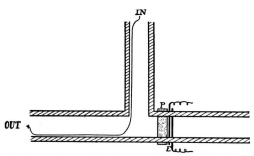

Fig. 52.—Diagram of T-shaped maze used by Yerkes in testing the learning of earthworms. The worm is admitted at the stem of the T, marked *IN*. It may turn to the left, in which case it will meet first a piece of sandpaper, *P*, then will receive an electric shock from the electrodes, *E*. The turn to the right leads directly out into a burrow. The course of a worm at the 30th trial after acquisition of the habit is indicated. It takes a course directly to the burrow, avoiding the left turn.

The evidence indicates that such acquired neuromuscular habits are executed by a modification of the action system of the whole body and are not due to modification of the brain only. It should be borne in mind that the brain of the earthworm is a very small part of the whole central nervous system and its dominance probably acts rather by setting the direction of responses than by controlling them during their execution. (The same is probably true of the human cerebral cortex to a very large extent.)

Summary. — The nervous system of worms, when compared with that of polyps and jellyfishes, shows several notable advances in organization correlated primarily with the habit of moving head-first and with the differentiation of the primary head-tail axis. In the simpler flatworms, like Planaria, progress in this direction has been slight yet sufficient to indicate clearly the fundamental functional and structural characteristics of (1) condensation of the diffuse nervous system into a central system, (2) cephalization, with development of a brain and pronounced head dominance, (3) bilateral symmetry, and (4) physiological isolation in relation to reproduction and tissue differentiation. These have been shown to be expressions of physiological gradients of the same type as in lower forms, *i. e.*, differences in rate of metabolism correlated with the excitation-conduction phenomena of protoplasm.

In the higher segmented worms, like the earthworm, the developmental tendencies which are only in their infancy in flatworms come to more mature expression in a pattern of organization which persists with no fundamental change throughout the entire group of segmented invertebrates (crustaceans, spiders and insects). The centralization of the nervous system is well advanced, each joint of the body possessing its own reflex apparatus and correlating nerve center. Cephalization has also advanced, with a small brain possessing limited but clearly defined functions of dominant control over the body and special nerve cells and fibers set apart as instruments of this control. Integration of the bodily processes has progressed so far that reproduction by fission through physiological isolation of parts takes a subordinate place, though there is a larger measure of segmental autonomy than in higher forms. The brain is doubtless concerned with the acquisition of habits, though it probably has no essential part to play in the retentiveness and actual performance of the habitual acts. In brief, these worms illustrate the general plan of the nervous system of all segmented invertebrates reduced to the lowest terms consonant with a clear exhibition of the common pattern, with no highly specialized development of any part of it.

CHAPTER XI

THE NERVOUS SYSTEM OF INSECTS

Segmentation of insects — Ganglia of the silkworm moth — Stable and labile types of behavior — Castes and social organization — Instinct and intelligence in insects — Biological plasticity contrasted with individual modifiability.

Segmention of insects. — Segmented worms of the same general type as the earthworm were probably the ancestors of all of the higher invertebrates grouped under the name of arthropods, including the crustaceans (crabs and their allies), spiders and insects. The infinitely diverse forms assumed by these animals are all clearly derived from a worm-like form by the elaboration of certain segments, giving much more complex structure and far more diversified functional powers, and especially by the fusion of some adjacent segments, giving more effective coöperative action of the regions thus more intimately united. In the insects the segments are arranged in three groups: (1) the head, containing the mouth and its appendages, the brain and the chief sense organs; (2) the thorax with three pairs of walking legs; (3) the abdomen. The head segments are the most highly modified, incidental to a high degree of cephalization and head dominance.

The arthropod type of nervous system, like that of the worms, consists of a brain composed of ganglia above and below the esophagus and a segmentally arranged series of ganglia along the ventral side of the body, but the brain is much larger, formed by the fusion of several segmental ganglia, and the ganglia of the other segments of the body may also be fused together in some regions. Some variations of this fundamental pattern are seen in Figure 53, which illustrates four species of flies. All of the ganglia of the head segments are united to form the brain and the remaining ganglia show different degrees of fusion in each case.

In these insects the ganglia which form the brain are the immediate servants of the sense organs of the head, especially the eyes, with which, as seen in Figure 53, they are in immediate contact; and the dominance which the eyes maintain over the behavior of many insects is well known. The reflexes in response to light (phototropisms) have been much studied. They are impulsions of the strongest sort and are ineradicable, as seen when the moth repeatedly darts into the flame which sears its wings.

Comparing the insect's nervous system again with that of the earthworm, we recall that in the latter the segments of the body are all very much alike, except those at the anterior and posterior ends, and in each of the segments its own ganglion has a large measure of independent control of its local activities. The body of the worm may be compared with a loose confederation of separate states, each with autonomous local self-government and responsible to a central power only in respect to its foreign relations. In the insect, to carry out the analogy, the central governing power (head dominance) is stronger,

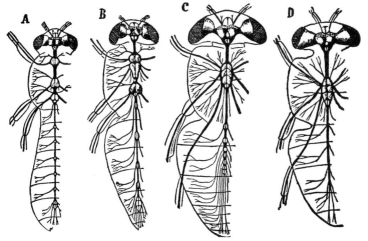

Fig. 53.—The nervous systems of four species of flies, to illustrate the various degrees of concentration of the ganglia: *A*, Chironomus plumosus, with three thoracic and six abdominal ganglia; *B*, Empis stercorea, with two thoracic and five abdominal ganglia; *C*, Tabanus bovinus, with one thoracic ganglion and the abdominal ganglia moved toward each other; *D*, Sarcophaga carnaria, with all thoracic and abdominal ganglia united into a single mass. (After Brand, from Lang's Text-book of Comparative Anatomy.)

the states (segments) are united in three subsidiary federations (head, thorax and abdomen), and yet each state retains a measure of autonomy. The machinery of government is almost entirely inflexible, as if it were merely the execution of a code of immutable laws.

Ganglia of the silkworm moth. — How far the head ganglia do actually dominate the insect's behavior and how far the ganglia of the segments can act independently has been tested experimentally in the case of the silkworm moth by Miss McCracken (1907). These moths after emergence from their cocoons live from ten to twenty days. Their behavior during this part of the life cycle is very simple. They are incapable of feeding, though the caterpillars are voracious enough, and are occupied chiefly with mating and laying the eggs. The female lays from 300 to 500 eggs, which are carefully arranged in a single layer in a definite pattern on a leaf of mulberry or other suitable food plant for the caterpillars when they emerge. This is all a matter of inherited reflex and instinctive organization. The moths show very little capacity for modifying this fixed action system.

The nervous system of this moth consists of the brain and thoracic ganglia and four abdominal ganglia arranged much as in the fly, Empis (Fig. 53, B), save that there is no ganglion in the first abdominal segment. The last (fourth) ganglion is a fusion of those of the three most posterior segments and supplies the muscles and other organs employed in egg-laying.

These moths can be decapitated by snipping off the head with fine scissors without loss of blood or any serious injury to the rest of the body, and the headless moths live as long as normal ones; in fact, they do not seem to mind the operation very much. If mated, either before or after decapitation, the females may by appropriate stimulation be induced to lay the normal number of fertile eggs, which are arranged as laid in the normal manner. The decapitated moths will not, however, spontaneously lay eggs as the normal moths do, nor can they select the appropriate kind of leaf on which to deposit them.

In other moths both head and thorax were snipped off either before or after mating. These females were incapable of mating and the length of life was shortened to about five days. The specimens which were first mated and then deprived of head and thorax laid no eggs spontaneously but they could be induced to lay eggs by rubbing the abdomen. In the absence of the legs, which were of course removed with the thorax, the eggs cannot be arranged as laid in the normal way although attempts were made to do so by twisting the abdomen about during deposition of the eggs.

Further experiments were then made by cutting the connectives between the four abdominal ganglia one after the other in specimens deprived of head and thorax. After separating the first abdominal ganglion from the others there was no obvious change in the behavior. Eggs could still be laid upon appropriate stimulation of the abdomen. When the connectives between the second and third and third and fourth ganglia were cut, there was still no important change in the egg-laying process; but cutting the nerves from the last abdominal ganglion abolished the reflexes.

These experiments show that the mating and egg-laying reflexes can be initiated by stimuli received by the brain, that they do not begin spontaneously without the brain, and that the selection of the proper kind of leaf on which to lay the eggs requires the brain. The brain of the earthworm has been shown (p. 140) to be unessential in the acquisition of habits, though it plays a considerable part in the normal reflex and instinctive behavior. The brain of the insect is here seen to play an essential part in setting off a complicated system of instinctive activities, involving some rather fine sensory discriminations, such as the selection of mulberry leaves in distinction from all other objects. In both cases when the activity of the body segments is once initiated it can be executed perfectly without the brain.

In the silkworm moth the act of deposition of the eggs is controlled directly by the last abdominal ganglion, but the coöperation of the thoracic ganglia and the organs innervated by them is necessary for the performance of the accessory movements involved in properly arranging the eggs. Miss McCracken summarizes her observations in these words:

"The coördination of movement in various segments, after each operation, is progressively lost. The ovipositor, throughout, makes the same effort to avoid placing one egg upon another, by moving from side to side. With abdominal ganglia intact, this effort is successful. It becomes noticeably less and less so as each abdominal ganglion is severed, until when but two remain, muscular coöperation of the segments is so far reduced that the combined efforts of the last three abdominal segments is not sufficient to pull the body around and the eggs (after the first three or four, which are placed side by side) are piled one upon another. The results from the last series of operations show the high degree of independent activity exhibited by the controlling center of the reproductive apparatus, namely, the last abdominal ganglion, and the coördination of the functions of this ganglion with those of the preceding ganglia in the ventral chain. . . . Each thoracic and abdominal ganglion in the silkworm is so organized that the reflexes carried on in the last segment of the abdomen are accompanied by a set of reflexes in other segments of a kind altogether different from that of the initial reflex. The functioning of the ovipositor is perfected by the movements in space of the legs, or in the absence of these, of the anterior segments of the abdomen."

These experiments show that we have in the insect the same type of physiological dominance as in worms (p. 135), viz., strong head dominance with a diminishing gradient backward and a secondary center of dominance at the tail end of the body for the control of the last body segments.

Stable and labile types of behavior. — It has repeatedly been emphasized and illustrated that two fundamental factors in animal behavior are, (1) a fixed invariable inherited action system of the reflex and instinctive type, and (2) individual modifiability or learning by experience. In the insects we find the first of these factors very highly developed and the second factor at a minimum, so that these animals are favorable objects for the study of reflexes and instincts. The simpler reflexes (often called tropisms or taxes) are remarkably stable and inflexible. Under normal conditions they serve useful purposes in feeding, mating, avoiding enemies, and the like; but in unusual situations where they are harmful they are nevertheless carried through with the same machine-like precision, as illustrated by the moth's reaction to the flame.

Many physiologists regard these reflexes as structurally determined orientations of the animal to the stimulus acting upon a body so organized that it must respond mechanically in a fixed manner. Others think they are inaugurated by selection of certain adaptive movements from a number of random turnings. But whatever the mechanism employed, it seems apparent that they are expressions of fixed patterns of the innate action system, unintelligent and capable of very little modifiability. Each species of insect has a limited range of behavior, which, like its bodily form, is nicely adapted to its own special mode of life. The species vary in these respects among themselves widely, but the individual insect has very little capacity for deviation from its own innate reflex and instinctive pattern.

The light reactions of insects are sometimes positive movements toward the source of light and sometimes negative movements away from it, and under experimental conditions the same insect may at one time show the positive reaction and at another time the negative. It has been shown by Allee and Stein (1918) that in the larvæ (nymphs) of the mayfly these reactions may be reversed by changing the rate of metabolism by Child's method (p. 71). These responses are, therefore, not inflexible but are individually modifiable, at least to the extent of change of sign from positive to negative.

One of the most interesting exhibitions of the fixed type of behavior is the so-called death-feigning reflex. Many insects if disturbed by anything unusual immediately "freeze" into rigidly motionless attitudes. If they are protectively colored, the attitude taken is such as to display the protective coloration to advantage. This is well shown by the caterpillar of the moth, Selenia, which feeds on birch trees (Fig.

54). When disturbed it takes a position on the stem like that of a short branch and holds itself motionless. The attitude, together with its natural markings, gives so close a resemblance to a twig as to deceive even a close observer. These reactions are usually regarded as typical products of natural selection. They cannot be explained on the tropism theory of Loeb.

An instructive illustration of a complex instinctive cycle is given by the mason wasps, or mud daubers. These insects lay their eggs in hollow cylinders about an inch long skilfully fabricated of mud which is manipulated into the desired form. Before the chamber is sealed with the last daub of mud, spiders are captured and so stung as to paralyze the animals (usually without killing them), an egg is laid on a crippled spider, and the chamber is crammed full of the unfortunate victims, which are then entombed by closing the opening. The mud dries into a prison cell with firm but porous walls. In a few days the eggs hatch, the larvæ de-

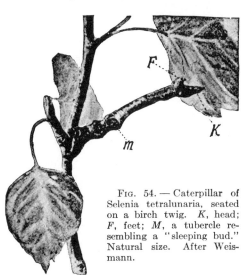

FIG. 54. — Caterpillar of *Selenia tetralunaria*, seated on a birch twig. *K*, head; *F*, feet; *M*, a tubercle resembling a "sleeping bud." Natural size. After Weismann.

vour the meat so bountifully supplied, and when sufficiently mature dig their way out to freedom. This highly adaptive performance is purely an inherited instinct. The mother wasp apparently has no understanding of what she does nor why. She never sees her offspring and can have no intelligent prevision of their requirements.

Castes and social organization. — Among the insects we find also highly elaborated social or community organizations, such as the hive of bees and the ant colony. Here there are numerous castes — queen, drones, workers, soldiers and the like — each with special duties to perform and with special structure which forbids any other activities. In some cases these castes cannot live independently of the others and the community as a whole cannot survive unless all óf them are functioning normally. This type of social division of labor is most highly developed in the termites and ants (Wheeler,

1913, 1923). The various forms taken by different castes of the colony of a single species of ant are shown in Figure 55.

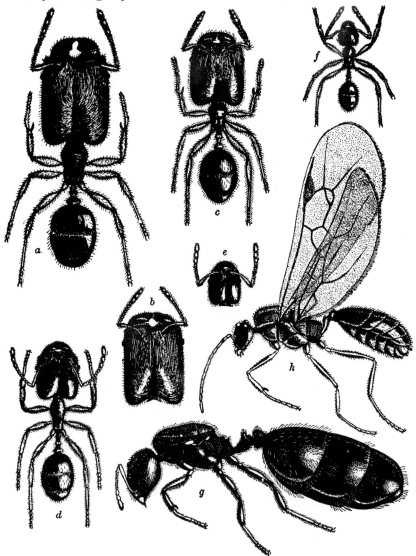

Fig. 55.—The various castes of the ant, Pheidole instabilis. *a*, soldier; *b–e*, intermediate workers; *f*, typical worker; *g*, dealeated female; *h*, male. After Wheeler.

We have compared the organization of the body of the individual insect to a federation of separate states. Here we have a larger state in which the persons are bound together on a coöperative basis, with division of labor among the individuals more rigidly carried out than in a human industrial community, though with fewer kinds of specialization represented (Child, 1924, Chap. 16).

This again is not intelligently planned by the insects themselves. They have little to say about it. Each does what it is structurally adapted to do and refrains from interference with procedures for which it is incapacitated. Miss Thompson (1916, 1917, 1919, 1922) has examined the nervous systems of different castes of termites (the so-called white ants) and finds that each caste has its own type of brain, as well as external bodily form, and that these characteristics of the castes are in some cases distinguishable at the time of hatching by internal structure. They are not developed on account of differences in food or any other external influences. In the sexual forms the eyes and optic lobes of the brain are larger than in the workers and soldiers and there are other differences. On the behavior of termites, see Andrews (1911).

In the case of bees, wasps and true ants it is said (Lameere, 1922) that the castes are determined by, or correlated with, differences in the nourishment supplied to the larvæ and are not due to germinal differences. But the males or drones of bees appear to develop from unfertilized (parthenogenetic) eggs of queens and workers from fertilized eggs (Phillips, 1917, pp. 186–191).

In the true ants (Thompson, 1913) the queen has a typical generalized type of brain, from which the greatly modified brains of the other castes have been derived by reduction of some parts and enlargement of other parts in each case. The eyes and optic lobes are large, and these are still larger in the males which have the other parts of the brain reduced. The large eyes in these forms are correlated with the mating habits, in which the male must be able to follow the female in the nuptial flight. The worker brain has greatly reduced eyes and optic lobes. This is well illustrated in Pheidole, whose various castes are shown in Figure 55. The relative development of the brain and eyes in four of these castes is shown in Figure 56.

In the brain of the ants there are large lobes, the pedunculated bodies or mushroom bodies, which are supposed to be the chief motor and psychic centers. These are larger in the workers than in the other castes (Fig. 56).

Instinct and intelligence in insects.— The cases of insects' behavior hitherto considered are largely expressions of the innate action system, executed perfectly as soon as the necessary organs have reached maturity and the proper stimuli are presented. They require no practice or training and are little, if at all, improved by repetition. Bees build comb, gather honey, and swarm at the appropriate time quite spontaneously and as perfectly the first time as the last (or nearly so). The fact that the design of the honeycomb is mechanically perfect to provide the maximum strength and containing capac-

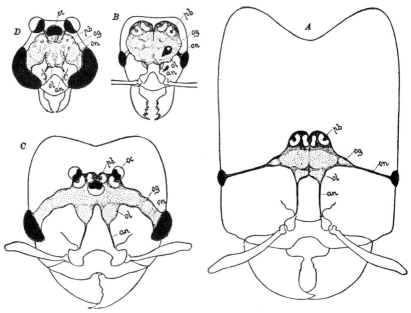

Fig. 56.—Heads of soldier (*A*), worker (*B*), female (*C*), and male (*D*) of Pheidole instabilis, drawn under the same magnification, with brain, eyes and ocelli viewed as transparent objects. *an*, antennary nerve; *oc*, median ocellus; *og*, optic ganglion; *ol*, olfactory lobe; *on*, optic nerve; *pb*, pedunculate bodies. After Wheeler. Figures 55 and 56 are taken from Professor Wheeler's book on Ants by kind permission of the publishers and owners of the copyright, The Columbia University Press.

ity with minimum expenditure of material, and countless other instances of wonderful adaptive skill in the lives of these lowly creatures led some of the older naturalists to ascribe to them almost superhuman intelligence. As a feat of engineering the honeycomb is undoubtedly wonderful, but this is no proof that either the bees or their ancestors ever consciously designed it in the full understanding of these engineering principles or even with any comprehension of the purpose for which they worked.

The higher insects show wonderfully developed stereotyped reflex and instinctive action with a minimum admixture of modifiability, docility or intelligence; in fact they probably offer more favorable opportunities for the study of this type of behavior than any other animals. But this does not mean that they have no capacity for modifying their behavior or profiting by experience. This modifiability is a fundamental property of all organisms and experiment shows that insects are not exceptions to the rule. But the modifiability has not been increased in proportion to the development of the fixed action systems, whose perfection and diversity are truly marvelous.

In studying the behavior of wasps Mr. and Mrs. Peckham (1905) have shown that some species find their way back to their nests by taking note of surrounding landmarks, and if these are moved during their absence they become confused and search much as a man would do (see also Rau, 1918). Turner (1907) in an experimental study of the homing of ants presents many clear instances of learning by experience, including cases where different individuals of the same caste in a colony showed marked differences in the way they learn to adjust to the same unfamiliar situation.

Turner in many experiments would transfer ants and pupæ from their nests on an artificial "Lubbock island" to a cardboard stage elevated 10 cm. and connected with the nest by an incline of cardboard. The ants quickly learned the way back to the nest and soon removed all of the pupæ, though they showed much individuality in the time and method of learning. In one case two marked workers, A and B, were placed on the stage with a number of pupæ. The ant A quickly learned the way to the nest and made repeated trips up and down the incline.

"But to B this was an insoluble problem. It continued for a long time to move at random over the stage, reaching down over first one edge and then over another, as though it were reaching for a support that was not to be found; but nothing prompted it to pass down the incline. In experiments where the time required to learn the trick was not the point to be investigated, I had sometimes helped ants to learn the way by forcing them with a forceps or spatula, to move in the right direction. I thought I would thus help B to learn. So with my forceps I pushed it along. Several times I succeeded in getting it to the incline, but nothing that I did would induce it to go down. I had failed, but this was not the first time that I had failed in similar attempts with other ants.

"Prompted by another thought, I shoved the section-lifter under the ant and transferred it to the island. The ant then stepped off and carried the pupa into the nest. As soon as B returned to the island, I shoved the section-lifter under it and transferred it to the stage. B stepped off and picked up another pupa. With the section-lifter I again transferred it to the island.

After this had been repeated several times, the moment I presented the section-lifter, whether on the island or on the stage, the ant immediately mounted it and rested quietly thereon until it had been removed to the stage or to the island; then it stepped off and picked up a pupa or else went into the nest. I usually held the section-lifter from two to four millimeters above the surface of the island or stage. In this manner the industrious creature passed to and from the stage about fifty times in something less than two hours.

"Whenever I presented the section-lifter to other ants of the same colony, they would attack it, or avoid it, or else mount it and roam over blade and handle and sometimes even my hand. When the same section-lifter was presented to A (the one that all this time had been conveying pupæ down the incline) it would avoid it and pass on.

"Thus I had two individuals of the same colony, at the same time and under identical external conditions, responding to the same stimulus in quite different ways. To the one the incline had no psychic value, to the other it was a stimulus to pass to and from the stage. To one the section-lifter was a repellent stimulus, to the other an attractive stimulus. Each had acquired a different way of accomplishing the same purpose and each had retained and utilized what it had gained by experience."

Darwin in his "Descent of Man" has remarked, "It is certain that there may be extraordinary activity with an extremely small absolute mass of nervous matter; thus the wonderfully diversified instincts, mental powers, and affections of ants are notorious, yet their cerebral ganglia are not so large as the quarter of a small pin's head. Under this point of view, the brain of an ant is one of the most marvelous atoms of matter in the world, perhaps more so than the brain of man."

Wheeler in commenting upon this quotation shares Darwin's wonder at the marvelous complexity of behavior controlled by the minute brains of ants. The marvel grows with our increased knowledge of insect life. But in partial explanation attention may be called to two features: first that the individual ant leads a rather simple routine existence, the complexity being largely a matter of the relations of the individuals to one another, and second that much of this behavior is the same sort of physiological response exhibited by protozoans and may not require highly developed nervous apparatus.

Biological plasticity contrasted with individual modifiability. — The three final chapters of Wheeler's book on Ants (1913) are devoted to The Sensations of Ants, The Instinctive Behavior of Ants, and The Plastic Behavior of Ants. This comprehensive and critical analysis should be read by everyone who is interested in insect behavior and all related questions, including the mental life of lower animals, psychogenesis and instincts. Throughout Wheeler's book stress is placed on the plasticity of ants and their adaptability to their surroundings. There are two factors here which others have not always so clearly distinguished:

(1) Diversity in the innate organization of different species and castes so that the entire group shows a great variety of adaptations. Ants as a whole are extraordinarily adaptable in this sense, the several species being adjusted to a great variety of natural conditions, and the different castes of a single species in the same way adapt themselves to many conditions. The high development of this type of innate adaptability in ants is the chief reason for their conspicuous efficiency in the biological sense. Ants are found everywhere, the number of species is very great (about 5000 species have been described), and they outnumber in individuals all other terrestrial animals (Wheeler, 1913, p. 2).

(2) Individual modifiability, plasticity of behavior, and docility. Ants probably show more of this sort of adaptability than any other invertebrates. Nevertheless their individual capacities in this direction are not conspicuously great and are far inferior to their biological adaptability mentioned under the first head, and their dominant position among the invertebrates is due primarily to the first factor rather than to the second. It is only in the vertebrate phylum that we find these relations reversed (p. 291).

What has just been said about ants applies to the insects as a whole. Their dominant position is due to a type of biological plasticity which is not dependent upon highly developed individual plasticity of behavior but upon hereditary organization. Their behavior is undoubtedly to some extent modifiable by individual experience, but this is not the decisive factor in establishing their unique position in the animal kingdom.

The insects form a terminal branch of the phylogenetic tree; they have given rise to nothing higher. They exhibit highly elaborate systems of reflex and instinctive action more nearly pure, that is, unmixed with intelligent modifiability, than are to be found elsewhere. Somewhat analogous conditions are to be found in the higher fishes and in birds, though in these cases, and especially in the latter, there is a much larger proportion of intelligent adjustment in the behavior complex.

Wheeler concludes his book on Ants with these words: "It is, in fact, quite futile to attempt a phylogenetic derivation of the automatic from the plastic activities or *vice versa*, for both represent primitive and fundamental tendencies of living protoplasm, and hence of all organisms. As instinct, one of these tendencies reaches its most complex manifestation in the Formicidæ, while the other blossoms in the intelligent activities of men."

This is the main thesis which we are expounding in this work. Both innate stable and individually modifiable plastic factors are present in all behavior, and the higher forms of behavior especially cannot be understood apart from the analysis of these component factors. The neglect of this analysis is responsible for the futility of so much of the enormous literature on instinct and intelligence. That which usually goes by the name of instinct is a composite thing. Throughout this work when the terms instinct and instinctive action are used the reference is intended only to the innate component of the behavior, not to the unanalyzed complex as a whole.

CHAPTER XII

THE GENERAL PLAN OF THE VERTEBRATE NERVOUS SYSTEM

Vertebrates and invertebrates — Development of the vertebrate brain — The subdivision of the brain — Segmental and suprasegmental apparatus — The reflex centers — The correlation centers — Summary.

Vertebrates and invertebrates. — The segmented worms and insects, together with the allied crustaceans and spiders, in the aggregate comprise the articulate branch of invertebrate animals. They are conspicuously jointed animals, characterized by more or less evident segmentation of the body. The fundamental similarities of the nervous organization throughout this phylum have been commented upon.

There are several other important invertebrate branches whose bodies are not obviously segmented — echinoderms (starfishes), mollusks, brachiopods (lampshells), tunicates, etc. — and whose nervous systems are very differently arranged. These must be left out of consideration entirely in this survey and our attention will next be turned to the type of nervous system found in the vertebrate branch.

The ladder type of central nervous system as exemplified in the articulates is an expression of the pronounced segmentation of the body — a pair of ganglia in each segment serving primarily as adjustors for local activities of that segment. Each segment is to some extent physiologically isolated from the others and its nerve center is master of its own little realm with, however, a limited but very definite subordination to a center of higher dominance in the brain.

The plan of organization of the vertebrate central nervous system is as different from this as it can well be when the fundamental similarity of the neurons in the two cases is taken into account. The nervous elements of the vertebrate spinal cord and brain are woven together to form a continuous fabric which was originally shaped in the form of a hollow cylinder, the *neural tube,* extending throughout the length of the body. This tubular character is a conspicuous feature of all vertebrate embryos (Figs. 64, 65) and it is in all cases preserved throughout life, though modified in form in different regions as required by local conditions (Fig. 57).

There is an obscure transverse segmentation of this neural tube
in early embryos, but this is overshadowed and in most places entirely
obscured in the adult by an extensive and complex system of longitudinal correlating nervous elements.   In the invertebrates hitherto
considered the segmental ganglia and their reflexes dominate the
architectural pattern, but even in the lowest vertebrates the dominant
feature of the central nervous system is the longitudinally directed
elements which more effectively correlate all parts of the system and
integrate its activities.   Peripherally the vertebrate nerves are more or
less clearly segmentally arranged in conformity with the segmentation

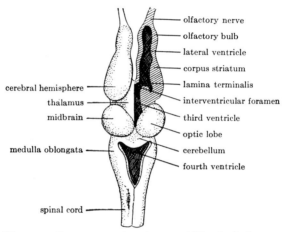

Fig. 57.—Diagrammatic representation of an amphibian brain from which the roof
of the thalamus and cerebral hemisphere has been dissected off on the right side, exposing the third ventricle and one of the lateral ventricles.   The membranous roof of
the fourth ventricle has also been removed.   There is a communication between third
and fourth ventricles which is not exposed in this dissection.

of the skeleton (vertebræ and ribs) and body muscles; but centrally
this arrangement is scarcely evident.

These structural differences imply on the physiological side that the
parts of the vertebrate body are more closely knit together, the
reflex pattern is more unified, there is more efficient central correlation of part with part, there is greater capacity for diversity of
response, and in general there is, accordingly, possible a wider range
of individual adjustments to diverse external situations.   This manifests itself in two phases: (1) the innate neuromotor mechanisms are
more complex with corresponding increase in range of variety of
reflex and instinctive capacity of the individual; (2) there is greater
modifiability and plasticity of behavior.   This plasticity is due wholly

to the greater ability of the organism to rearrange the reflex units of the innate neuromotor apparatus in new, that is, individually acquired combinations.   In addition to and superposed upon the innate action systems represented by the more or less complex reflex and instinctive patterns, there is in the central correlation centers more elaborate apparatus for recombining the behavior units in ways determined by past experience of the individual.   The individual vertebrate learns to do new things or to react to situations in ways which are not predetermined by innate structure more readily than does the invertebrate.   And this capacity increases as we ascend from lower to higher vertebrates.

The central nervous system of articulates is developed from the skin of the ventral side of the body (Fig. 41, p. 127); in contrast with this the tubular nervous system of all vertebrates arises from the skin of the dorsal side of the body and it always lies dorsally of the digestive tract.   In all vertebrate embryos the central nervous system rests upon a supporting rod, the notochord, which persists in adult life in the lowest forms but in higher classes is enveloped and ultimately replaced by jointed skeletal elements forming the vertebral column, from which the phylum receives its name — Vertebrata.

The solid ganglia of the articulate animals are correlated with fixed or stereotyped reflex and instinctive patterns and in no case do these species show any highly developed plastic or individually modifiable behavior types.   They go about the business of life industriously and efficiently, but apparently for the most part unintelligently. There is, to be sure, some evidence of associative memory and whatever of psychic life (if any) that implies; but this is never highly developed, and among the countless swarms of insects there is relatively little evidence of intelligent adaptation or any other form of mentality.

The tubular nervous system of vertebrates in its simpler forms seems but little better endowed with these higher functional capacities. But clearly it can serve and integrate the activities of larger and more complex bodies.   And the very complexity of bodily organization thus made possible permits a more diversified and richer life.   The progressive elaboration of the machinery of living and widening the content of experience is, no doubt, the biological basis on which is built the greater capacity for profiting by experience of higher vertebrates.   The highest invertebrate phylum early reached a limit of bodily size and complexity of nervous organization and behavior which in this phylum has not been exceeded.   Further specialization was in the direction of multiplication of diverse species and castes on the plane already reached rather than by passing beyond to higher levels of organization.

Among vertebrates, on the other hand, the increasing diversification of form and function within the individual goes on progressively. This phylum is of the indeterminate rather than determinate type of growth, to borrow a botanical analogy; that is, instead of producing its first and finest flower at the end of the axis of growth and thus blocking further development in the ascending line like a sunflower, the growing point seeks ever higher and higher levels like a spruce tree. Even in man, the culmination of this ascending stem, progress (let us hope) is not yet terminated — possibly so in physical prowess but not in resources of brain and mind.

Development of the vertebrate brain. — The best approach to an understanding of the plan of the vertebrate nervous system is through its embryologic development, which in broad lines is surprisingly uniform in the earlier stages throughout the whole phylum from the lowest fishes to man. How far this development is an actual recapitulation of phylogenetic history is a difficult problem[1] which has not been fully solved. Clearly the embryologic development of the brain in no particular species follows exactly the pathway of the preceding evolutionary movements; yet in its main outlines the recapitulation is more evident in the vertebrate nervous system than in most other organ systems and an intimate knowledge of the comparative anatomy and comparative embryology of the nervous system is an indispensable foundation for a full understanding of the complexities of the human brain. If attention is fixed upon the development of particular parts of the human brain, some of these are seen to recapitulate the phylogeny very closely, even though these parts in their mutual relationships and in the time sequence of their differentiation may be so combined as to result in great distortion of the pattern of the phylogenetic history of the brain as a whole (Hines, 1922, p. 166).

As we have seen (p. 97), the physiological gradients which determine the chief body axes appear to have been laid down in the general organization of the bodies of multicellular animals in advance of the differentiation of the nervous system and the latter organs were shaped in conformity with these preëxisting gradients. This history is repeated in the embryonic development of the vertebrate body. Gradients in rate of metabolic activity have been demonstrated in vertebrate embryos by the susceptibility method and otherwise. These gradients define a chief head-tail axis or apico-basal polarity,

[1] See Child, 1924, Chap. 9; Herrick, 1922 a; Hertwig, 1918; Montgomery, 1906.

dorso-ventral polarity, and medio-lateral polarity long preceding the appearance of differentiated tissues of nervous or any other kind. The nervous system is laid down within the dynamic field thus prepared, and its primary morphological and physiological features are to this extent predetermined.

Bellamy (1919, 1922) has shown by an extensive series of experiments which cannot be summarized here that frog's eggs and embryos exhibit general bodily axial gradients of the same physiological type as those previously described by Child and others in lower invertebrates and plants. These gradients are reducible to quantitative differences of physiological condition, of which rate of metabolism

FIG. 58.—The early neural plate of the egg of the amphibian, Cryptobranchus. The outer layer of the egg (ectoderm) has thickened to form an epithelial plate bounded by elevated ridges, the neural folds. Compare figure 61. The entire central nervous system is developed from this plate. This and the two following figures are redrawn from B. G. Smith (1912).

FIG. 59.—The late neural plate, or neural groove, of Cryptobranchus. The neural folds are higher and are approaching each other preparatory to closure of the neural tube. Compare figure 62.

FIG. 60.—The same egg seen at the time of closure of the neural tube. The neural folds have fused in the mid-dorsal line. Compare figure 63.

is one important factor. "If a gradient in physiological condition is a fundamental ordering factor in the process of physiological axiation, it should be possible to obtain as many expressions of this gradient as there are aspects into which fundamental activity and the physical constitution of the protoplasm may be analyzed." In fact, a large number of these expressions have been brought to light experimentally in both early and later stages of development of the frog's egg and the foundation is thus laid for an analysis of the dynamic factors in vertebrate development (see further, Child, 1924, Chap. 8).

The developing nervous system first appears as a thickened plate of the outer (ectodermal) epithelium along the mid-dorsal surface of the body, this plate being folded inward to form first a trough, then a tube, which is pinched off from the outer skin. The process of formation of this neural tube can easily be watched from hour to hour with the aid of a hand lens in the living egg of the frog or salamander. The steps will be clear from Figures 58 to 64.

In an early stage of embryological development the epithelium forming the epidermis is thickened along the mid-dorsal region of the egg, thus forming the neural plate bounded by elevated ridges, the neural folds (Figs. 58, 61). The two neural folds which form the lateral borders of the neural plate gradually approach each other in the mid-dorsal line (Figs. 59, 62), and here they finally meet and fuse (Figs. 60, 63). The outer skin heals over along the seam of fusion, below which the neural tube is separated from the skin. The relations of the neural tube to surrounding structures shortly after its closure and separation from the skin as seen in longitudinal section are illustrated in Figure 64.

In all young vetebrate embryos the walls of the neural tube are relatively simple epithelial membranes throughout. There is some enlargement at the head end, which is the morphological expression of the strong head dominance of the vertebrate body. The epithelial tube of the trunk regions in the adult becomes the spinal cord with walls greatly thickened by local differentiation of nervous elements and other specialized tissues. In form the spinal cord does not otherwise greatly differ from that of the early neural tube.

The neural tube of the head, however, undergoes much more radical change to become the brain, whose primary major subdivisions can be

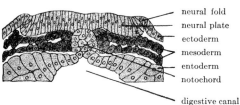

neural fold
neural plate
ectoderm
mesoderm
entoderm
notochord
digestive canal

FIG. 61.—Cross section through the neural plate of the newt, Triton, at about the stage represented in figure 58.

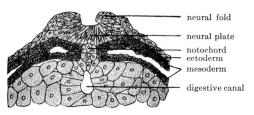

neural fold
neural plate
notochord
ectoderm
mesoderm
digestive canal

FIG. 62.—Through the neural groove at about the stage represented in figure 59.

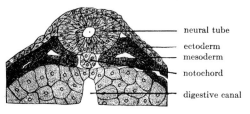

neural tube
ectoderm
mesoderm
notochord
digestive canal

FIG. 63.—Through the closed neural tube. Compare figure 60. After Hertwig.

identified in all vertebrates in fundamentally the same arrangement. Both spinal cord and brain retain their tubular character throughout life, the original cavity remaining as the ventricles of the brain and central canal of the cord.

It must, then, be borne in mind that the vertebrate brain is a hollow organ and the astonishing variety of forms which it assumes has been brought about through inequalities of growth which produce various flexures, local thickenings, outfoldings and infoldings of different parts of the walls of a tube which was originally a thin-walled and relatively simple epithelial cylinder. The cerebral hemispheres are derivatives of this primitive neural tube, and some of the factors

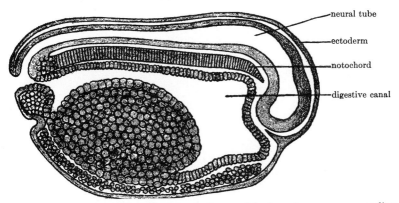

neural tube

ectoderm

notochord

digestive canal

FIG. 64.—A longitudinal section through the egg of the frog at an age corresponding approximately to the stage of development shown in figures 60 and 63. After Marshall.

which may have operated in the early stages of their evolutionary history are considered beyond. The profound significance of the distance receptors and the correlation centers related with these so-called organs of higher sense in shaping the course of differentiation of the brain is also commented upon in another connection.

The subdivision of the brain. — The human brain is so inconceivably complex that a functional analysis is very difficult and a rational method of subdivision has been slow in developing; a rational nomenclature has not yet been attained or even approximated. The names in most common use are those adopted by the German Anatomical Society at its meeting in Basel in 1895 and known as the Basel Nomina Anatomica (BNA). The neurological terms are based on the embryological researches of the late Professor His. They are rather cumbersome in their Latin form, and since they are readily available in all textbooks of anatomy it will be necessary here to give only a very brief account of them. These names and their more common synonyms are listed by Eycleshymer and Shoemaker (1917). We shall examine a few embryological stages of the human brain, and these are typical of those of vertebrates in general.

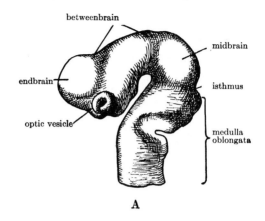

A

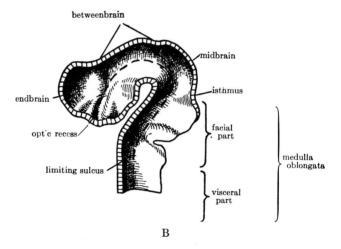

B

Fig. 65.—Enlarged drawings of the brain of a 6.9 mm. human embryo (about four weeks). A, from the left side; B, the right side as seen in median longitudinal section exposing the ventricular cavities. In B the broken line marks the position of the limiting sulcus (separating ventral motor from dorsal sensory centers) as described by His; some recent students place the anterior end of this sulcus somewhat farther back than here shown.

The brain is the encephalon and its chief subdivisions are indicated by prefixes as shown in Figures 67 and 68. These embryonic subdivisions conform in the main to the regions as functionally defined in lower brains to be surveyed in the next chapter. In very early stages the embryonic neural tube shows a series of constrictions and dilations due to inequalities in rate of growth of different parts. These look forward to differences in the functional significance of the parts in the adult brain and hence are of great significance. Each of the transverse regions so defined comprises several primitive segments; they are not truly segmental structures but are functionally determined. The true segments are more or less evident in still earlier stages.

The external and internal surfaces of the neural tube in the region of the future brain of a human embryo 6.9 mm. long (about four weeks old) are illustrated in Figure 65. There is a longitudinal groove in the ventricular wall of each side of the neural tube known as the limiting sulcus; this separates ventral motor from dorsal sensory regions. Its position is indicated by a broken line in Figure 65. Comparison with later stages shows that motor centers in general lie below this sulcus and sensory centers above it. The cerebral cortex is developed wholly from

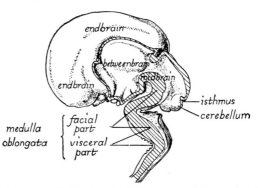

FIG. 66.—Median longitudinal section of the brain of a human embryo in the third month. Comparison with figure 65 B shows that some parts have enlarged much more rapidly than others, the endbrain most rapidly and the betweenbrain next.

the sensory region, a point of considerable interest (p. 241).

About midway the length of the brain tube there is a sharp transverse constriction, the isthmus, which is an area of arrested growth and is one of the most important structural landmarks in the brain. The region below the isthmus is rhomboidal in shape and is known as the rhombic brain (rhombencephalon); the region above it is the cerebrum (as defined by the BNA).

The rhombic brain comprises the medulla oblongata or bulb, cerebellum and pons in the adult, but in the stage shown in Figure 65 the last two have not yet made their appearance. In Figure 67 a small cerebellum is visible, but the pons has not yet developed. The V to

XII pairs of cranial nerves are related to the medulla oblongata, the I to IV pairs to the cerebrum.

The lower part of the rhombic brain may be characterized as the visceral part of the medulla oblongata (termed myelencephalon in the BNA), for, though not exclusively visceral in function, it is dominated by these activities. The upper part of the medulla oblongata in a similar way is chiefly devoted to the innervation of the skin and muscles of the face, including the jaws, and the internal ear; it may therefore be called the facial part of the medulla oblongata. To this part of the

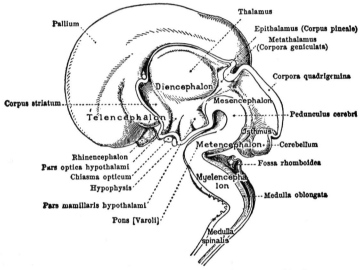

FIG. 67.—Drawing of the same brain as shown in figure 66, with the parts named according to the BNA nomenclature. (After His, from Spalteholz's Atlas.)

brain there are added in late developmental stages the cerebellum and (in mammals) the pons, which is really an appendage of the cerebellum.[1] The cerebellum is the balancing brain, devoted chiefly to unconscious coördination of bodily movements and maintenance of posture and equilibrium.

In front of the isthmus the cerebrum is divided into the midbrain (mesencephalon) and forebrain (prosencephalon). The midbrain contains ventrally the motor centers of the eyeballs and important longitudinal conducting pathways. This part is called the cerebral peduncle, for the forebrain in front is borne upon it like a flower on a

[1] For some inexplicable reason this part of the medulla oblongata is called pons in the BNA, though the true pons does not appear in it at all in lower brains and in man only after the medulla oblongata is fully developed.

stalk (Fig. 68). Dorsally of the ventricle there are two pairs of eminences, the quadrigeminal bodies (double twins). The superior pair is comparable with the optic lobes of fishes and amphibians and is a reflex center for vision (eyebrain); the inferior pair is not separately represented in fishes (which lack the cochlea) and in mammals is a reflex center for hearing (earbrain).

The forebrain is further subdivided into the betweenbrain (diencephalon) and endbrain (telencephalon). The walls of the betweenbrain in very early embryonic stages are evaginated to form the retinas of the eyes (Fig. 65, optic vesicle). The remainder of this region is

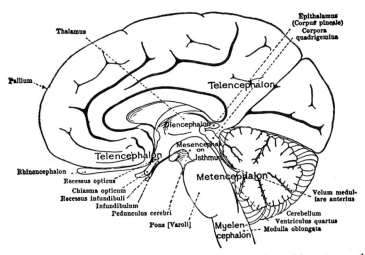

Fig. 68.—Median longitudinal section of the adult human brain, with parts named as in figure 67. From Spalteholz's Atlas.

very small in fishes and is chiefly occupied by centers for olfactory reflexes. It is, in fact, the narrowest part of the brain. In man the olfactory parts of the betweenbrain are relatively small (epithalamus and hypothalamus, Fig. 67) and between them is the very large thalamus, which is chiefly concerned with the transmission of sensory impulses forward into the cerebral cortex. The size of the thalamus varies with the development of the cortex, with which it is in functional connection. In higher vertebrates the optic nerves have important connections with the thalamus and hence the whole betweenbrain is sometimes improperly called the optic thalamus.

The endbrain contains three important structures: (1) the primary and secondary centers for smell (nosebrain), these comprising nearly the whole of this subdivision in fishes; (2) the corpus striatum, a large subcortical mass of gray and white matter which attains its maximum importance in reptiles and birds but in mammals is overshadowed by the cerebral cortex; (3) the cerebral cortex, the apparatus of the highest correlations and associations.

The endbrain in early stages is simply the terminal portion of the neural tube (Fig. 65). As development proceeds the side walls of this region evaginate to form hollow hemispheric vesicles (Fig. 67), the cerebral hemispheres, whose walls later become greatly thickened. In fishes, however, this evagination is very much less extensive and a considerable portion of the endbrain remains as a median area (primitive endbrain, telencephalon medium) between the greatly reduced cerebral hemispheres.

In this hasty survey of the human brain the larger functionally defined regions have been identified and in a human embryo of five or six weeks their form relations are found to resemble those of fishes rather closely. In the adult these resemblances are not lost, but they are obscured by the enormous overgrowth of the cerebral cortex, which not only enfolds all of the brain in front of the isthmus but sends its roots downward into all lower regions with resulting profound modifications of both structure and function. In its broad lines the neurological pattern is the same in fishes and men, and the same holds true for all of the intermediate types. Differences in the importance of individual reflex systems and in the complexity of their interrelations are accurately reflected in the form relations of the central nervous system, and differences in the capacity for labile, individually acquired and intelligent behavior are related to changes in the size and arrangement of the higher centers of correlation and association, especially those of the cerebral cortex.

Segmental and suprasegmental apparatus. — None of the fishes possess differentiated cerebral cortex, though the regions in which the cortex of higher vertebrates is developed can be identified with more or less precision and these are called cortical primordia. The cerebellar cortex is, however, well developed in most fishes. In higher forms that portion of the brain which remains after removal of the cerebellum and cerebral cortex is called the brain stem, and if we further remove those portions of the brain stem which are subsidiary to the cortex of the cerebrum and cerebellum, the residue is termed the segmental apparatus (A. Meyer, 1898), because it is regarded as derived directly from the segmented nervous system of the primitive vertebrate ancestor. The cerebellum and the cerebral cortex are mechanisms of higher control of later evolutionary origin and are termed the suprasegmental apparatus.

The brains of all fishes comprise the segmental apparatus and cerebellum only, and in the most primitive forms (cyclostomes) the cerebellum is very small. It is, accordingly, not surprising to discover that the entire brain of fishes (and this includes the cerebellum) is concerned chiefly with reflex and instinctive activities and that in their behavior we can recognize but little of that which in higher vertebrates we term intelligent behavior. Fishes do exhibit associative memory and they do profit by experience; but, as in insects, these functions are far from dominating their behavior. The reflex and instinctive patterns, on the other hand, are much more complex than in any insects and the fishes lead a much more diversified life.

The reflex centers. — It is possible to recognize in the brain regions or centers, each of which is connected by peripheral nerves with a single physiological type of sense organ or organ of response and is concerned chiefly with the regulation of reflexes of some specific sort. These are the primary centers of the corresponding functions or functional complexes. From this expression it is not to be inferred that these functions reside here or are performed exclusively in these centers. The organ of a reflex function is the entire peripheral and central apparatus which is activated, but the so-called center is a nodal point in the conduction system whose significance may be roughly compared with that of the telephone switchboard in relation to the rest of the telephone system.

Those nerve fibers which conduct toward such a center are called afferent with reference to it; those which conduct away from it are efferent. The brain and the spinal cord together constitute the central nervous system and are often treated as a single great center of correlation. Accordingly, all nerve fibers which discharge their impulses into this central apparatus are classed as afferent or sensory and those which conduct away from it are called efferent (sometimes these are motor, sometimes they activate other effectors, such as glands).

The limits of many of the reflex centers are externally manifest and when these regions are all marked out in the brains of fishes it is found that almost the entire brain has been thus included. This implies that almost every part of the fish brain is dominated by some particular sense organ or system of similar sense organs (nose, eye, skin, taste buds, etc.) or, in the case of efferent centers, that it controls a particular functional system of muscles or other effectors. Few, if any, of the sensory centers, however, are pure in the sense that they receive only the one kind of sensory fibers which give them their dominant sensory character. The optic centers, for instance, receive all of the afferent fibers from the eyes, and also some correlation fibers from the centers of hearing, cutaneous sensibility, etc. Thus each primary sensory center is also in some degree also a correlation center.

The correlation centers. — The various centers of the brain are connected among themselves by complex systems of internal correlation fibers. Fibers of like origin and termination tend to run together in bundles which are termed *tracts*. The details of the courses and connections of these correlation tracts differ greatly from species to species, depending on the sensori-motor organization and mode of life. Or, to state it the other way about, the action system or reflex pattern of each species of animal is the expression in behavior of its physical equipment of receptors, sensory centers, motor centers, centers of correlation and coördination, and organs of response, and the arrangement of the peripheral nerves and central correlation tracts which connect these organs in definite anatomical patterns.

The correlation and integration of the units of behavior in reflex patterns appropriate to the mode of life of any species can be effected by central connections of the primary sensori-motor centers among themselves without the addition of any special centers devoted exclusively to correlation. The colligation of certain types of peripheral excitation, such as vision and hearing, which normally coöperate in the execution of some particular adaptive response, may be effected in the primary centers themselves with the aid of correlating tracts passing between these centers.

In all higher animals, however, the larger part of the brain substance is occupied by adjusting mechanisms which are not dominated by any single sensory or motor system. Here the reflex units, or units of behavior as these were defined on page 12, are combined and rearranged as the exigencies of the moment demand. But it should be borne in mind in this connection that in both lower and higher brains the primary sensori-motor centers are so connected with one another by direct correlation tracts that they are capable of performing rather complex adjustments in the absence or inactivity of any special correlation centers. With the development of such special or higher centers in the brains of the more noble animals the capacity for making these more elementary correlations is not lost, though it is subordinated to and dominated by the special correlation centers of later phylogenetic origin.   The persistence of these more primitive sorts of reflex and instinctive tendencies with their strong unconscious impulsions is a factor in the development of human personality and conduct too often ignored.

Summary. — The vertebrate central nervous system is organized on a quite different plan from those of any of the invertebrates.   It is fundamentally a dorsal tubular structure, whose parts are closely knit together by longitudinal and transverse fiber tracts in such a way as to ensure a closer correlation and higher integration of all bodily activities than is possible in the more detached ganglionic systems of the invertebrates.   This neural tube in primitive forms is locally enlarged by the differentiation of central adjustors for specific reflex systems, and in higher forms there are added very elaborate correlation centers which provide further control and integration of the reflex units.   Of these the most important are the cerebellum and the cerebral cortex.

CHAPTER XIII

THE NERVOUS SYSTEM OF THE DOGFISH

The fishes — The brain of the dogfish — Components of the peripheral nerves — Functional analysis of the brain — Conclusion

The fishes. — The fishes, like the insects, comprise a highly specialized and diversified group of animals. All exhibit the typical vertebrate characteristics very clearly and their nervous systems are alike in fundamental plan, though this plan is very differently worked out in detail. Some, like the cyclostomes (lamprey, hagfish, etc.), are very generalized and primitive, while others show very highly developed special adaptations. The latter group includes the teleosts, or bony fishes, comprising by far the larger number of species and individuals and including most of the common food fishes. These are exceedingly diverse in structure and mode of life; but the diversification, like that of insects, is spread out on a rather low plane (as measured by vertebrate standards) and none of these specialized groups are in the direct line of ancestry of the higher vertebrates. The elasmobranchs (sharks, skates, rays) comprise an ancient and highly efficient stock which has survived in the sea from Silurian times until now. They have diverged somewhat from the direct line of ascent to the land vertebrates but are on the whole generalized and rather primitive.

The brain of the small shark commonly called dogfish is chosen as a typical vertebrate pattern and its structure will next be reviewed. This type is selected partly for the reasons just stated and partly because it is widely used in the schools for laboratory dissection and specimens are easily obtainable for this purpose. Laboratory directions for the dissection of the nervous system of this fish are available.[1]

The brain of the dogfish. — The brain of the adult dogfish (Fig. 69) differs from the simple neural tube of the embryo (Fig. 70) far less than do the brains of higher vertebrates, as will be seen by comparison of Figure 71 with Figures 76 and 68. These modifications of the early neural tube during embryological development in all cases arise mainly from local thickenings of the walls of the tube and various

[1] Herrick and Crosby (1920). Directions for the dissection of the entire animal of this and allied species are also published — Marshall and Hurst (1899), T. J. Parker (1900), Kingsley (1907), Griffin (1922), Hyman (1922).

bendings, infoldings and outpouchings of portions of the wall resulting from inequalities of growth.

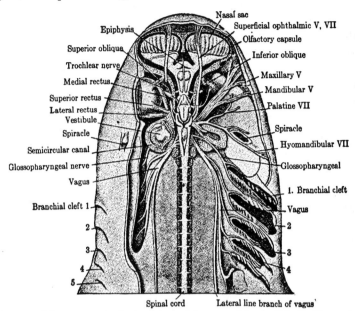

FIG. 69.—Dissection of the brain and cranial nerves of the dogfish, Scyllium catulus.
The right eye has been removed. The left internal ear is partly dissected. (Marshall
and Hurst from Ranson's Nervous System).

Portions of the dorsal wall of the tube near the anterior and posterior ends of the brain remain thin and non-nervous epithelial plates.

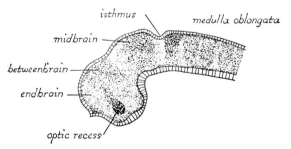

FIG. 70.—Sketch of a median longitudinal section of the brain of the dogfish, Acanthias vulgaris at stage with 30 primitive segments. The brain at this age has attained
about the same stage of development as the human brain illustrated in figure 65. Redrawn from Sterzi.

The overlying brain membrane becomes highly vascular and crumpled
and forms the choroid plexuses of the forebrain and hindbrain (Fig. 71),

which are concerned with the secretion of the cerebrospinal fluid which fills the brain cavities. The remaining portions of the neural tube are more or less thickened by the development of the nerve cells and fibers which compose the primary sensory and motor centers and the apparatus of correlation.

The primary sensory centers which receive the peripheral sensory nerves and the primary motor centers from which the motor nerves arise are enlarged by the development within them of the nerve cells and fibers which mediate their respective functions and, as already mentioned, in the dogfish these primary centers in the aggregate make up almost the entire brain. The portions of the brain, except the correlation centers of the forebrain, which intervene between the primary

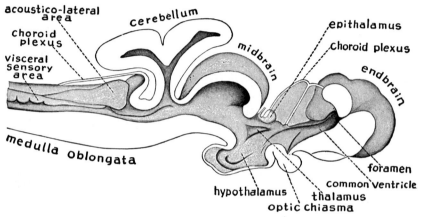

FIG. 71.—Median longitudinal section of the brain of the adult dogfish, Squalus acanthias.

centers are less active functionally, they contain a smaller number of nerve cell bodies, and accordingly the walls of the neural tube are here thinner. The result is that the adult brain exhibits on both external and internal surfaces a series of eminences separated by depressed regions which gives a characteristic sculptural pattern or relief which is functionally defined.

The general configuration of the brain and the relations of its parts to the other organs of the head are shown in Figure 69. The peripheral nerves here indicated are in most cases mixed in the sense that each nerve contains bundles of nerve fibers of different functional systems.

A *functional system* of nerve fibers is defined as all fibers of like peripheral and central connections which therefore mediate functions of the same physiological type, such as the gustatory system, general cutaneous system, etc. All of the fibers of a given functional system may be concentrated in a single pair of cranial nerves, like the olfactory and optic nerves, or they may be distributed along with those of other systems through a number of mixed nerves. Thus in the dogfish, fibers of the gustatory system are distributed to the taste buds through various branches of the VII, IX and X pairs of cranial nerves, and these nerves may also contain fibers of other functional systems (for lateral line organs, various muscles, etc.).

Components of the peripheral nerves. — Before an adequate physiological analysis of the central nervous system is possible it is necessary that the functional composition of the peripheral nerves be accurately known, for these are the avenues of communication between the peripheral end-organs and their central adjusting apparatus. The acquisition of this knowledge has been a slow and very difficult task,[1] but it has been successfully accomplished so far as the chief functional systems are concerned in representatives of most groups of vertebrates; and the general plan of functional composition of cranial and spinal nerves is found to be uniform throughout the vertebrate phylum, though with great variation in the details in correlation with diverse modes of life and unequal differentiation of the sensory and motor end-organs. The classification and nomenclature of functional systems of nerve fibers and brain centers follows that of the peripheral end-organs with which they are connected, as given in Chapter IV.[2]

Those functional systems whose end-organs are widely distributed throughout the body (tactile, gustatory, visceral motor, etc.) are represented in several or many peripheral nerves, usually in mixed nerve trunks. But as these mixed nerves enter the brain the fibers of each functional system separate from those of other systems and converge from their respective nerve roots toward a common region which is the primary cerebral center of that system. This central conver-

---

[1] As illustrations of this extensive literature the following works may be cited: Strong (1895), Herrick (1899, 1903 a, 1922, Chap. 9), Coghill (1902), Johnston (1902 a, 1905, 1906, 1909), Norris (1908, 1913), Landacre (1914), Willard (1915), Norris and Hughes (1920). A tabular analysis of the human cranial nerves in accordance with the same principle has also been published (Herrick, 1914 b, 1922, Chap. 9).

[2] On the senses and sense organs of the dogfish the following recent works, among others, may be consulted. The bibliographies accompanying them will cite the older literature. Bethe (1899), Daniel (1922), Johnson (1917), Maxwell (1923), Norris and Hughes (1920), Parker (1905 a, 1908 b, 1910, 1910 a, 1914, 1918), Parker and Sheldon (1913), Parker and van Heusen (1917 a), Sheldon (1909, 1911).

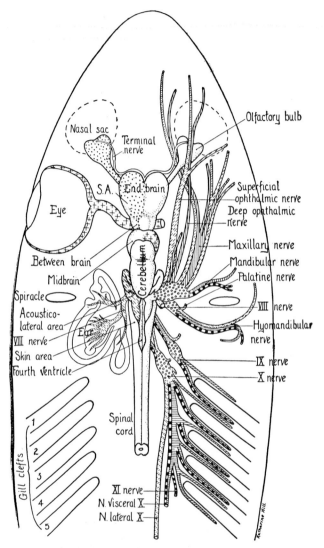

FIGS. 72, 73, 74.—Diagrams of the brain and nerve components of the dogfish, Squalus acanthias. These figures are taken (with slight modification) by permission of the publishers from Herrick's Introduction to Neurology (Philadelphia, Saunders, 1922); the same conventional markings are used throughout the peripheral nervous system and the brain for corresponding functional systems of nerve fibers and reflex centers, as follows: nosebrain (olfactory centers), coarse dots; eyebrain (retina, optic nerve and optic lobes), crosses; auditory and lateral line nerves and earbrain (acoustico-lateral area), broken oblique lines; general cutaneous nerves and skin area of the brain, longitudinal lines (skinbrain unshaded in fig. 72); visceral sensory and gustatory nerves and brain area, transverse lines; motor nerves, black and white rectangles.

FIG. 72.—Diagram of the brain and cranial nerves, seen from above, natural size.

The functional composition of the cranial nerves is schematically indicated after the researches of Norris and Hughes (1920). Nerve fibers of like functional character, such as smell, taste, and general cutaneous sensibility, enter in each case a particular region of the brain. In the dogfish the regions thus seen to be directly connected with various peripheral functional systems of nerve fibers make up nearly the entire brain. This brain is, accordingly, made up largely of simple reflex centers. The somatic area of the endbrain (S. A.) is a higher correlation center.

gence of fibers of like functional significance into a single center facilitates the correlation of this particular function with others.

A detailed analysis of the functional components of the cranial nerves of the dogfish has been made by Norris and Hughes (1920), and thus the way is prepared for a similar analysis of the brain. In Figure 72 the functional composition of the cranial nerves is schematically indicated, and in Figures 72, 73, 74 the primary cerebral centers of the more important functional systems (or groups of related systems) are shown.

Functional analysis of the brain. — When the primary sensory and motor centers of the dogfish are thus mapped out (including certain

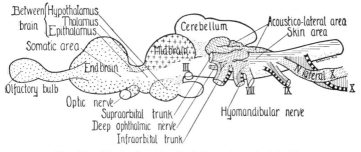

Fig. 73.—The brain of the dogfish seen from the left side.

olfactory correlation centers of the forebrain) it is found that almost the entire brain is included within them, and we can designate parts of it as nosebrain, eyebrain, earbrain, skinbrain, etc. These comprise the segmental apparatus (p. 166). The cerebellum is the largest remainder and is the only suprasegmental apparatus represented. It is an outgrowth of the earbrain and may be called the balancing brain. The other apparatus of correlation is for the most part distributed through the primary centers, though there are some regions which may be regarded as true correlation centers. Chief of these are the secondary olfactory centers of the forebrain, in which the olfactory function clearly predominates; these have a very special significance in the further development of the higher correlation mechanisms, to be considered more in detail later.

The form of the dogfish brain is thus seen to reflect very directly the sensori-motor activities of the animal. These activities are for the most part responses to excitations of the receptive organs, which are therefore the sources of the directing energies which determine the specific behavior of the individual. They have high metabolism of excitation-conduction type and are, therefore, local centers of physiological dominance (p. 55). The primary sensory centers into which these excitations are discharged are so organized as to reinforce and strengthen the excitations and the apparatus of correlation still further steps up the energy efficiency of the process (p. 266). The result is that the various sensory and motor centers are regions of high physiological dominance in the body — the primary centers for those reflex systems with which they are in most direct functional connection — and the correlation centers are regions of highest dominance for a wider range of integrated activities.

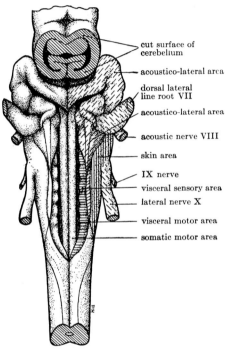

cut surface of cerebellum

acoustico-lateral area

dorsal lateral line root VII

acoustico-lateral area

acoustic nerve VIII

skin area

IX nerve

visceral sensory area

lateral nerve X

visceral motor area

somatic motor area

FIG. 74.—The medulla oblongata of the dogfish seen from above after removal of the membranous roof of the fourth ventricle.

Each of the regions of the brain which we have mentioned above (nose-brain, eyebrain, etc.) is, accordingly, a center of high physiological dominance for the reactions colligated with this particular system of sensory excitations. And the relative physiological importance of each of these functional systems in the action system or reflex pattern of the species can be roughly measured by the relative size and complexity of organization of the related end-organs and brain-centers.

The distance receptors naturally lie near the rostral end of the body in the leading segments during forward progression. In the dogfish the most important of these are clearly the nose and the eye, and the related parts (nosebrain, eyebrain) comprise about half of the brain.

Behind the eyebrain is a region which receives no peripheral sensory fibers; it is physiologically neutral territory and accordingly it is reduced in size. This constricted portion of the brain is the isthmus. The portion of the brain in front of it is now-a-days called the cerebrum; the portion behind is the rhombic brain, including the medulla oblongata and cerebellum.

The medulla oblongata is divided functionally into two parts. The lower part (myelencephalon) connected with the spinal cord is concerned chiefly with visceral reflexes and as a whole may be termed the visceral brain, though somatic reflex centers are represented here also. The ventricular surface on each side is marked by four longitudinal ridges (Fig. 74, and in cross section, Fig. 75) which contain in order

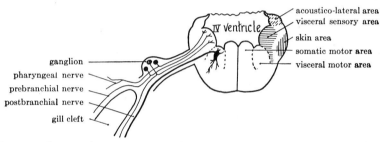

FIG. 75.—Cross section through the region of the IX cranial nerve of the dogfish brain to illustrate the innervation of the gills and the arrangement of the longitudinal functional columns of the medulla oblongata in the visceral brain.

from dorsal to ventral borders the primary centers for the following functional systems: (1) somatic sensory (acoustico-lateral area and skinbrain), (2) visceral sensory (tastebrain and general visceral sensory centers), (3) visceral motor, (4) somatic motor.

In fishes the lower part of the medulla oblongata (region of the IX and X cranial nerves) is concerned chiefly with the visceral functions of respiration, nutrition, circulation of blood, etc., and the same is true in man, though with many secondary changes. In air breathing vertebrates the respiratory mechanism is totally different from the gills of fishes and most of the muscles concerned are innervated from the spinal cord, yet even in man the center responsible for maintaining the respiratory rhythm is in its primitive position in the medulla oblongata. Most of the gill muscles of fishes have disappeared in the human body; but some survive in the pharynx and larynx with greatly changed functions, and these muscles in man are innervated from the visceral motor column as in fishes, even though their functions have been secondarily transformed to the somatic type (Herrick, 1922, pp. 265–270, 1922 b).

The upper part of the medulla oblongata as a whole may be termed the facebrain, for here are located the chief sensory and motor reflex centers for facial movements served by the V and VII pairs of cranial nerves.   The skinbrain area extends backward across the entire length of the medulla oblongata and into the upper end of the spinal cord.   Above the skin area (and probably phylogenetically derived from it) is the earbrain, or acoustico-lateral area, which includes the primary centers for the VIII cranial nerve, both its vestibular fibers for equilibratory reactions and the auditory fibers for the sense of hearing, and also the centers of the related lateral line sense organs (p. 35).   The relations of the longitudinal columns of the medulla oblongata in the region of the facebrain are shown in Figures 73, 74 and 76.

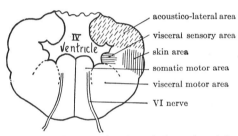

FIG. 76.—Cross section through the region of the VIII cranial nerve of the dogfish to illustrate the arrangement of the longitudinal functional columns of the facebrain.

The internal ear contains two very distinct sense organs, (1) in the saccule the organ of hearing which is feebly developed in the dogfish, there being no cochlea, and (2) in the semicircular canals the organ of equilibrium which here is as well developed as in man.   The earbrain of the dogfish is probably concerned mainly with the latter function, together with the still imperfectly known functions of the lateral line organs.   Near its upper end it makes a wide curve outward, then turns medialward and joins the corresponding area of the opposite side under the cerebellum, into which the upper ends of both areas are merged.

The cerebellum is a higher center of correlation and coördination for equilibratory and allied reactions.   Its size varies in proportion to the activity and equilibratory requirements of the species, being very small in sluggish animals like salamanders which lie flat on their bellies and larger in free swimming, flying and running animals which execute rapid and diversified movements.   It is highly developed in the dogfish.

Above the isthmus is the cerebrum, which is subdivided first into midbrain (mesencephalon) and forebrain (prosencephalon), and the forebrain in turn into betweenbrain (diencephalon) and endbrain (telencephalon). The betweenbrain is again divided into thalamus, epithalamus (pineal body and habenula), and hypothalamus (tuber cinereum, mammillary bodies, and hypophysis).

The eyebrain in lower vertebrates is chiefly in the retina and midbrain, with very small representation in the thalamus. In higher vertebrates these relations are reversed, the thalamic optic centers becoming so much enlarged that the entire betweenbrain is sometimes (incorrectly) called the optic thalmus. In fishes the nosebrain includes the primary olfactory centers in the olfactory bulbs and secondary olfactory correlation centers which make up the larger part of the endbrain, epithalamus, and hypothalamus; but in mammals the non-olfactory parts of the thalamus and endbrain assume far greater importance. The cerebral hemispheres arise from the endbrain, but the hemispheres are very poorly developed in fishes and there is no differentiated cerebral cortex.

Conclusion. — The general plan of the vertebrate nervous system as typified by the dogfish may now be reviewed and summarized. Parallel with the differentiation of each functional system of sensory nerves which enters the brain a special receptive area is set apart, whose increase in size is roughly proportional to the relative functional importance of the system in question. This enlargement is caused by increase in the number of neurons required to handle the volume of business to be transacted; but it does not necessarily involve any increase in the actual complexity of organization. This latter depends on another factor, the range of diversity of the possible number of responses, and this type of business, when it attains large volume, is transacted in another set of offices in the higher correlation centers. These higher centers are not well developed in any fishes.

In the absence of any considerable enlargement of higher correlation centers (except the cerebellum) in the dogfish, the primary reflex apparatus can be analyzed with great clearness and the general functions of the parts diagrammatically indicated, as on Figures 72, 73, 74. But these lower vertebrate types, no matter how elaborately their reflex centers are developed, do not shed much light upon the problem of the apparatus of associative memory and the higher integrative functions.

Not all associations are cortical. The fish has no differentiated cerebral cortex, yet gives unmistakable evidence of associative memory as this is defined by the physiologists. On the other hand, the higher associations are undoubtedly functions of the cerebral cortex, and further knowledge of the structural and functional evolution of the cortex and the steps by which it has emerged from lower subcortical sorts of correlation tissue can legitimately be expected to shed light upon the origin, nature, and biological significance of essential factors in the psychic life. An indispensable preliminary to a fruitful study of the origin and biological significance of the cerebral cortex is a fuller analysis than has yet been made of the subcortical correlation centers in the forebrains of lower vertebrates which precede in evolution the appearance of the cortex itself.

CHAPTER XIV

REFLEX PATTERNS IN FISHES

Relationships of fishes — Olfactory apparatus of fishes — Gustatory apparatus of fishes — Apparatus of cutaneous sensibility — The acoustico-lateral system — The cerebellum — The motor centers — Electric organs — Neurobiotaxis — The reactions of fishes — Conclusion

Relationships of fishes. — The dogfish, whose nervous system was reviewed in the last chapter, is a typical member of the very ancient group of elasmobranch fishes and in most respects may be regarded as representative of fishes as a class. But some features of this brain, notably in the forebrain, are peculiar to the elasmobranchs and decidedly aberrant. The sturgeon is a generalized ganoid fish, also of ancient lineage, which may be regarded as a type much closer to the primitive stem from which the various groups of fishes, and land vertebrates as well, have diverged. The still more primitive cyclostome fishes (lampreys and hagfishes) have diverged from the main axis of vertebrate development in some respects, though in general they give a helpful insight into the characteristics of the probable ancestral type. The accompanying diagram (Fig. 77) expresses the probable relationships of the chief groups of fishes and some lower and higher allied stocks.

The brain of the lamprey (Fig. 78) shows very little enlargement of the embryonic neural tube. Internally, too, the neurons are arranged in embryonic patterns. The sturgeon's brain (Fig. 79) shows some advance beyond that of the lamprey, though in both external form and internal structure it is more primitive than that of most other fishes. The microscopic structure of this brain has been very fully described by Johnston (1901). The medulla oblongata is very similar to that of the shark; the cerebellum is much smaller for the sturgeon is a less active fish; the sense organs are fairly evenly developed, no sensory system being unusually elaborated. Using the sturgeon or dogfish as a norm or reference type, it will be of interest to review some selected illustrations of the brains of fishes which show especial deviations from this type.[1]

---

[1] For a comprehensive summary of the comparative anatomy of the vertebrate nervous system the reader is referred to the large work recently published by Kappers (1920–21). See also Johnston (1906), Edinger (1908, 1911) and Elliot Smith (1902).

Olfactory apparatus of fishes. — In both the lamprey and the dogfish the nose and cerebral olfactory centers are greatly enlarged as compared with most other fishes. In the dogfish the nose is clearly the dominant receptor. The nasal sac is filled with closely packed lamellæ covered with the specific olfactory receptive epithelium (Figs. 80, 81). Measurements of the total surface of this olfactory epithelium in three adult dogfish made in the anatomical laboratory of the University of Chicago by three observers (Forrest A. Kingsbury, Evelyn Garfiel, and the author) gave for each nasal sac 2100

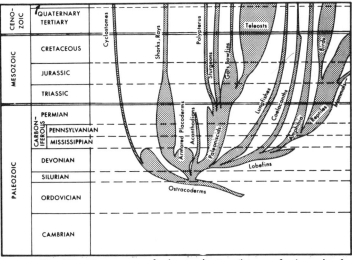

Fig. 77 Diagram of the relationships of the chief groups of fishes and higher allied stocks. The era and period time spans are shown proportionately to one another as determined by the most recent investigations.

PREPARED BY THEODORE EATON   THE UNIVERSITY OF KANSAS

sq. mm., 2080 sq. mm., and 3084 sq. mm. (the last a very large fish). The average area is 2421 sq. mm., or 4842 sq. mm. for both nasal sacs. This is about 7.36 square inches, a very considerable area in a fish less than a meter long. When it is remembered that throughout this area the specific olfactory cells are very closely packed together in the sensory epithelium, the inconceivable number of the olfactory receptors is evident, and it is not surprising to find that the olfactory nerve is the largest nerve in the body and that the primary olfactory centers and the correlation centers in which the olfactory function is dominant make up about one-third of the total weight of the brain (see Figs. 72, 73).

In the cyclostomes (Fig. 78) the olfactory apparatus makes up a still larger proportion of the total mass of the brain, and throughout the groups of fishes, amphibians and reptiles this system is large and evidently functionally very important, though generally not so highly developed as in the two fishes just cited. This functional system not only dominates the functional activity of the rostral end of the brain in all of these cases, but clearly it has been the chief factor in shaping the morphological evolution of this part of the brain in all vertebrates below birds and mammals.

The endbrain (telencephalon) of fishes generally consists of two well separated parts, (1) the olfactory bulbs, which form the primary olfactory center within which the olfactory nerves terminate, and (2) farther back a larger portion. The latter may take the form of thickened lateral walls of the neural tube, as in the sturgeon (Fig. 79), and is then termed primitive endbrain (telencephalon medium); or it may be formed by a lateral outpouching of the walls of the tube, thus producing two hollow cerebral hemispheres, as in all types above fishes.

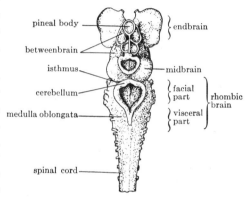

FIG. 78.—Dorsal view of the brain of the larval lamprey, Petromyzon (Ammocoetes). Membranous portions of the roof of betweenbrain, midbrain and medulla oblongata have been removed, exposing the cavities of the brain ventricle. Note that this brain is only slightly larger than the spinal cord and that the medulla oblongata and nosebrain are relatively large, the latter comprising nearly all of the endbrain and betweenbrain. The cerebellum is minute.

The olfactory bulbs usually lie close to the remainder of the endbrain, as in the cases already cited. But in some of the bony fishes (teleosts) the nasal sacs lie far removed from the brain. In these cases the gap may be bridged in either of two ways. In the first case the olfactory bulbs may retain their primary position close to the primitive endbrain and the olfactory nerves are elongated to reach the nose, as in the eel (Fig. 82). In the second case the olfactory bulbs may lie close to the nose far removed from the primitive endbrain and the intervening space is traversed by greatly elongated olfactory stalks (Figs. 83, 85, 91). In the carp and catfish the olfactory stalks may be much longer than all the rest of the brain. In

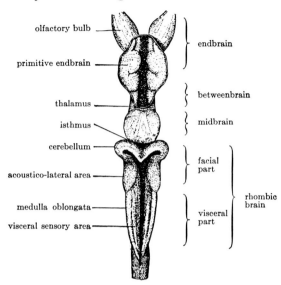

olfactory bulb

primitive endbrain

thalamus

isthmus

cerebellum

acoustico-lateral area

medulla oblongata

visceral sensory area

endbrain

betweenbrain

midbrain

facial part

visceral part

rhombic brain

FIG. 79.—Dorsal view of the brain of the sturgeon, Acipenser, natural size. Membranous portions of the roof of endbrain, betweenbrain and medulla oblongata have been removed exposing the ventricle. Olfactory centers of endbrain and betweenbrain are relatively large. The cerebellum is larger than in Petromyzon (fig. 78), but smaller than in the dogfish (fig. 72). The figure is redrawn from Johnston (1901).

Figures 84 and 87 the olfactory bulbs and most of their stalks are removed.

Gustatory apparatus of fishes. — In some fishes the organs of taste are enormously increased in number and widely distributed both within the mouth and in

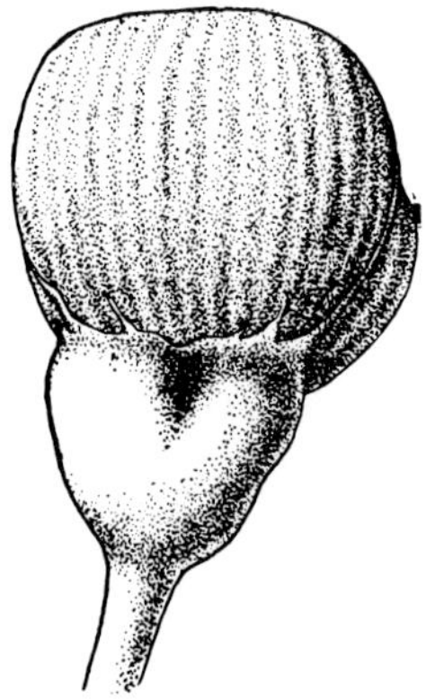

FIG. 80.—The nasal sac and olfactory bulb of the dogfish, Squalus acanthias, twice natural size. The olfactory bulb of the brain below partially incloses the nasal organ and a few filaments of the olfactory nerve are seen to spread over the surface of the nasal sac.

FIG. 81.—Transverse section through the nasal sac of Squalus acanthias, showing the arrangement of the lamellæ which are covered with the olfactory sensory epithelium.

the outer skin. This is notably true in the catfishes (siluroids) and the carps and suckers (cyprinoids). In the carp there is a curious palatal organ in the roof of the pharynx which is very thickly covered with taste buds arranged on comb-like ridges. During feeding this is enlarged by congestion with blood and serves to sort food particles out of the mud which is taken into the mouth for this purpose. The brain center for these taste buds is greatly enlarged, the so-called vagal lobes (Figs. 84, 85). Inclosed between the two vagal lobes is a smaller center, the facial lobe (Figs. 85, 86) which receives nerve fibers from the cutaneous taste buds. In the brain of the catfish the vagal lobes are smaller and the facial lobes exceed them in size

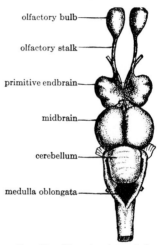

olfactory bulb

olfactory stalk

primitive endbrain

midbrain

cerebellum

medulla oblongata

Fig. 82.—Dorsal, lateral and ventral views of the brain of the common eel. After C. L. Herrick. At the top of the figure are the olfactory nerves terminating in the olfactory bulbs, which are close to the primitive endbrain. Then follow the enlargements of midbrain, cerebellum and medulla oblongata. Compare figure 83.

Fig. 83.—Dorsal view of the brain of the fresh-water mooneye, Hyodon tergisus. After C. L. Herrick.

(Fig. 87). Taste buds are distributed over the entire cutaneous surface of these fishes, even to the tail fin, being especially numerous on the barblets around the mouth. These cutaneous taste buds are all supplied by branches of the facial nerve (Fig. 88), whose nerve fibers terminate centrally in the facial lobes. Both vagal lobes (for mouth-tasting) and facial lobes (for skin-tasting) are local enlargements of the visceral sensory brain as illustrated in the dogfish (Fig. 74). The behavior of these fishes has been studied and interesting correlations between these remarkable sense organs and the methods of feeding brought to light (Herrick, 1903, 1903 b, 1905; Parker, 1908 b, 1910, 1911; Olmsted, 1918).

It has been shown experimentally that catfish locate food with both olfactory organs and cutaneous taste buds, the former being far more sensitive and acting as typical distance receptors, while the latter are practically contact receptors. The barblets around the mouth are richly supplied with both tactile and gustatory nerve endings and these coöperate in the selection of food. These fishes are bottom feeders and as the barblets are trailed along the ground the fish quickly turns and snaps up any food object with which it comes in contact. The tomcod, Microgadus, in a similar way trails the filiform pelvic fins along the bottom and as these are also supplied with both tactile and gustatory nerve endings the feeding reactions are in principle similar to those of catfish, though the reactions involved are different. In this case the fish, having sensed the food with the pelvic fins, must "back water" until the mouth can reach the edible

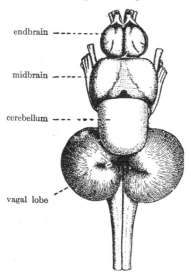

endbrain

midbrain

cerebellum

vagal lobe

FIG. 84.—Dorsal view of the brain of the fresh-water buffalofish, Carpiodes tumidus. After C. L. Herrick.

morsel. The central reflex mechanism is here, accordingly, differently arranged from that of the catfish (Herrick, 1903, 1907).

The searobin, Prionotus, and the allied European Trigla are also bottom feeders, and here the food is located by the finger-like rays of the pectoral fins which feel about among the stones and other furnishings of the ocean floor for small edible creatures. Taste buds are not present on these fin rays and the reactions are purely tactual reflexes with an entirely different type of central apparatus from that of the catfish or tomcod (Morrill, 1895; Herrick, 1906, 1907 a).

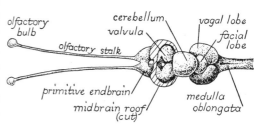

olfactory
bulb

olfactory stalk

cerebellum

valvula

vagal lobe

facial
lobe

primitive endbrain

midbrain roof
(cut)

medulla
oblongata

FIG. 85.—Dorsal view of the brain of the carp. The roof of the midbrain has been dissected away to expose the valvula of the cerebellum lying in the ventricle of the midbrain. Modified from Elliot Smith (1902).

Apparatus of cutaneous sensibility. — Within and beneath the skin of fishes are end-organs of pressure, pain and probably temperature which are doubtless in a general way comparable with our own, and in addition there are several types of receptors of which we have no

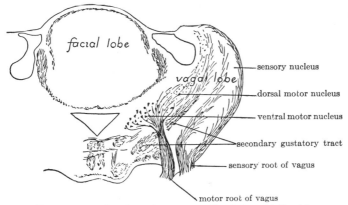

FIG. 86.—Transverse section through the right side of the medulla oblongata of the carp. The vagal lobe (for mouth tasting) is not so large as in Carpiodes (fig. 84), and the facial lobe (for skin tasting) is relatively larger. Redrawn from Herrick (1905).

experience. For example, Sheldon (1909) found the skin of the dog-fish everywhere sensitive to a number of different chemical substances, though there are in this fish no cutaneous taste buds or other special chemo-receptors. The central mechanisms which mediate this type of sensibility are unknown. There is a similar general chemical sensitivity on moist mucous surfaces of the human body with high threshold of excitability which is probably mediated by free nerve endings in the epithelium.

The nerves of general cutaneous sensibility from the skin of the head converge, as we have seen, into the "skin area" where they end in a longitudinal column of gray matter on the lateral aspect of the medulla oblongata which has long been

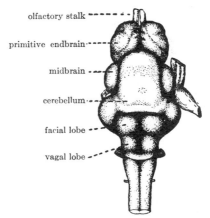

FIG. 87.—Dorsal view of the brain of the catfish, Pilodictis olivaris.

known in the human brain as the gelatinous substance of Rolando. This column extends back into the spinal cord as the dorsal gray column or dorsal horn and here it receives the nerves of general cutaneous sensibility from the trunk and fins. In most fishes (and other vertebrates as well) this gray column is of fairly uniform size throughout its length from the upper part of the medulla oblongata to the lower levels of the spinal cord. In quadrupeds and in man it is enlarged where the nerves from the skin of the arms and legs enter the spinal cord (cervical and lumbar enlargements of the cord). In a similar way the searobin, to which reference has been made (p. 186), presents in the upper levels of the cord a series of considerable enlargements which receive the great tactile nerves from the finger-like rays of the pectoral fins.

The acoustico-lateral system. — The organs of the lateral line system have already been briefly considered (p. 35). Embryologically

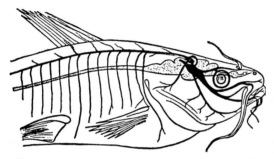

these organs arise from the skin in common with the internal ear, anatomically their nerve endings resemble those of the internal ear, their physiological functions (so far as known) are intermediate between those of tactile and auditory organs, and the nerves from the entire lateral line system and the internal ear converge into a common acoustico-lateral area (earbrain) within the brain.

FIG. 88.—The small catfish, Amiurus melas, seen from the right side, upon which are projected the outline of the brain and spinal cord (stippled) and the cutaneous branches of the VII cranial nerve which supply the taste buds distributed over the skin of the entire body, especially freely on the head and barblets. From Herrick (1903).

In cyclostomes this center is found to be in process of differentiating from the general cutaneous center (Johnston, 1902). These and other facts which might be mentioned suggest that the lateral line system and the internal ear were derived in some ancestral stage from cutaneous sense organs of the tactile series.

The acoustico-lateral area of fishes receives all nerve fibers from the internal ear and from the several kinds of lateral line organs, and the central terminations of these different kinds of fibers are so intertwined within this area that it has hitherto not been possible to separate completely the reflex centers of the many diverse functions represented in this complex system of peripheral sense organs. There is, however, an incomplete separate localization within this area of several specific functions, but the reflexes served by all of the organs of the acoustico-lateral complex are evidently in very close physiological association. These reflexes fall into three groups: (1) equilibratory and postural, served chiefly by the semicircular canals of the ear; (2) auditory, served by end-organs of the saccule; (3) reactions following excitations of the lateral line organs by slow water vibrations and probably by other agents as yet imperfectly known.

The semicircular canals of fishes apparently serve substantially the same functions as do those of man. They have recently been restudied in the dogfish physiologically by Maxwell (1920, 1923). The sense of hearing is poorly developed in fishes, but certainly is present. The receptive organ is in the saccule (Parker, 1918) and perhaps also in a small diverticulum from the saccule known as the lagena which is the primordium from which the cochlea of mammals has been developed.

The nerves from the lateral line organs are very large in most fishes and the greater part of the acoustico-lateral area is undoubtedly concerned with the correlation of the functions of these organs. In the dogfish (Fig. 74) these areas are large ear-shaped lateral projections from the medulla oblongata which are called the auricles and

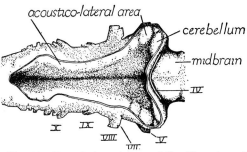

Fig. 89.—Dorsal view of the medulla oblongata and cerebellum of the larval salamander, Amblystoma tigrinum (Herrick, 1914 a). × 21. The membranous roof of the fourth ventricle has been removed. Roman numerals refer to the cranial nerves. In the adult of the still more primitive amphibian, Necturus, the cerebellum is even smaller (Herrick, 1914).

are still sometimes incorrectly termed restiform bodies. In this fish the two acoustico-lateral areas bend inward in front and meet under the cerebellum. In fact, the cerebellum is an outgrowth of these both embryologically and phylogenetically considered. In amphibians the cerebellum is very small and in some of the simpler types it is clearly merely a slightly enlarged anterior portion of the acoustico-lateral areas (Herrick, 1914, 1914 a), as shown in Figure 89.

The aquatic amphibians, including the tadpoles of air-breathing forms like the frog, all have lateral line organs and acoustico-lateral areas in the brain similar to those of fishes but smaller. These organs disappear in land vertebrates (reptiles, birds, mammals) and their nerves and cerebral centers vanish with them. In the development of the frog this history is repeated in very dramatic fashion. At the time of transformation from tadpole to frog the entire lateral line system fades away and simultaneously the organ of hearing shows a pulse of growth and differentiation and seems in a way to take the vacant place. The details of this metamorphosis have not been worked out.

The cerebellum. — This organ varies in size directly with the motor activity of the species and it is evidently the chief center of reflex coördination of bodily movements. It is primarily the balancing brain, with control of equilibrium, posture, motor coördination and muscular tone. In the cyclostomes, which are sluggish and in some cases parasitic, it is small. In the dogfish, which is very active, it is well developed (Figs. 72, 73); various other forms which it assumes in fishes are illustrated in Figures 79, 82, 83, 84, 85, 87. Deviations from the fish pattern are seen in amphibians, reptiles and birds, the greatest size being seen in the latter group.

As has been pointed out, the cerebellum develops from the forward ends of the acoustico-lateral areas, which in fishes are mixed auditory, vestibular and lateralis correlation centers, in most fishes the last mentioned system predominating. In these animals the cerebellum is in very intimate anatomical and physiological relationship with the lateralis component of the mixed area, its characteristic structure in many species extending backward over almost the whole extent of the lateral line centers in form known as cerebellar crest. The vestibular component of the mixed acoustico-lateral area is smaller than the lateralis and it also is intimately related with the cerebellum, while the small auditory component is not known to have any cerebellar connections.

In cyclostomes and the lower amphibians (Fig. 89) the cerebellum is merely an expansion of the front end of the acoustico-lateral area, to which are added connections with the spinal cord and higher correlation centers of the midbrain and betweenbrain. In the dogfish this part of the cerebellum is preserved in similar form, though larger, forming the auricles. To these there is added the medial body of the cerebellum which receives chiefly fibers from the spinal cord and also the fibers from the midbrain and betweenbrain. This type of cerebellum is characteristic (in many variant forms) of other fishes, reptiles and birds.

In the bony fishes there is a special part of the cerebellum termed the valvula which is found in no other animals. This projects downward and forward into the ventricle of the midbrain and appears to be

functionally related with the lateral line centers of the medulla oblongata. It is small in the cod (Fig. 90), larger in the carp (Fig. 85),

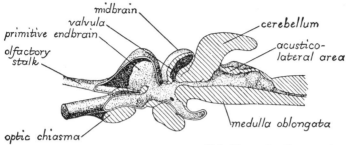

Fig. 90.—Median section of the brain of the codfish, illustrating the arrangement of the ventricles, the small valvula of the cerebellum and the fusion of the acoustico-lateral areas of the two sides above the fourth ventricle. Modified from Elliot Smith (1902).

and largest of all in a group of peculiar African fishes (the Mormyridæ, Fig. 91).

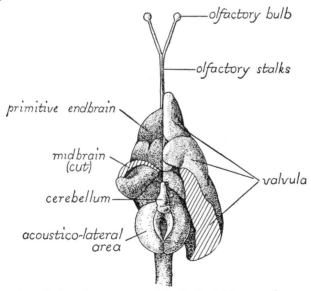

Fig. 91.—Dorsal view of a dissection of the brain of Mormyrus kannume. Most of the valvula cerebelli has been removed on the left side and the postero-medial part of it on the right to expose the underlying structures. On the left side the roof of the midbrain has also been removed, exposing a portion of the valvula within its ventricle. The body of the cerebellum is very small; the acoustico-lateral areas of the medulla oblongata are greatly enlarged and fused medially. Figs. 85, 90, 91, after R. H. Burne from Elliot Smith (1902).

In Mormyrus the lateral line system is highly developed (van der Sprenkel, 1915) and the acoustico-lateral area of the medulla oblongata is correspondingly enlarged. The cerebellum itself is small, but the valvula attains enormous size. The resulting brain form is unique and indeed amazing. The valvula, a part which is not represented at all in the human brain, is here so large that it not only dilates

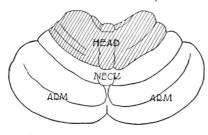

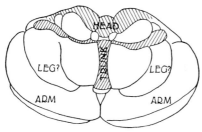

FIG. 92.—Sketches of the upper and lower aspects of the human cerebellum. (For the anatomical names of the parts here shown see Herrick, 1922, fig. 88.) Different regions of the cerebellum which are supposed to regulate reflex motor coördination of various parts of the body are indicated by the words printed across the diagrams. The areas shaded with oblique lines are those regarded by Ingvar (1918) as more primitive. The unshaded areas, of later phylogenetic origin, are concerned largely with movements initiated in the cerebral cortex. These areas are enormously enlarged in the human brain as compared with those of other mammals.

the ventricle of the midbrain and spreads the inclosing parts outward and downward, but it overflows the confines of the midbrain, mushrooms out and envelopes nearly the entire brain. In this species of fish the valvula is larger in proportion to the remainder of the brain than are the cerebral hemispheres of man in proportion to the underlying brain stem. The physiological features correlated with this monstrous hypertrophy of the valvula are as yet imperfectly understood. Since this structure seems to be enlarged in correlation with highly developed lateral line organs, these fishes would seem to be favorable objects for the solution of some of the baffling physiological puzzles presented by the lateral line system.

In mammals the cerebellum as commonly described comprises five ill defined regions, a median vermis or worm, paired lateral hemispheres, and ventrally the paired flocculi and paraflocculi; but these subdivisions do not correspond exactly to the significant physiological and morphological regions. Viewed phylogenetically the mammalian cerebellum consists of a marginal part, which is ancient and probably derived from the cerebellum of fish types, and a central part of more recent evolutionary origin. The new or central part is small in lower mammals and in higher forms it increases in proportion to the enlargement of the cerebral cortex until in man it comprises by far the larger part of the cerebellum, as illustrated in Figure 92.[1]

In mammals the inferior part of the old cerebellum (uvula, nodulus, flocculi) receives direct vestibular fibers, as in lower forms. The flocculi are probably roughly comparable with the auricular lobes of the dogfish. Fibers from the spinal cord reach the remaining sub-divisions of the older or marginal part of the cerebellum, and also to some extent the marginal parts of the new cerebellum. The newer part is developed in correlation with the cerebral cortex, with which it is in functional relation through the pons. In man it reaches truly enormous proportions. Its more lateral portions in particular are greatly enlarged and form the larger part of the human cerebellar hemispheres. These last are real cortical dependencies and probably regulate movements of cortical origin in much the same way that other parts of the cerebellum regulate the simpler reflexes arising from vestibular excitation, muscle sense, and other proprioceptive receptors.[2]

In summary, the cerebellum arises embryologically in all vertebrates from the forward part of the acoustico-lateral area (fishes and amphibians) or vestibular area (higher vertebrates). Its phylogenetic origin was apparently similar. In all cases, even in man, it receives direct root fibers of the vestibular nerve. To this region there have been added correlation fibers from all other parts of the central nervous system which are concerned in the reflex maintenance of posture, equilibrium and motor coördination.

The cerebellum does not appear to participate in the analysis of sensory impressions for determining what the appropriate response shall be; but after the character of the response has been established, unconsciously in lower centers or consciously in the cerebral cortex, as the case may be, the cerebellum participates in the execution of the movements. Its own activities are wholly unconscious and are largely of the invariable, innate structurally predetermined type.

The motor centers. — In all vertebrate embryos the motor centers develop in the ventral part of the neural tube, while the dorsal part contains sensory centers and correlationt issues (Fig. 120, p. 242).

---

[1] The old and new cerebellum are here defined according to Ingvar (1918). Edinger (1911, pp. 260–263) makes a somewhat different subdivision, assigning all of the vermis to the old cerebellum.

[2] For an excellent description and summary of the comparative anatomy and physiology of the cerebellum see Kappers (1920–21, Chap. 7); further discussion of the functions of the cerebellum will be found on page 242; on its phylogenetic development see Herrick (1924).

In many adult brains this primitive relation is more or less distorted, but it is always evident. The adult dogfish illustrates the primitive condition very well.

In the floor of the ventricle of the medulla oblongata there is in the dogfish on each side a ventral ridge below which are the centers of origin of the somatic motor nerves (III, IV, VI and XII cranial nerves) and an extensive series of nerve fibers, the longitudinal medial bundle, which coördinate the activities of these centers. Lateral to this is the "visceral motor area," within which are the centers of origin of the nerves of the visceral motor series (V, VII, IX, X cranial nerves). The visceral motor centers are of two sorts. The first, the special visceral motor series, supply striated visceral muscles of the jaws, hyoid and visceral arches; the second, the general visceral motor series, supply unstriated visceral muscles of the digestive tract, heart muscle, glands and other viscera innervated through the sympathetic nervous system. Both of these series are fairly uniformly developed in the brain stem of vertebrates, but one part or another may be enlarged in response to the development of some special peripheral apparatus. Thus in the carp there is, as already mentioned (p. 185), a very complex palatal organ covered with taste buds which assists in sorting food particles from mud. The interior of this organ is filled with vascular and muscular tissue. The taste buds are innervated from the visceral sensory area in the vagal lobe and the muscles from the deeper layers of the same lobe (Fig. 86) which are enlargements of the general visceral motor centers.

Electric organs. — The most interesting functional adaptation of the motor systems is perhaps seen in the electric organs of some fishes. The torpedo fish is a large elasmobranch whose brain is essentially like that of the dogfish except for the presence in the medulla oblongata of a pair of great enlargements known as electric lobes. Some of the muscles of the gill region have been enlarged and structurally highly modified to form powerful electric batteries whose discharge is sufficiently powerful to shock the prey and facilitate capture. Mere contact with a large fish, which may reach a weight of 200 pounds, can disable a man and hence the creatures are much dreaded by fishermen. The electric lobes in this case are enlarged special visceral motor nuclei (Fig. 93).

There are several other electric fishes in which various parts of the body musculature are similarly modified into electric organs and the innervation is from cells of the motor area of the region of brain or spinal cord from which the modified muscles receive their nerve supply.

Neurobiotaxis. — The motor mechanisms, like the sensory, show a great range of diversity in adaptation to varied modes of life. These have of late been very exhaustively investigated. Between the sensory centers and the motor centers which have just been described there is a diffuse coördinating tissue known as the reticular formation and the motor nuclei of the tegmentum. This contains the pathways of connection between sensory and motor limbs of the reflex arcs, the details of whose arrangements differ from species to species depending on the reflex patterns of the animal (for the arrangement in a typical fish see Bartelmez, 1915).

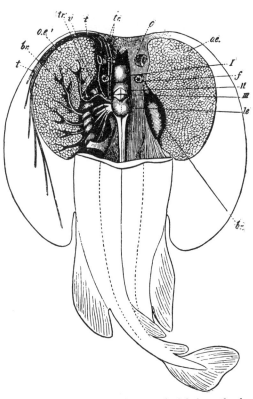

In some fishes and amphibians a single pair of nerve cells of this nucleus, the so-called cells of Mauthner, is greatly enlarged and serves as the final common path for nervous impulses involved in the motor coördinations of swimming and equilibration. Connecting fibers from all sensory centers which contribute to these functions converge into

Fig. 93.—Dissection of the torpedo fish from the dorsal side. The electric organs (*o. e.*) are exposed on both sides, and on the left the nerves which supply them. *I*, forebrain; *II*, midbrain; *III*, cerebellum; *br.*, gill chambers; *le.*, electric lobes; *o.*, eye. After Gegenbaur.

these two neurons, from each of which a single giant fiber passes down the entire length of the spinal cord making collateral connections along the way with the spinal centers from which the motor nerves of the swimming muscles arise (p. 114).

The primary motor nuclei of different vertebrate brains show interesting shiftings of position in correlation with the functional connections through which they receive their dominant innervation.

Since these connections differ from species to species, the resulting phylogenetic movements of the motor nuclei shed interesting sidelights upon fundamental problems of functional factors which have operated in shaping the internal structure of the brain during its evolutionary history.

An instructive series of special adaptations of this sort has been elaborated by Kappers under the name neurobiotaxis, a principle which establishes that if in the nervous system, by a change in the mode of life of the species, a particular center receives its dominant stimuli from a new direction or by a different tract from the former connections there will be a tendency for the chief dendrites of the nerve cells of this center to be extended in the direction from which the new dominant nervous impulses are derived, and eventually the bodies of these neurons will migrate in the same direction. In the course of phylogeny many nuclei within the brain have changed their positions in accordance with this principle and the particular functional adaptations involved have been carefully investigated.[1] In this connection Davidson Black (1917, p. 558) remarks,

"Among teleosts the capacity for apparently unlimited variations in the reflex pattern of the brain stem nuclei reaches its acme among the vertebrate series. Within this group the extreme specialization of any of the organs of special sense is followed by a corresponding amplification of the primary afferent nucleus or nuclei involved, together with a modification of the motor nuclear pattern in perfect harmony with the reflex needs of the animal. Further, the specialization of effectors of whatever nature is also followed by an adequate corresponding adjustment of the reflex connections of the sensory and motor neurons involved."

The applications of the principle of neurobiotaxis have been worked out in most detail in connection with the motor centers of the brain; but the principle applies equally elsewhere and many features of the nervous system, including the arrangements of correlation centers in the brain stem and patterns of cortical localization of function, are believed to have arisen in accordance with it.

The reactions of fishes. — In reviewing the fishes from the standpoint of the nervous system it is necessary to separate the primitive forms from the more highly specialized types. The primitive ganoids, elasmobranchs, and lungfishes lie close to the main stem of vertebrate

[1] For a review of the extensive literature upon this subject see Kappers (1920–21, Chaps. 5 and 6). In a survey of the motor nuclei in representatives of the entire vertebrate series Davidson Black (1917–1922) has given especial attention to the correlation of their anatomical differences with diversities in mode of life.

evolutionary development (Fig. 77, p. 182) and are generalized in structure and behavior; the bony fishes (teleosts), on the other hand, are very highly specialized and include most of the fresh and salt water species of fishes.

The teleosts comprise a group of very diverse types with remarkable adaptations to special modes of life. The individual fish also leads an active and diversified life. The nervous system bulks large in the general organization of the body because of the great complexity of the reflexes. In even the highest fishes the increase in size of the brain is due almost wholly to larger reflex centers of the simpler types of adjustment.

Though fishes have no differentiated cerebral cortex, yet experiments show that they can learn and do modify their behavior through individual experience. They possess a primitive type of associative memory which is similar to that found in invertebrates.

A catfish ordinarily selects its food by touching it with its barblets, and experiment shows that this is a mixed tactile and gustatory stimulation, for the barblets are supplied with both tactile nerve endings and taste buds (p. 186). The fish will respond to either a pure gustatory stimulation of a barblet, as when meat juice is diffused in the water, or to a pure tactile stimulation by contact. If a barblet is touched with a piece of meat, the fish turns and snaps it up and it will react in the same way to cotton soaked in meat juice. In both cases the tactile and gustatory stimuli reinforce each other. But if cotton alone is used, the fish will snap at it for a few times and later ignore the contact with the unsatisfying substance. This acquired discrimination is like that of the lowest animals described more fully elsewhere (p. 287), but unlike the latter it may persist for several days.

Thorndike (1899) and Churchill (1916) have shown that fishes can readily learn to thread a labyrinth. Möbius (1873) and Triplett (1901) have shown that one of the most fundamental of the feeding instincts of fishes can be inhibited by training. In the first case a pike and in the second case a perch was confined in a tank in which it was separated by a glass partition from the minnows which form its natural food. After repeatedly dashing against the glass both fishes learned to abandon the attempt to capture the minnows, and so thoroughly was this lesson learned that when the glass partition was removed and they could swim freely around among the minnows they still refrained from trying to capture them. A review of the sense physiology and behavior of fishes together with some experiments on their associations is given by Miss White (1919).

If we compare in general the behavior of the higher fishes with that of the insects, and especially with the most highly specialized of these, the ants, there are many points of similarity which are the more striking in view of the profound differences in the structure of their nervous systems.

The complexity of the behavior of ants is largely brought to pass by divergent specialization of the different species and of the castes within each species, so that, though the aggregate is a marvel of perfection of adjustment to a great variety of conditions, the part played by each individual ant is very simple and sharply circumscribed by its own structural limitations. The group as a whole is remarkably plastic, as Wheeler says, but the capacity of each ant to make individual adjustments to changing conditions is slight though not totally lacking. The plasticity, in other words, is biologically determined and acts through slow modification of the hereditary reflex and instinctive mechanisms; there is but little personal plasticity or capacity for individual adjustment to unfamiliar conditions on the part of the individual.

In the higher fishes we have much the same situation. There are many species, each nicely adjusted to a particular habitat in adaptation to which it is structurally modified. As in insects, the highest centers of adjustment are solid nervous masses (that is, in this case massive local thickenings of the wall of the neural tube) which seem to be structurally poorly adapted to give rise to the more elaborate mechanisms of individually modifiable behavior requiring complex associations and concrete memories of past experience. Neither phylum, therefore, is ancestral to anything higher. But fishes have much larger nervous systems than insects and the behavior of the individual is much more complex. The reflex pattern is much more elaborate, providing for stereotyped adjustments to a wider range of conditions. They are probably also capable of more individual modifiability and profit more by personal experience, though of the limits of these powers we have no very satisfactory evidence.

Conclusion.—In this chapter we have reviewed selected examples of lower vertebrates from the point of view of differences in anatomical structure in correlation with diverse degrees of elaboration of their several functional systems. The changes in brain form here illustrated grow out of differences in mode of life and the relative importance of specific sensori-motor reaction types in the ordinary behavior of the species examined. In some cases one system of sense organs, in other cases another, may be very elaborately developed; and these differences are accurately reflected in the size and internal organization of the related reflex centers. Each of these functional systems has a central adjusting mechanism which is physiologically dominant over the activities of that system, and in fishes the extent of this dominance may be roughly measured (in the absence of higher correlation centers) by the relative size of the reflex centers concerned.

The reactions here considered are chiefly on the plane of reflex and instinctive behavior. The extent to which this behavior is individually modifiable has been briefly considered. As we pass from fishes to higher vertebrates, the organization of the reflex systems is found to be similar in principle to that already discussed; but the apparatus of more plastic, that is individually modifiable, behavior is superposed upon the lower reflex centers in progressively larger measure. These centers of higher adjustments, of correlation and association, are developed chiefly in the forebrain and especially in the cerebral cortex. In the higher vertebrate types, accordingly, our interest centers largely in the forebrain, to which attention will next be directed.

CHAPTER XV

THE EVOLUTION OF THE FOREBRAIN

The forebrain of fishes — The primitive forebrain — The sturgeon — The dog-fish — The bony fishes — The lungfishes — The amphibians — The reptiles — The birds — The mammals

The forebrain of fishes. — The entire central nervous system of fishes is devoted so largely to adjustments of fixed reflex and instinctive types that, as has been illustrated, when the sensory and motor centers known to be concerned with these classes of functions are delimited but little tissue remains unassigned. This is true not only in spinal cord and medulla oblongata, but in the forebrain as well. There is no extensive region of the fish brain which is not dominated by a single functional system as this term was defined on page 172, and such correlations as are effected are done for the most part within the primary sensori-motor centers and with the aid of fiber tracts which connect these centers by passing directly from one to another in various complex patterns. It should be noted, however, that the olfactory area of the forebrain (p. 175) is in a somewhat more advanced stage of differentiation.

The cerebellum is the most notable exception to the rule just stated, for in the more active species this organ is very highly developed, it receives afferent fibers from all sensory areas which may assist in the maintenance of equilibrium and the orientation of the body, and, though the vestibular area is its parent tissue, it is not in its more elaborated forms dominated by any single sensory system. The cerebellum, however, is an executive, not a deliberative organ. Its chief duty is not to determine what is the appropriate reaction to a situation, but to coöperate in the execution of movements whose character is elsewhere determined and to maintain posture and balance reflexly.

Within the forebrains of higher vertebrates, and especially in the cerebral cortex, there are correlation and association centers of very different type, centers which are not dominated by any single sensori-motor system but are reached by fiber tracts from several lower sensory centers. Here the more difficult problems of conduct are solved; these are deliberative reactions, the occasion for which arises only when the innate instinctive and reflex modes of response prove inadequate to make the desirable adjustment.

These higher mechanisms of correlation are not well developed in fishes. Their forebrains are clearly dominated for the most part by the olfactory system. There are, however, small regions at the base of the endbrain (somatic area of Johnston, see Figs. 72, 73) and in the center of the betweenbrain (thalamus proper) which are true correlation centers, that is, centers of adjustment superposed upon the lower primary centers and not under the dominant influence of any one of the functional systems. The olfactory centers of the endbrain below the olfactory bulbs, the ventral part of the betweenbrain (hypothalamus) and the roof of the midbrain (optic lobes) approach this condition, but in the first two the olfactory system exerts a controlling influence and in the last the optic system. It is probable that in fishes the hypothalamus is the dominant center of the highest correlations of olfactory, gustatory and general visceral senses and that the roof of the midbrain similarly serves the highest correlations of the somatic sensory or exteroceptive senses of which these animals are capable.

The non-olfactory centers of the thalamus and somatic area of fish brains are small and their functions are not well understood; but it is clear that from these regions and from parts of the olfactory area of the endbrain the highest centers of adjustment of mammalian forebrains have arisen — thalamus, corpus striatum, cerebral cortex. Much attention has been devoted to these centers in lower vertebrates and to the problem of the origin of the cerebral cortex and this literature is too extensive and involved to be reviewed here. My own interpretations of some of the physiological and morphogenetic factors which have operated in shaping the forebrains of lower vertebrates have been published in two recent papers (1921, 1922 c), and some of these conclusions will next be briefly presented.

The primitive forebrain.—In early embryonic stages the vertebrate central nervous system is a simple epithelial tube somewhat dilated in the region of the future brain (p. 160). Evidence from embryology and comparative anatomy suggests that the form of the brain of the ancestral vertebrate was somewhat similar in form. Early in vertebrate evolution the eye and the nose were highly elaborated and the related primary cerebral centers were enlarged. The visual receptive cells were developed within the neural tube itself (p. 165) in the region of the betweenbrain, and this part of the brain wall, rapidly enlarging, pouched outward on each side and ultimately formed the retinas of the eyes. This history is repeated in the development of every vertebrate body. In later embryonic stages fibers of the optic nerve grow inward from the evaginated retina and terminate in the optic centers of the betweenbrain and midbrain.

The nose develops in the outer body wall opposite the endbrain, and from this peripheral sensory epithelium fibers of the olfactory nerves grow inward to the brain. The enlargements of the brain wall on each side which accommodate the apparatus of olfactory adjustment comprise the nosebrain. These enlargements were at first probably merely local thickenings of the lateral walls of the neural tube in the endbrain region where the peripheral olfactory nerve fibers terminate, as they are today in early embryonic stages of some vertebrates (Fig. 94).

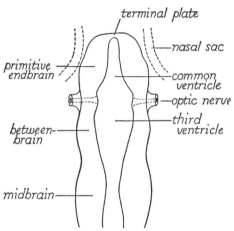

Fig. 94.—Diagram of the anterior end of the early neural tube of the embryo of a salamander (Amblystoma). The stage of development here depicted is not far from that of the human embryo shown in figure 65. In both cases the neural tube is sharply bent in the region of the midbrain. This diagram is drawn as if that flexure were straightened out and then the tube cut through in the horizontal plane midway between dorsal and ventral borders. The thickenings in the lateral walls of the primitive endbrain as here illustrated are in later developmental stages enlarged and laterally evaginated to form the hollow cerebral hemispheres.

With further enlargement of the primary olfactory center (that is, the region within which fibers of the olfactory nerve terminate) the entire brain wall of this region increases in extent but not in thickness, resulting in a lateral bulging or evagination of the whole thickness of the wall. Thus arose the olfactory bulbs which are hollow lateral diverticula from the forward end of the primitive endbrain. These hollow lateral evaginations are the beginnings of the cerebral hemispheres. This slight modification of the simple neural tube probably represents an early ancestral form of vertebrate forebrain, a form which is preserved to-day but little changed in some of the more generalized fishes. Figure 95 illustrates in a schematic way this forebrain pattern, which may be taken as a point of departure for a consideration of the further evolutionary history of the vertebrate forebrain.

The adult internal structure of the olfactory bulbs is in principle similar throughout the vertebrate series; but the differentiation of the olfactory correlation centers at the bases of the olfactory bulbs, which in the lowest vertebrates compose nearly all of the endbrain, has taken so diverse forms as to present one of the most remarkable series of evolutionary changes known in biology. In following this series of changes through the series of lower vertebrates we shall omit consideration of the more aberrant types (or pass them over very lightly) in an endeavor to trace the probable steps in the history of the elaboration of the cerebral hemispheres to their culmination in the human brain.

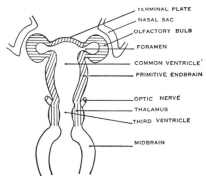

The cerebral hemisphere is a hollow outpouching of the lateral wall of the endbrain, giving in effect an increase in the mass of tissue without undue thickening of the wall. Not all of the endbrain in any vertebrate is thus evaginated to form the cerebral hemispheres, and the residual portion which remains in the unevaginated neural tube is the primitive endbrain (telencephalon medium). The cavity of the primitive endbrain is the common ventricle (ventriculus impar) and the cavities of

Fig. 95.—Diagram illustrating the probable primitive vertebrate type of forebrain as seen in longitudinal section. A portion of the endbrain behind the terminal plate has evaginated in correlation with the differentiation of the adjacent nasal organ and olfactory nerve. This forms the olfactory bulb which here comprises the entire cerebral hemisphere. The cavity of the olfactory bulb is the lateral ventricle. The remainder of the endbrain is unevaginated (primitive endbrain or telencephalon medium).

In this and the following diagrams (figs. 96-105, 107, 108, 110-112) the cut surfaces of the walls of the neural tube are conventionally marked, as follows: primitive endbrain, diagonal lines; evaginated endbrain (cerebral hemispheres), horizontal lines; betweenbrain, vertical lines; midbrain, unshaded.

the cerebral hemispheres are the lateral ventricles. Each of these communicates with the common ventricle by an opening, the interventricular foramen, or foramen of Monro. In the diagram (Fig. 95) the primitive endbrain and its common ventricle are relatively large, being bounded in front by the terminal plate (lamina terminalis); the cerebral hemispheres are small and are limited to the primary olfactory centers, or olfactory bulbs.

As the endbrain increases in size in higher animals, a relatively larger proportion of it is incorporated in the evaginated hemispheres until in man there is only a very small residual primitive endbrain in the vicinity of the terminal plate and optic chiasma. Figures 96 to 103 illustrate various steps in this process of elaboration of cerebral hemispheres at the expense of primitive endbrain.

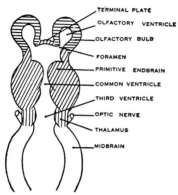

FIG. 96.—Diagrammatic longitudinal section of the forebrain of the sturgeon, Acipenser. The cerebral hemispheres comprise only the olfactory bulbs, the remainder of the endbrain being unevaginated but thickened laterally.

The sturgeon. — The form of the brain of the sturgeon has been illustrated (Fig. 79, p. 184) and further examination of the forebrain shows that it conforms very closely to the schematic pattern just presented (compare Figs. 95 and 96), the chief difference being a thickening of the side walls of the primitive endbrain, thus providing space for the neurons of the olfactory correlation centers. These centers receive the great descending olfactory tracts from the olfactory bulbs and also ascending fibers from sensory centers of diverse sorts in lower regions of the brain.

The olfactory centers at the bases of the olfactory bulbs, which in the aggregate are known as the olfactory area or olfactory nuclei, are correlation centers, but they receive so much larger proportion of olfactory fibers than of other sensory sorts that they must be classed with the other primitive centers of the brain stem and cannot be compared with the cortical association centers of higher brains which are not physiologically dominated by any single sensory system. There are, however, in the sturgeon some small regions of the forebrain in the thalamus proper and somatic area of Johnston which are really higher correlation centers in the sense just defined. These are connected directly or indirectly with the olfactory area and also with other sensory centers, but they are not dominated by any single sensory system as is the olfactory area.

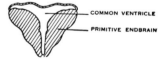

FIG. 97.—Cross section through the middle of the thickened primitive endbrain of the sturgeon. Figures 96 and 97 are based on figures of Johnston (1901).

The dogfish. — Reëxamination of the forebrain of the dogfish (Fig. 98) from this point of view reveals considerable modification of the more primitive pattern seen in the sturgeon. Here the olfactory bulbs are very large and widely evaginated and the remainder of the endbrain is modified in a direction peculiar to the elasmobranchs, consisting anteriorly of paired lateral lobes and posteriorly of primitive endbrain. The brains of these fishes have been much studied and Johnston (1911) in particular has analyzed the olfactory and somatic areas. The position of the somatic area is indicated in Figures 72 and 73 (pp. 174, 175). In this region various non-olfactory exteroceptive senses are brought into correlation with one another and with the olfactory sense. This is apparently the region from which in higher vertebrates the corpus striatum has been elaborated.

The dorsal part of the olfactory area of the dogfish, that is the part which has been removed in opening up the ventricles in the diagram, Fig. 98 (*cf.* Figs. 72 and 73), is obviously of different structure and functional significance from the remainder of this area (Johnston, 1911, 1923, part V); and the same is true of the corresponding part in all other fishes. The whole of this appears to have been primitively a part of the olfactory area, but it also receives special fiber tracts from other parts of the brain, including probably the underlying somatic area. These relations, the details of which we cannot here enter into, have led nearly all students of the question to regard this dorsal olfactory area as a region from which the cerebral cortex of higher forms (or at any rate a part of it) has been derived. That the olfactory cortex (hippocampal formation) has arisen from it is quite generally believed and this region is, accordingly, often called the primordium of the hippocampus. Very recently Holmgren (1922) and Johnston (1923, part V) have published observations which lead them to conclude that the primordia of the non-olfactory cortical areas also are to be sought in this same region.

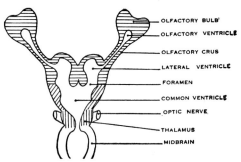

FIG. 98.—Diagram of the relations of the walls of the forebrain and its ventricles in the dogfish, Squalus acanthias, as seen in longitudinal section.

OLFACTORY BULB

OLFACTORY VENTRICLE

OLFACTORY CRUS

LATERAL VENTRICLE

FORAMEN

COMMON VENTRICLE

OPTIC NERVE

THALAMUS

MIDBRAIN

Though the forebrains of fishes present quite satisfactory evidence of an incomplete localization of function and of the presence of correlation centers differing among themselves in the particular reflex patterns which they serve, yet there is no well developed cerebral cortex in any of these forms. The primordial cortex of fishes is not cerebral cortex, though it does show definite structural modifications and fibrous connections which look forward in that direction.

The bony fishes. — Of the remaining groups of fishes two merit special mention in this connection, namely, the teleosts (bony fishes)

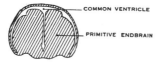

FIG. 99.—Cross section through the thickened primitive endbrain of a teleost.

and dipnoans (lungfishes or mudfishes). The teleostean fishes are the most numerous of all and their brains are specialized in many different directions (for illustrations see Figs. 82, 83, 84, 85, 87, 90, 91); but in all of these cases the primitive endbrain is similar in general plan. The lateral thickenings which are evident in the sturgeon (Figs. 96, 97) are here greatly increased, especially by enlargement of their middle portions, so that the membranous roof of the common ventricle is widely expanded and attached at the ventrolateral borders. The result is that these thickenings themselves are attached only at their basal or ventral sides and project upward into the common ventricle. Fig. 84 illustrates the appearance when the greater part of the membranous roof is removed; Fig. 90 shows the thickening as it appears in median section of the brain; and Fig. 99 presents a cross section through this type of endbrain.

The teleosts are very successful fishes; that is, they have adapted themselves to a wide variety of conditions in fresh and salt waters and they are very numerous, both in number of species and of individuals. But they resemble the insects in that this specialization is all on a rather low plane, is in aberrant directions, and does not lead up to anything higher. Their forebrains are quite unlike those of any other vertebrates and never attain to great size. The solid masses into which their nervous material is condensed are adequately organized for efficiency on the fishes' plane of living, but appear not to have been capable of further development along the lines taken by the higher vertebrates.

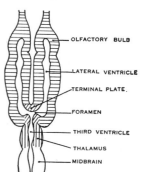

FIG. 100. — Diagrammatic longitudinal section of the forebrain of the lungfish, Protopterus, illustrating the fully evaginated cerebral hemispheres.

The lungfishes. — The Dipnoi are all mudfishes and the three existing genera are survivals of a much more extensive group which lived in former times. The surviving types are the African Protopterus, the Australian Ceratodus, and the South American Lepidosiren. All of these show modifications of the forebrain in the direction of the Amphibia and the higher land vertebrates in general.[1]

In these cases the larger part of the side wall of the primitive endbrain on each side has joined the olfactory bulb in the lateral evagination, thus forming extensive cerebral hemispheres (Figs. 100, 101). The primitive (unevaginated) endbrain is reduced to a small region near the terminal plate and a larger area on the ventral surface not shown in Figure 100. This is the definitive form of cerebral hemispheres as seen in all vertebrates above the fishes. Here the hemispheres are hollow thin-walled vesicles separated by a deep median fissure, whose rostral ends are formed by the olfactory bulbs and whose remaining parts include tissues which in most other fishes are represented in the unevaginated primitive endbrain.

Fig. 101.—Cross section through the cerebral hemispheres of Protopterus taken between the olfactory bulbs and the terminal plate.

These hemispheric vesicles are evaginated not only laterally but forward so that they project far beyond the terminal plate.

The amphibians. — In both the tailed Amphibia (Urodela), including salamanders and their allies, and the frogs and toads (Anura)

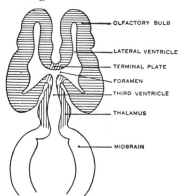

OLFACTORY BULB

LATERAL VENTRICLE

TERMINAL PLATE

FORAMEN

THIRD VENTRICLE

THALAMUS

MIDBRAIN

Fig. 102.—Diagrammatic longitudinal section of the forebrain of an amphibian.

cerebral hemispheres are formed in substantially the same way as in mudfishes (Fig. 57, p. 156). As seen in Figures 102 and 103, almost the entire endbrain is represented in the evaginated cerebral hemispheres whose walls are, however, thicker and internally much more highly organized than in mudfishes. From the dipnoans, through the lower and higher amphibians, we have a graded series of forms of cerebral hemispheres which lead directly up to those of higher vertebrates, including man, all constructed upon the same plan and differing chiefly in the size and internal complexity of the walls of the evaginated hemispheric vesicles.

In amphibians the olfactory bulbs occupy the anterior or antero-

[1] This is true even of Ceratodus, as Holmgren (1922) has recently pointed out, thus correcting some earlier descriptions.

lateral parts of the hemispheres and behind these are various localized correlation centers, most of which are reached by olfactory fibers from the bulbs. The number and complexity of these correlation centers can be increased indefinitely without great thickening of the wall by simply enlarging the size of the hemispheric vesicle. In the course of further elaboration of the hemispheres in still higher forms advantage has been taken of this possibility until in the human brain the cerebral hemispheres make up more than three-quarters of the total weight of the brain and have expanded so as to project forward far beyond the terminal plate and backward as far as the cerebellum, inclosing and concealing from view the entire betweenbrain and midbrain. Yet even these enormous hemispheres are hollow vesicles; their walls, it is true, are considerably thickened, but this thickening

FIG. 103.—Cross section through the amphibian cerebral hemispheres taken between the olfactory bulbs and the terminal plate.

is due chiefly to the white matter composed of fibers connected with the cortical gray centers which are strictly superficial.

It should be borne in mind in this connection that the walls of the cerebral hemispheres are never uniformly thin. Even in mudfishes there is some irregularity in thickness of the wall, the thicker regions containing the chief collections of correlation neurons and the thinner zones being physiologically less active. With increase in the size and complexity of the correlation centers these local thickenings become more pronounced. Throughout these progressive changes in the complexity of the cerebral walls there are manifest two structural tendencies which have very significant functional corollaries. These are, first, that pronounced local thickenings are usually centers of innate, that is, reflex and instinctive, types of behavior; and, second, that the centers concerned with more labile individually acquired behavior are spread out in thin sheets of tissue usually superficial in position. Thus arise in the first place the so-called basal ganglia, or better basal nuclei, and in the second place the cerebral cortex.

Even in the Amphibia the beginnings of these lines of divergent specialization are evident. In the lowest urodeles, like the mudpuppy, Necturus, the walls of the cerebral hemispheres are thin and but little more complicated internally than are those of the mudfishes. But in higher members of this group, like the frog, the specialization has gone considerably further. Here we can recognize the beginnings of the basal nuclei, or basal lobes (corpus striatum, etc.) and in the

dorsal convexity of the hemisphere a rudimentary cerebral cortex
(P. Ramón y Cajal, 1922).   On the behavior side it is obvious even
to casual inspection that the frog leads a more varied and enterprising life than the mudpuppy and salamanders.

The reptiles. — The two developmental tendencies to which
reference has just been made come to full expression in the reptiles.
From the primitive reptilian stock, which the fossil history shows to
have arisen at least as far back as the Upper Carboniferous (Fig. 77,
p. 182), further evolution of the forebrain took two widely divergent

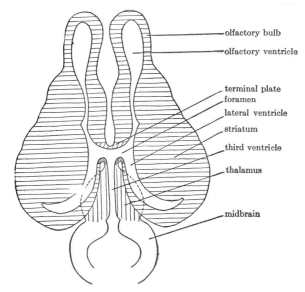

FIG. 104.—Diagrammatic longitudinal section of the forebrain of the box-tortoise
Cistudo. This and the next figure are based on descriptions of Johnston (1915).

directions; one with massive basal lobes in the lateral wall of the
hemisphere led up to modern saurians and birds, the other with
thinner cerebral walls and more elaborate cerebral cortex led up to
the mammals.

The turtles are the most generalized of existing reptiles and they
show both of these tendencies in moderate degree.   Fig. 104 illustrates a horizontal longitudinal section through the forebrain of the
turtle and Fig. 105 a transverse section taken between the olfactory
bulb and the terminal plate.   The lateral wall of the hemisphere is
seen to be considerably thickened; this is the corpus striatum complex.
The dorso-medial wall, however, is thin; this region contains true

cerebral cortex of primitive structure but unmistakable nature. From this type of brain differentiation led away in two directions.

From forms with brains like those of turtles the mammalian brain was derived by further elaboration of the cerebral cortex. From the same point of departure the brains of saurians (lizards and crocodiles)

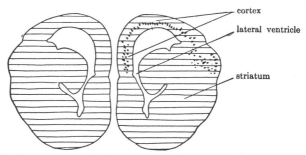

FIG. 105.—Transverse section through the cerebral hemispheres of the box-tortoise taken between the olfactory bulbs and the terminal plate.

and of birds were derived by further elaboration of the basal lobes. The brain of the American alligator illustrates an advanced step in this direction. Fig. 106 shows a side view of this brain with the dorso-lateral wall of the hemisphere removed, thus exposing the big basal lobe (striatum complex) which projects inward from the ventro-lateral wall so as nearly to fill the lateral ventricle; compare the longi-

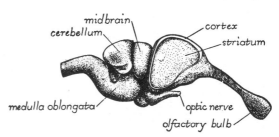

FIG. 106.—The brain of a young alligator 55 cm. long seen from the right side, one and one half times natural size. The lateral cerebral cortex has been removed, opening the lateral ventricle and exposing the underlying basal lobe or corpus striatum complex. Redrawn from Crosby (1917).

tudinal section, Fig. 107. As shown by the transverse section (Fig. 108), both the basal lobes and the cerebral cortex are more extensive than in the turtle.

It is well known that alligators and crocodiles rank higher in the behavior scale than do the turtles. Not only are the reflex and instinctive acts very complex, in correlation with the large size of the basal lobes, but they lead a much more active, diversified and apparently intelligent life, in correlation with the considerable enlargement of the cerebral cortex.   They are, in fact, in all respects the most highly organized of any of the reptiles.

The birds. — From an ancestral type of brain not far from that of the alligator the brains of the birds have apparently been derived by further increase in the size and complexity of the basal lobes (striatum complex) and an actual degradation of the cerebral cortex.

Visual, auditory and tactual sensibility are very highly developed in birds with a noteworthy reduction in the sense of smell, especially in the higher species. This is reflected in the small size of the olfactory bulbs of the brain, as seen by comparison of Figs. 106 and 109. The cerebral hemispheres of birds are much larger than in any reptile, but the cerebral cortex is reduced in amount and, what is more significant, is of more primitive histologic type.

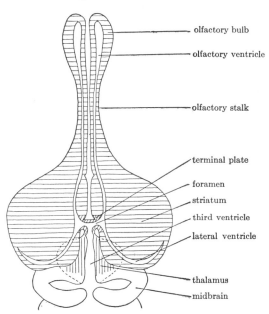

olfactory bulb

olfactory ventricle

olfactory stalk

terminal plate

foramen

striatum

third ventricle

lateral ventricle

thalamus

midbrain

FIG. 107.—Diagrammatic longitudinal section of the forebrain of the alligator.   Drawn for this work by Dr. Elizabeth Crosby.

In the mammals, where the cerebral cortex attains its culmination, this cortex has three main subdivisions: (1) The dorsal convexity of the hemisphere is covered by cortex related with somatic sensorimotor activities, the somatic cortex, general cortex, or neopallium. (2) Below the somatic cortex on the medial side of the hemisphere is the hippocampal formation, and on the lateral side (3) the pyriform lobe cortex.   The last two are dominated by olfactory and visceral functions and are called the archipallium because they attained to full development earlier in phylogenetic history than did the somatic cortex or neopallium.   In reptiles and lower mammals the lateral and medial parts of the archipallium converge in front at the base of the olfactory bulb and also behind in the posterior pole of the hemisphere. The olfactory cortex thus comprises the entire margin of the cortical field, while the non-olfactory or somatic cortex is developed within this ring of older cortex on the dorsal side of the

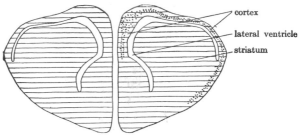

Fig. 108.—Transverse section through the cerebral hemispheres of the alligator taken immediately in front of the terminal plate.

hemisphere. This latter cortex is hardly recognizable in reptiles, well defined though of limited area in very primitive mammals, and progressively larger as we ascend the series until in man it forms by far the larger part and crowds the more primitive archipallium into crevices and crannies at the inferior margin of the cortical territory.

Examination of the cerebral hemispheres of the birds with this analysis in mind brings to light some very peculiar features. By far the larger part of the reptilian cortex is archipallium. With the reduction of the olfactory apparatus in birds, the archipallium is nat-

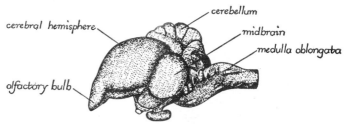

Fig. 109.—The brain of the pigeon, side view.

urally also shrunken to an insignificant vestige, yet the cerebral hemisphere as a whole is notably larger than in reptiles. This increase is not in the cortex, but in the subcortical basal lobes, especially the corpus striatum complex of the lateral wall. So great is this enlargement that the lateral ventricle has been reduced to a narrow slit (Figs. 110, 111) and the hemisphere is nearly solid. There is no corresponding increase in the somatic cortex. A cellular area which is probably comparable with the neopallium of mammals covers the dorsal surface of the hemisphere, as indicated by the coarse stipple of Fig. 111; but these cells nowhere show as well-defined cortical characters as in mammals or even reptiles, and if any of this

tissue is real cerebral cortex, it is certainly cortex of a very low order. This last conclusion is confirmed by the physiological experiments of Rogers (1922, 1922 a).

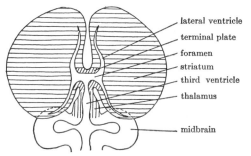

The experiments to which reference has just been made show that removal of the rudimentary cerebral cortex

Fig. 110.—Diagrammatic longitudinal section of the forebrain of the pigeon. The thalamus is in reality much larger in proportion to the other parts than here drawn.

of the pigeon leaves the animal deficient in intelligence, ability to learn by experience and personal memory, and since these functions are not very highly developed in the normal bird the behavior is not as greatly modified as would be the case in a mammal. The reflex behavior is practically unaffected. The reflexes are, however, seriously impaired if the basal lobes are injured, and removal of progressively more of these lobes and of the thalamus results in a corresponding progressive loss of reflex and instinctive powers.

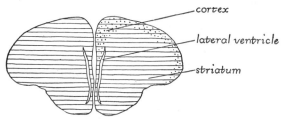

Fig. 111.—Transverse section through the cerebral hemispheres of the pigeon taken immediately in front of the terminal plate.

It is everywhere recognized that birds possess highly complex instinctive endowments and that their intelligence is very limited. The preceding analysis, therefore, gives us the facts necessary for an evaluation of the parts played by cortical and subcortical correlation mechanisms in general. Amplification of the innate endowments goes hand-in-hand with enlargement of the subcortical basal lobes of the cerebral hemispheres; enlargement of the powers of personal learning by experience, memory, and adjustments of the intelligent type is correlated with enlargement and diversification of structure in the cerebral cortex.

The comparison of the forebrains of birds and bony fishes is very instructive. Both of these groups are terminal members of their phylogenetic branches, neither has given rise to any higher type. Each has very numerous species with great variety of specialization in detail, though all are organized on the same general plan, the differentiation in each species being in adaptation to a particular mode of life. Each phylum as a whole is plastic in the sense that it exhibits great numbers of particular and very special adaptations to environmental conditions; but the plasticity is largely biologically determined and works out through the hereditary organization as instinctive behavior rather than as individually learned behavior for the most part. In this both of these groups resemble the insects (p. 152). Fishes, however, show more individual modifiability and docility than do any insects, and the birds have much more capacity for intelligent modification of their instinctive patterns than the fishes.

Attention has been called (p. 206) to the fact that the solid form of endbrain in bony fishes seems to have presented structural limitations to differentiation in the direction leading toward greater individual plasticity of behavior. The same factor seems to be operative in birds. This type of hemisphere is nowhere endowed with capacity for highly intelligent behavior, nor has it in any case given rise to the apparatus necessary in such behavior. This seems to be an orthogenetic limitation of the sort which I have elsewhere discussed (1920).

This does not mean that birds are incapable of highly complex behavior. Observation shows quite the contrary. The individual bird leads a very diversified life, much more so than any fish. But this very elaborate behavior pattern is largely cast in stereotyped molds and takes the form of hereditary instinct. The mating, nesting and brooding habits of birds illustrate this very well, as has been pointed out by F. H. Herrick (1905, 1911); see also Whitman (1919). These authors give numerous illustrations of the inflexibility of the instinctive cycles.

The reproductive cycle in many birds is made up of a series of terms which must follow in a definite sequence. Eight of these terms are distinguished by Herrick, and if the cycle is broken at any point the whole process may be abandoned and the bird begins the cycle anew. There are divers capacities for readjustment of disturbed cycles, but in general the original innate sequence cannot be greatly altered.

The tissues of the solid cerebral masses of birds are adequate for the performance of these hereditary instinctive cycles of great complexity. There is also capacity for a considerable degree of intelligent modification of the instinctive acts; that is, this behavior, as with ourselves, is always a mixture of inherited and individually learned factors. But in birds the inherited factors predominate, with ourselves the individually learned. Breed (1911) has analyzed these factors experimentally by studying the feeding and other reactions of newly hatched chicks.

In the preceding review emphasis has been placed on the dominance of the stable inherited factors in the behavior of birds; these factors here probably reach their highest expression, though they do not appear in so pure a form as in insects. Yet it must not be overlooked that there is a considerable measure of plasticity and probably of intelligence in these behavior complexes, the individual modifiability playing a relatively larger part than in the somewhat similar case of the insects. Intelligence as used here is not synonymous with consciousness. Intelligence seems not to be highly developed in birds; on the other hand, the emotional and impulsive components of consciousness appear to be very strong, so far as can be judged by objective behavior.

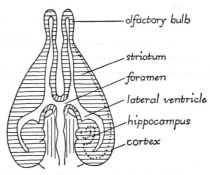

Fig. 112.—Diagrammatic longitudinal section of the forebrain of the rabbit.

The social factors in birds' behavior are highly developed and on a very different plane from that of the social insects (p. 147). The social control appears to be largely through conscious and especially through emotional appeal (see the papers by Craig, 1908–1911).

For detailed observations and critical analyses of the behavior of pigeons and its inherited and acquired components, together with very interesting data on their social relations, homing instincts, the limits of their intelligence, etc., the reader should consult the posthumous works of Whitman (1919).

The mammals. — In primitive reptiles the foundations were laid for the elaboration of two very different types of forebrain; one with amplification of basal lobes and reduction of cortex led to the birds, the other with amplification of the cortex led to the mammals. In the more primitive mammals the basal lobes are perhaps as well developed as in the reptiles, though on a very different plan; but the cortex in all mammals is well differentiated and as we pass from lower to higher forms it increases progressively, while the basal lobes do not.

In Figure 112 we see the general plan of the cerebral hemispheres of a lower mammal very schematically presented. The olfactory bulbs are large and the olfactory cortex is, accordingly, very well developed. The medial olfactory cortex is for the most part rolled into the lateral ventricle in very complex formation and appears in the section figured as the hippocampus. The remaining cortex is superficial. The somatic cortex occupies the entire dorsal wall (the portion removed in the section figured) and parts of the medial and lateral walls. The somatic cortical areas of the two hemispheres are connected in all but the lowest mammals by a large bridge of association fibers which cross the median plane above the interventricular foramina. This is the corpus callosum (removed with the somatic cortex in Figure 112).

Since we are concerned in this work with foundations rather than with the details of the completed superstructures, it will be impossible in the space at command to follow further the history of the successive stages of mammalian differentiation which have led up to that noble edifice, the cerebral cortex of man. In the most primitive existing mammals the cortex presents the three subdivisions to which reference has already been made (p. 211), viz., (1) the medial part of the archipallium or hippocampal formation, (2) the lateral part of the archipallium or pyriform cortex, and (3) the dorsal neopallium or somatic cortex. The archipallium in these primitive forms has already attained its maximum development; it is within the somatic cortex that those profound changes have taken place which are correlated with the rise of intelligence as the controlling factor in behavior and, in man, the acquisition of speech, the reasoning powers, and those refined sentiments which make for self-culture and social advancement.

CHAPTER XVI

FUNCTIONAL FACTORS IN FOREBRAIN DEVELOPMENT

Analysis of functional influences — Oxygen supply of the forebrain — Innate functional factors — Correlation patterns in the forebrains of fishes — Correlation patterns, amphibians to mammals — Conclusion

Analysis of functional influences. — The preceding review of the structural differences between the forebrains of various vertebrates suggests further inquiry into the physiological factors operative in this series of changes.

Among the agents which have acted in shaping the forms of the forebrain are: (1) the mechanical factors of space requirements of the parts, their mutual pressures and tensions; (2) the nutritive requirements of the parts, the blood supply, oxygen supply, movements of lymph and cerebrospinal fluid, etc.; (3) the functional connections of the parts, the nature and magnitude of the nervous impulses entering and leaving them, the complexity of internal organization required for correlating and integrating these nervous impulses and the resulting differential growth processes. The second and third of these groups of factors are directly physiological and will be briefly considered.

Oxygen supply of the forebrain. — In comparing the forebrains of the more highly specialized fishes with those of higher vertebrates the most characteristic difference lies in the more complete evagination of the primitive endbrain into the cerebral hemispheres in higher forms. The movement in this direction did not begin in the Amphibia, for we find fully evaginated hemispheres in the lungfishes. Probably the trend in this direction began in the ganoidean stem ancestral to both Dipnoi and Amphibia. Can we discover the cause of this deviation from the directions of forebrain development taken by the other groups of fishes? As I have elsewhere (1921) suggested, the problem may be approached from the side of the nutritive requirements of the tissues, and especially the oxygen supply.

Now, the lungfishes are not the most successful types of fishes. From the standpoint of biological efficiency they are surpassed by the elasmobranchs which from early Silurian times have dominated the salt waters and by the teleosts which dominate the fresh waters and now compete with the sharks for the mastery of the oceans. The surviving members of the more archaic types of fishes exist to-day, not by reason of the functional superiority of their hollow cerebral hemispheres over the massive solid thickenings of the primitive endbrain seen in teleosts, but rather because they have, as it were, hidden themselves away in crannies of the environment not sought after by the more enterprising groups of fishes. In fact, they live in waters which periodically dry up and are therefore not habitable by other kinds of fishes. And here perhaps is the key to the solution of our problem.

Fishes with evaginated cerebral hemispheres are inhabitants of sluggish waters; they and their allies, the primitive ganoids, are mudfishes. Lull (1918) has called attention to the fact that this type of fishes came into prominence at a geological period (the late Silurian and early Devonian) when extensive continental fresh-water lakes and streams were drying up. The fish fauna of these waters was faced with the alternative of gradual modification in adaptation to seasonal drought or extinction. The more highly specialized species inhabiting these stagnant waters undoubtedly perished, as their "senile" type of organization was unable to make the necessary readjustment; but the more generalized forms, whose undifferentiated tissues retained the plasticity and adaptability of the "young" type, met the emergency by supplementing their water-breathing apparatus by air-breathing organs of various sorts. Thus arose the lungfishes and the Amphibia.

For fishes living in imperfectly aërated water the oxygen supply of the brain is a vital matter. The vascular supply of the brain of lungfishes is very rich. The brains of these fishes and of all the more generalized ganoids are, moreover, provided with extraordinarily enlarged choroid plexuses which are highly vascular and probably ensure the highest possible oxygen supply to the cerebrospinal fluid within the wide brain ventricles and in the extensive surrounding endocranial spaces. Many larval and adult urodeles which thrive in stagnant waters also possess unusually extensive and vascular choroid plexuses.

It has been shown[1] that oxidases are present in brain tissue, in

[1] See Pighini (1912), Katsanuma (1915), Marinesco (1919, 1922), Mott (1921). Kappers (1922, 1920–21, p. 1275) has briefly reviewed some of this literature. It is interesting in this connection to note that Cole (1921) has investigated the source of oxygen supply of various invertebrates (insect larvæ, worms, etc.) living in water entirely deficient in oxygen, and he concludes that such a supply may be derived from decomposing organic matter in mud with the aid of enzymes

larger quantity in the cerebrospinal fluid, and most of all in the choroid plexuses (Pighini, 1912). The exact relation of oxidase to the processes of oxidation in living tissues is not altogether clear, but it is commonly believed to play an important part in the facilitation of this type of metabolism and in the case of brain tissue there is independent evidence that this is true. These facts suggest that probably the mudfishes and the lower amphibians possess an internal mechanism more highly developed than in many other vertebrates, located especially in the choroid plexuses of the brain, which promotes oxidation and may serve to make more efficient use of a limited oxygen supply than is possible in other species.

Obviously, this arrangement is well adapted to make the largest possible use of a deficient supply of oxygen, for the nervous tissues can take up oxygen directly from the blood-vessels which envelop and penetrate their mass and also from the cerebrospinal fluid by which they are bathed. But the latter source of oxygen is available only on the ventricular and external surfaces, and the interior of any considerable thickenings such as characterize the forebrains of teleosts would be dependent upon a single source of oxygen only, viz., the penetrating blood-vessels. This latter source is obviously adequate for species living in well aërated water, but for mudfishes, and especially those subjected to periods of drought, the interior of such thick masses might suffer asphyxiation without the collateral source of oxygen furnished by the cerebrospinal fluid.

The thin walls of the forebrains of the lungfishes, accordingly, have two possible sources of oxygen supply, in contrast with the thickened masses of the brains of teleosts which have but one, and if the supply is deficient this may be sufficient to maintain the life of the tissue during critical periods of drought. Indeed, in the total suppression of gill breathing, skin respiration may be adequate to supply the minimal amount of oxygen necessary to keep such a brain alive while the animal remains inactive. This minimum of oxygen might well be quite inadequate to prevent asphyxiation of a brain of teleostean type.

Now the form of the forebrain is not an essential factor in this situation in the case of lowly organized fishes of sluggish habit, provided only that the walls are thin and highly vascular and there are extensive choroid plexuses. But only in the evaginated forms does there reside the potentiality of indefinite further differentiation under more fortunate conditions of life.

within and without their bodies. This may be a possible source of oxygen in the case of some of the mudfishes, though we have no direct evidence of such a thing.

On the basis of these considerations it may be assumed that a primitive ganoid type in late Silurian or early Devonian times, whose brain form was not far from that indicated in Figure 95 (p. 203) and whose histological structure was primitive and generalized, was subjected to periodic drought. This climatic change is believed to have been very pronounced and widespread at this time (Lull, 1918, p. 121). In adaptation to this environmental change the forebrain of the generalized type in question differentiated in one or several of the directions presented by modern ganoids and lungfishes. One such form, viz., the thin-walled evaginated hemispheres, proved capable of further progressive differentiation in air-breathing Amphibia and in their later descendants.

By reason of the limitations imposed by their modes of life, these animals in the early stages of this differentiation undoubtedly remained on a low level of organization, as do the modern mudfishes, passing a sluggish and uneventful existence. But with the elaboration of an efficient pulmonary respiratory mechanism (which indeed is only imperfectly realized in many living urodele Amphibia), these limitations were removed, the oxygen supply of the brain was adequate, and the evaginated type of cerebral hemisphere, acquired during a period when the vital currents were at lowest ebb, developed possibilities of further evolutionary advance forever denied to those types of fishes which diverged in other and (for fishes) more favorable lines of specialization.

Innate functional factors. — Besides strictly mechanical influences and the nutritive requirements of brain tissue there remain to be considered the structural modifications correlated with the specific nervous functions. This is by far the most important morphogenetic factor, for, after all, the neurons themselves take the leading part in shaping the nervous system. The adult arrangement of these nervous elements is conditioned upon two sorts of processes. There are, first, obviously adaptive features which are firmly hereditary and common to all members of a species, such as the reflex patterns and their neuromotor apparatus. In the second place there is the immediate effect of active function upon the progress of development of the individual — facilitation by use, trophic response of the tissue to excitation, direct action of physiological gradients of excitation and conduction upon direction and rate of growth, the bioelectric phenomena of excitation and differentiation and their directive influence upon contiguous differentiating neuroblasts, hormone action, and probably many others. The researches of Child (1921, 1924) have been directed especially to the analysis of this second group of influences.

In the analysis of the adaptive modifications of the nervous system it is very difficult to separate those features which are strictly inherited from those which are individually acquired during the early life of the individual; for, in the early stages of development especially, all eggs of a given species are growing in very similar environments and the external influences (external, that is, to the developing egg) which impinge upon them and determine their forms and physiological gradients and so shape the course of development normally act so uniformly upon all the individuals as to give substantially the same end-effects as would be the case if the characters in question were determined by true germinal heredity (Child, 1924, Chap. 13).

Fortunately for the purpose of this analysis it is not necessary to determine whether the characters under consideration are really hereditary or are acquired in early prenatal life under identical conditions with resulting uniformity in all the individuals; for up to the time when the newborn or newhatched individuals are launched upon their individual careers in the manifold complexities of the external environment it is of little practical import whether their common capacities and limitations were determined in the germ or in the prenatal environment. What does matter is that to this extent future behavior is structurally predetermined, and uniformly so in all members of a race or species. This is what is meant by innate structure and innate behavior in this work. The question whether these innate characteristics are truly hereditary is not prejudged.

Whether the postnatal behavior of these individuals will rank high or low in our scale (p. 13) will be measured by one or both of two different standards. If the innate behavior is of a very complicated pattern with a wide range of very precise adjustments to particular external conditions and the whole carried on with mechanical precision, we recognize a high grade of stereotyped or instinctive behavior. If, on the other hand, during postnatal life the individual is capable of recombining the behavior units (p. 12) of the innate endowment in a great variety of new patterns in adaptation to his particular experience, we say that he shows a high grade of plastic, individually modifiable, or intelligent behavior.

The varied assortment of special adaptive modifications of the brain which were illustrated in Chapter 14 all lie chiefly within the field of the innate apparatus; those of the forebrain discussed in Chapter 15 include both the innate apparatus of the olfactory system and the higher correlation centers which mediate the more labile individually acquired components of the behavior. I have recently reviewed (1922 c) comparatively some of the functional factors which have shaped the innate organization of the forebrains of lower vertebrates. The details of this analysis are too intricate to be presented here, but a few general considerations may be summarized.

Correlation patterns in the forebrains of fishes. — In all fishes the greater part of the forebrain is dominated physiologically by the olfactory system, this entire region being designated the nosebrain. In the dogfish the nosebrain comprises about one-third of the entire brain (p. 182). It can be separated into two physiologically distinct

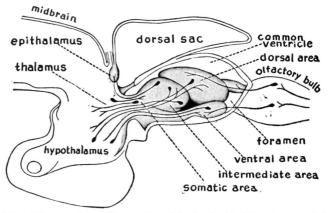

FIG. 113.—Diagram of a median section of the forebrain of the sturgeon, Acipenser, to illustrate the relations of the dorsal, ventral and intermediate nuclei of the olfactory area to the parts of the betweenbrain. Based on the researches of Johnston. Compare figures 79, 96 and 114.

parts. In front is the olfactory bulb, the primary olfactory center within which the fibers of the olfactory nerve end; here are the first synapses in the afferent olfactory path. Behind the bulb is the olfactory area, containing correlation centers which are reached by fibers of the second or third order transmitting excitations of the olfactory system which descend from the olfactory bulb. Here synaptic junctions are made between these descending fibers and those of various non-olfactory functional systems which ascend from the betweenbrain.

Now, the fibers which descend from the olfactory bulb into the olfactory area are, so far as we now know, all of the same physiological type. The olfactory component of the correlation complex represented in the olfactory area as a whole is, accordingly, the same in all parts of this area; nevertheless the area itself is differentiated into several regions or nuclei of very different structure. These differences must, then, be accounted for in terms of the non-olfactory fiber systems which ascend into the area from the betweenbrain to effect correlational junctions with the olfactory fibers.

The betweenbrain itself is a complex of correlation centers of three distinct sorts. (1) Above is the epithalamus (habenula) which is chiefly a link in the chain of efferent discharge from the olfactory area. (2) Below is the hypothalamus, a much larger center which receives gustatory and various visceral and other correlation tracts ascending into it from the medulla oblongata and midbrain; it is connected by ascending and descending fibers with the olfactory area. (3) Between these is the thalamus proper which receives ascending fibers of the tactile, optic and other somatic sensory systems. This somatic correlation center of the thalamus is extended forward into the endbrain in substantially the same form, where it is known

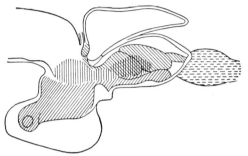

Fig. 114.—Scheme of the centers of the forebrain of the sturgeon as seen in median section to illustrate the relations of dorsal, ventral and intermediate olfactory areas to the olfactory bulb in front and to the betweenbrain behind. Compare figure 113. The primary olfactory center (olfactory bulb) is marked with broken horizontal lines; the dorsal zone (dorsal olfactory area and epithalamus) is marked with oblique lines; the ventral zone (ventral olfactory area and hypothalamus) is marked with oblique lines at an angle to the last; and the intermediate zone (olfactosomatic area, somatic area and thalamus) is marked by vertical lines. For fuller description see Herrick (1922 c).

as the somatic area of the endbrain, a region which is not a part of the nosebrain as this term is here defined, for it is not directly reached by any fibers of the olfactory system.

The primitive endbrain at its lower border is in contact with these three subdivisions of the betweenbrain and its physiological organization is profoundly influenced by these relationships. In a generalized fish like the sturgeon (Fig. 79, p. 184, and Fig. 96, p. 204) these relations are diagrammatically expressed in Figure 113 and still more schematically in Figure 114. The olfactory area of the primitive endbrain is incompletely separated into dorsal, ventral and intermediate or lateral parts or nuclei. The dorsal nucleus is in still more primitive fishes (cyclostomes) directly continuous with the epithal-

amus; here in the sturgeon these regions are separated and related
only by descending fibers of the olfacto-habenular tract. The ventral
(or medial) nucleus is in direct contact with the hypothalamus and
the lateral nucleus is similarly directly continuous with the somatic
area which, in turn, is extended backward into the thalamus.

Comparative evidence, the details of which we cannot here enter
into, suggests that the olfactory area of the endbrain was primitively
a homogeneous field within which correlations were effected between
the olfactory system and various non-olfactory systems. The contiguous non-olfactory areas of the betweenbrain sent correlation
fibers forward into this field and, in response to the diverse physiological characteristics of these ascending nervous impulses and differences in type of response appropriate to each, the olfactory area itself
underwent progressive internal modification. The ventral nucleus was
influenced chiefly by
gustatory and visceral
systems ascending from
the hypothalamus, the
lateral nucleus by so-
matic sensory systems
ascending from the so-
matic area ,while the history of the dorsal nucleus
is peculiar and will be
considered later.

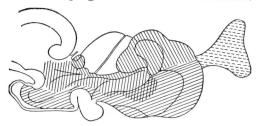

Fig. 115.—Scheme of the centers of the forebrain
of the dogfish as seen in median section. Compare
figure 71, p. 172. The conventional markings are the
same as in figure 114. From Herrick (1922 c).

In all other fishes which have been adequately examined similar
conditions prevail. As indicated in the diagrams of the sturgeon
(Fig. 114) and dogfish (Fig. 115), there are three physiologically
defined longitudinal columns or zones on each side of the forebrain
which in front converge toward the olfactory bulb and behind diverge
toward the three major subdivisions of the betweenbrain. In front
they are all purely olfactory; behind their characters are modified in
relation with the non-olfactory connections which have invaded them
from the betweenbrain. Local differentiation within the endbrain
occurred in response to the diverse physiological features of these
ascending systems, and also in connection with the development of
systems of correlation neurons intrinsic to the endbrain itself.

The hypothalamus is the most important correlation center of the
betweenbrain of fishes. The ventral part of the olfactory area is
adjacent to it and the two are intimately bound together by ascending
and descending correlation fibers. These physiologically related

regions form a ventral zone of correlation of olfactory, gustatory and visceral reflexes. These primitive relations are retained even up to the human brain, where they are represented by the medial olfactory nucleus, septum, tuber cinereum and mammillary bodies.

The small thalamus of fishes is devoted to exteroceptive or somatic sensori-motor correlations — optic, somesthetic, acoustico-lateral systems. The adjacent part of the endbrain, or somatic area, is of like physiological character. The lateral zone of the endbrain includes in front a lateral olfactory nucleus, then an olfacto-somatic correlation nucleus, followed by the purely somatic area and thalamus. These parts are connected by ascending and descending correlation fibers which are the precursors of the thalamic projection fibers of higher forms. Within this zone in higher vertebrates there appear the lateral olfactory nucleus, amygdala and corpus striatum complex.

The dorsal olfactory nucleus was probably primitively related with the epithalamus in much the same way that the ventral nucleus is bound up with the hypothalamus, but in existing vertebrates there are no ascending fibers from the epithalamus to the dorsal nucleus, though the descending olfacto-habenular tract is in all cases well developed. The results of this partial physiological isolation of the dorsal nucleus from the adjacent epithalamus have been peculiar. It has been invaded by ascending fibers from the hypothalamus (Fig. 113) and also by correlation fibers connecting it with the underlying somatic area and ventral nucleus. The dorsal nucleus, in short, begins to show a more complex pattern of correlation fibers than any other part of the forebrain, and these are largely short connections with other parts of the endbrain itself.

The tendency of the dorsal part of the olfactory area to develop the most complex associational connections and thus to serve as the center of the most complex reflex patterns which is here inaugurated in the most generalized fishes comes progressively to fuller expression as we pass from fishes up to the amphibians and higher vertebrates. This region, in fact, is now universally recognized as the point of departure for the elaboration of a part, at least, of the cerebral cortex; it is primordial cortex, though in no fishes does it contain well-differentiated cortical structure.

Correlation patterns, amphibians to mammals. — Now, as we pass from the generalized fishes, in which all of the endbrain except the olfactory bulbs is represented in the lateral walls of the primitive neural tube, up to the amphibians and higher forms, in which most of the primitive endbrain has been evaginated to form the extensive cerebral hemispheres, the functional factors which have just been reviewed continue to operate, but in new directions with resultant profound modification of forebrain patterns.

The exact method by which the primitive endbrain of generalized fishes was transformed into the fully evaginated cerebral hemispheres of lungfishes and amphibians is not yet known and there are sharp differences of opinion about this question. My own view of the probable relationship of the amphibian hemispheres to the primitive endbrain is expressed in the accompanying conventionalized diagrams (Figs. 116, 117).

The ventral zone extends forward beyond the interventricular foramen to form the ventro-medial sector of the evaginated hemi-

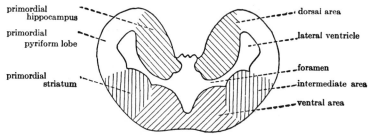

primordial hippocampus — dorsal area
primordial pyriform lobe — lateral ventricle
primordial striatum — foramen
— intermediate area
— ventral area

Fig. 116.—Diagrammatic cross section through the amphibian cerebral hemispheres at the level of the interventricular foramen with conventional markings similar to those of figures 114 and 115 to illustrate the author's view of the corresponding parts of the forebrain in amphibians and fishes. The unshaded area is of uncertain relationships, probably having been derived from both the dorsal and the intermediate zones of unevaginated types. For further discussion see Herrick (1922 c).

sphere. The lateral zone similarly extends directly forward from the thalamus past the foramen to form the ventro-lateral sector of the hemisphere. The dorsal zone forms the dorso-medial sector of the hemisphere. There remains a dorso-lateral sector of problematic relationships. It seems quite likely that this is a derivative of both the dorsal and the lateral zones of the primitive endbrain, for it has some of the functional connections characteristic of both.

Here in the amphibian cerebral hemisphere there are laid down in very elementary outlines all of the major subdivisions of the hemispheres of higher vertebrates. The subcortical or basal cerebral centers develop within the two ventral sectors, on the medial side various reflex centers in which the olfactory system is dominant, on the lateral side reflex centers of two sorts. The first and more primitive, going back to the lowest fishes, is an olfacto-somatic correlation system which in mammals is represented by part of the caudate nucleus of the corpus striatum and the amygdaloid complex (Johnston, 1923). The second is concerned wholly with non-olfactory somatic sensori-motor reflex and instinctive adjustments, represented in mammals by the remainder of the corpus striatum complex.

The dorsal sectors of the cerebral hemisphere are cortical areas. In the lowest Amphibia no true cortex is differentiated here, but the evidence is clear that the dorso-medial sector is primordial hippocampal cortex and the dorso-lateral sector is primordial pyriform lobe cortex. In the frog incipient cortex is found in these areas and in reptiles and all higher forms there is well differentiated cortex.

In amphibians both medial and lateral cortical primordia are strongly dominated by olfactory associational connections. In other words, there is here primordial archipallium but no area which can be

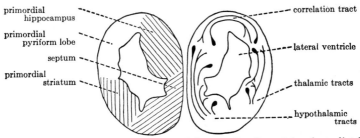

primordial
    hippocampus
primordial
    pyriform lobe
septum
primordial
    striatum
correlation tract
lateral ventricle
thalamic tracts
hypothalamic
    tracts

FIG. 117.—Cross section similar to that of the preceding figure taken immediately in front of the interventricular foramen, with diagrammatic indication of the arrangement of some of the neurons.

called primordial somatic cortex or neopallium. In reptiles (Figs. 105, 108) medial or hippocampal cortex and lateral or pyriform cortex are well developed and between these on the dorsal convexity of the hemisphere there is intercalated a sheet of cortex which is believed to be the precursor of the neopallium of mammals, though in a very rudimentary form.

The steps by which the mammalian type of cortex has been elaborated from an unknown reptilian ancestral type are obscure, and there is considerable difference of opinion amongst comparative neurologists regarding the part played in this process by the components of the corpus striatum complex which are so greatly enlarged in reptiles and birds (pp. 209, 213). For discussions of these questions see Elliot Smith (1910, 1919) and Johnston (1923).

As has already been pointed out, cortical differentiation within the mammals, so far as this history is indicated by existing types, has centered about the non-olfactory and especially the exteroceptive functions. The elaboration of the cortex, which is so notable a feature as one reviews the series of existing mammals from lower to higher members, has taken place almost wholly within the neopallium and this is probably to be correlated with the larger part which the distance receptors have played in the fabrication of the higher associations of intelligent type (p. 271).

Conclusion. — Some of the conclusions to which we have been led in this and the preceding chapters may now be summarized.

In the most primitive living vertebrates almost all of the brain in front of the midbrain is dominated by the olfactory system and the further differentiation of this region in all higher forms appears to have taken place largely under the influence of various systems of non-olfactory fibers which have grown forward into this olfactory territory. Increasingly complex correlations of the various other senses with smell have involved the elaboration of separate correlation centers in the forebrain for each of these reflex patterns, different in each species of animal according to its mode of life. The diverse patterns of cerebral architecture exhibited in the vertebrate series are, therefore, structural expressions of these functional relationships, namely, the various parts played by the olfactory and the different non-olfactory sensory systems.

The form relations of these correlation centers which have been assumed by the different groups of fishes are exceedingly diverse, each structural pattern probably reflecting some particular grouping of the sensori-motor elements of behavior characteristic of the species. It would almost seem as if nature had tried many experiments, each of which was successful within a certain environmental range. For life in an aquatic medium the most successful of these appears to have been the teleostean type; but this type, though capable of unlimited modification of detail on the plane of relatively simple forms of reflex behavior, has not proved adequate for differentiation in the direction leading up to the individually modifiable and intelligent forms of behavior.

Moreover, none of the more highly specialized kinds of fishes were able to make the structural readjustments required to maintain themselves in inland waters during the period of continental elevation and consequent drought known to have occurred in late Silurian times. On the other hand, certain very generalized species of ganoids were able to survive these periods of desiccation by developing accessory respiratory organs and so modifying the brain and its membranes as to facilitate its aëration in a reduced supply of oxygen. Of the several modifications of brain form which met the requirements of these adverse conditions, one in particular has proved susceptible of unlimited further differentiation.

Those primitive ganoids of Silurian or early Devonian times which were able to perfect the air-breathing apparatus and so to leave the water as amphibians probably possessed fully evaginated cerebral hemispheres similar to those of the lungfishes, for all modern amphibians, larval and adult, exhibit this type of brain. The more diversified conditions of life on land appear to require far more complex centers of higher correlation than those possessed by any fish, and it seems probable that of all known forms of morphological pattern of the forebrain only that which possesses widely evaginated thin-walled cerebral hemispheres capable of indefinite expansion without undue thickening of the wall is adequate to form the foundation on which the complexity of higher brains could be elaborated.

Mention has been made of the high efficiency on the reflex plane of solid cerebral masses of teleostean type. In higher vertebrates with fully evaginated cerebral hemispheres local thickenings of a different sort appear in the lateral walls of the hemispheres themselves in reptiles and especially in birds. Here again this structural form is correlated with the predominance of stable, heritable reflex and instinctive behavior patterns. In mammals, on the other hand, where individually modifiable behavior of the intelligent type is the most characteristic feature, so extensive solid thickenings of the walls of the hemispheres do not appear, but instead the highest correlation tissue of the brain is spread out in thin sheets as cerebral cortex (Kappers, 1913, 1914).

From a general survey of what is known regarding the correlation of forebrain patterns with behavior patterns, it appears that solid masses of cerebral tissue may be structurally well adapted for the performance of the most complex types of reflex and instinctive activity whose patterns are innate and relatively stable, as illustrated in teleosts and birds. High specialization in this direction, however, seems to have precluded the possibility of any great development of the more labile individually modifiable sorts of behavior and especially of the culmination of this kind of behavior as manifested by capacity for rapid learning by individual experience and intelligence in general.

Conversely, the development of the labile functional type goes hand in hand with the extensive elaboration of thin sheets of correlation tissue, as exemplified in the cerebral cortex, in which numerous functionally distinct fields are well separated in space and are at the same time in free communication through systems of association fibers of unlimited complexity, which find ample room in the sub-cortical white matter. There is no assignable limit to which structural specialization of this sort can extend. The nutritive requirements of the tissue are readily satisfied by its superficial position in close apposition with the rich blood vascular supply of the pia mater and with the cerebrospinal fluid of the spaces within the brain membranes.

CHAPTER XVII

MECHANISMS OF CORRELATION

Non-nervous correlation — Effector systems as integrators — Reflex correlation — Correlation and coördination — Correlation in the brain stem — Coördination in the brain stem — Sensory and motor differentiation — The cerebral cortex

Non-nervous correlation. — The orderly coöperation of different parts of the body in the performance of definite acts of adjustment to changes in the external environment or internal condition is the essential factor in preserving the life of the body and maintaining its unity. Certain norms or standards of form and behavior are characteristic of each species and the organism tends by reason of a sort of biological momentum to return to these norms if they are disturbed. The actual expression of this tendency is what is meant by biological regulation of form and behavior (p. 279).

The mechanisms of these integrating and regulatory forces have been in part analyzed (Chap. 5) and their sum in any given organism constitutes the organismic factors in behavior in contrast with the local intrinsic activities of the separate tissues. Our interest first centers in the excitation-conduction gradients of ordinary protoplasm from which the specific nervous activities have been derived, as we have attempted to show.

Effector systems as integrators. — Considerable attention has of late been paid to coördinations effected within the effector apparatus itself. Parker has called attention to the early differentiation in sponges of muscular tissue in the absence of any recognized sensory or nervous organs; but it has been noted (p. 86) that these so-called muscles are really neuromuscular organs and that the correlation mechanism here is probably not fundamentally different from that of excitation-conduction type of both lower and higher forms. The same is probably true of the "independent effectors" in the adult human iris, of the myogenic contractions of the fetal heart, and of the "aneural" movements of elasmobranch embryos described by Wintrebert (1921).[1]

---

[1] For further discussion of automaticity or self-excitation see Child (1924, Chap. 11).

In the higher animals there is undoubtedly a certain amount of coördination of the mechanical type to which reference is made on page 260 in the effectors themselves. It is reported (Fritz Edinger, 1913, p. 19) that Kreidl totally destroyed the brain and spinal cord of a frog and then tore out the peripheral nerves of the legs. If the denervated animal was put in a crouching position and an electric shock passed through its body so as to act directly upon the muscles, the frog "sprang far forward in an elegant leap only to fall down again as a limp mass of flesh."

Reflex correlation. — Attention has repeatedly been called to the fact that the chief instrument of non-nervous correlation and integration is the physiological gradients and the relations of physiological dominance and subordination incidental to these gradients, and also to the further fact that the greater efficiency of primitive nervous systems of non-synaptic type depends chiefly upon the better conducting powers of these elementary nervous strands, thus extending the range and facility of dominance of the more excitable regions and so more intimately knitting together the parts of the body and unifying their activities. With the appearance of the synaptic nervous system much more radical changes in the mechanism of correlation are effected, though the physiological gradients are still operative (Child, 1924, Chaps. 11, 12). Accordingly, there is a certain justification for the common practice of physiologists of limiting the term reflex to reactions involving synaptic mechanisms and calling the simpler reactions tropisms or taxes.[1]

A reflex act, as this term is usually defined by the physiologists, is a mechanically determined adaptive response to the stimulation of a sense organ, involving the use of a center of adjustment and the conductors necessary to connect this center with the appropriate receptor and effector organs. The act is not voluntarily performed, though one may become aware of the reaction during or after its performance. The term reflex is often very loosely applied to include non-nervous tropisms and nervous activities of very diverse sorts, but as generally used by physiologists it involves the rather complex nervous functions just described. If an electric shock is applied directly to a muscle or to the motor nerve which innervates that muscle the muscle will contract, but this direct contraction is not a reflex act.

---

[1] On the reflexes and the neuromotor mechanisms involved see Herrick (1922, Chap. 4) and other general treatments of the nervous system. Child (1924, Chaps. 13, 15) discusses the relations between trial-and-error, tropism, and reflex from the standpoint of the underlying general physiology.

In this connection we must clearly distinguish between: (1) non-nervous or non-synaptic tropisms; (2) automatisms in which no specific receptor mechanism is demonstrable, these being internally excited activities which may be of non-nervous type or cases in which an internal excitant acts directly upon motor nerve centers such as the stimulation of the respiratory center by carbon dioxid in the blood; (3) the so-called axon-reflexes in which participation of a nerve center seems to be unnecessary; (4) typical simple reflexes (probably never occurring singly in the adult mammalian body); (5) compound and complex reflexes in endless variety; (6) chain reflexes, a special variety of the last leading up in successive degrees of complexity to typical instinctive acts (Loeb); (7) associative memory, also a special form of complex reflex pattern with a specific mnemonic factor which in turn leads up to (8) conditional reflexes (Pavlov).

All of these cases are dependent for their basic patterns upon the presence of some sort of innate mechanism which is uniform (or nearly so) in all members of a race or species. These mechanisms may or may not be inherited, but they are provided ready-made at birth either by germinal heredity or by prenatal environment and so are uniform. To this extent the behavior conforms to what we have called the fixed or stable type, which may appear in pure form in some of the tropisms and simpler reflex patterns. But in all of these types, and especially in the more complex forms, the basic pattern is subject to more or less of individual modification through personal experience as typified by associative memories and conditional reflexes. Where this individual modifiability comes to be the dominant characteristic of the behavior we speak of learning by experience, association, intelligent behavior, and so forth, and this marks a great step in advance as measured by personal efficiency in adjusting to the conditions of life. Where these postnatal modifications become permanently incorporated into the action system we have habit, acquired automatism (an unfortunate term, for these acts are not truly automatic as defined above), lapsed intelligence, character.

The reflex has been the chief stock in trade of neurologists and psychologists from time immemorial. The clinician begins his examination of a neurological case with observations on the reflexes, the neuro-anatomist strives to unravel the intricately woven fabric of the nervous system into a warp of nerve fibers connected in systems of simple reflex arcs through which is shot a weft of cross-connections providing for all sorts of compounding of reflexes, the physiologist aims to reduce all known behavior so far as possible to reflex acts of various kinds and degrees of complexity, the psychologist usually begins his analysis of mind with an account of reflexes regarded as unconscious or subconscious nervous functions in some way significant in the analysis of conscious processes and by some regarded as their direct antecedents.

But the concept of the reflex is not a general master key competent to unlock all of the secrets of brain and mind, as some seem to suppose, and it has of late been subjected to very searching physiological analysis (*e. g.*, by Hough, 1915). Into the details of these discussions we cannot here enter, though attention should be especially directed to the futility of attempting to derive intelligence and the higher mental faculties in general from reflexes, habits, or any other form of fixed or determinate behavior. On the contrary, these owe their origin to the more labile and plastic components of behavior, which are determined, if you like, though not by rigid innate organization but rather by individual experience acting through and upon the innate units and recombining these in new patterns. The nervous system is more than an aggregate of reflex arcs and life is more than reaction to stimuli. After this digression let us return to the reflex apparatus as mechanism of correlation.

In the theoretically simple reflex there is a one-to-one relation between stimulus and response; the act follows as mechanically as the ringing of a doorbell when the button is pushed. The correlation here is of the simplest possible sort. But this condition is rarely, if ever, realized in the body. At every synaptic junction there is the possibility, and usually the actuality, of more or less modification of the direct nervous impulse by collateral discharge or by influences from other reflex arcs or centers. The simple reflex is a convenient abstraction. In actual practice each reflex center is usually a region where more or less complex compounding of simple reflexes is effected, where a single afferent impulse is distributed to all of the synergic muscles necessary for the complex motor response, where antagonistic impulses meet and struggle for possession of a final common path (Sherrington, 1906), or some other correlation of higher order is effected.

In searching for the probable mechanisms of these central correlations attention may again be directed to the neural rhythms to which reference was made on page 116. Our knowledge is not yet sufficiently complete to enable us to direct the clear light of experiment into all of the dark corners of the correlation centers, but it is sufficient to suggest at least the probability that the activities of the centers of nervous adjustment are in part determined by functional variations in synaptic refractory periods and neuronic rhythms.

It is commonly believed that the acquired correlations and associations of higher animals are effected by the opening up of new connections between previously established conduction systems so that the simpler elements of behavior may be linked in new combinations — and upon this assumption the following discussions are based. On this view learning and indeed the whole course of the development of individual behavior patterns depend structurally upon the spread of nervous impulses out of the already established channels across the barriers into unfamiliar paths and then the preservation and strengthening of these newly acquired nervous conductors by further use. There is anatomical evidence that all main nervous circuits are related by collateral cross connections permitting such overflow, presumably, however, only under stress of strong excitation or block of the usual paths of more open and free discharge. There is, it must be admitted, little specific evidence of the mode of formation of such collateral connections. Coghill (1924) has recently shown that in the very earliest stages of differentiation of functioning nervous elements the origin and development of new modes of behavior are correlated with the growth and differentiation of specific nerve cells while they are functioning as conductors. "In other words, the development of the behavior pattern, which is a process of learning in the broadest sense, is actually development structurally and functionally." What is here observed to take place in the elaboration of the simplest reflex circuits probably also occurs in the later development of more complex systems of interrelated circuits.

Correlation and coördination. — In all reflex systems, apart from the theoretical simple reflex arc, there are two aspects of the process of reaction which should be clearly distinguished and may be called the legislative and the administrative or executive aspects. The first determines what shall be the response to the particular stimulus or complex of stimuli which initiates the activity; the second is concerned wholly with the task of executing the reaction thus determined. Both of these aspects of the reaction may be very complex, but the complexity is of different type and the apparatus employed may be very dissimilar. In discriminative reactions the "choices," whether physiologically or consciously made, are all enacted in the legislative chamber, which is a deliberative body. In short, in both reflex and deliberative (including voluntary) reactions we may say that the nature of the neural process is abruptly changed when it "turns the corner" from the afferent to the efferent limb of the arc.

This is the basis for the distinction drawn by Professor Landacre (see Herrick, 1922, p. 36) between correlation and coördination. The term *correlation* is applied to those combinations of the afferent impulses within the sensory centers and of mnemonic vestiges of previous reactions which determine which of several possible efferent pathways will be activated or what is the appropriate reaction to the situation. This may be done promptly or it may take a quite appreciable time; in fact, in the case of conscious choices the deliberation may be indefinitely prolonged. As soon as the nature of the response has been determined the demand is to get the thing done as quickly as possible, and this employs a very different sort of nervous apparatus on the efferent side of the system from that of the afferent side. Every reaction, even the simplest actual reflex, involves the combined action of several different muscles or other effectors, and the ordering of these so as to effect the appropriate response is *coördination*. Here anatomically fixed arrangements of the motor nervous centers and tracts are employed and each of these is so organized as to act quickly, powerfully and invariably.

Physiologically these phases of reaction are clearly distinguishable in any concrete instance of response to stimulation. There is, of course, a corresponding structural basis for the change in physiological character of the process as it passes from the afferent to the efferent limb of the arc. But within the central nervous system the main conduction pathways, the highways of through traffic which serve the great fundamental reflex systems of the routine activities of each animal species, are not detached fiber tracts like the insulated wires of a telephone system. On the contrary, all of the parts of each such reflex system are so intimately and variously connected with one another and with parts of other systems by collateral branches of the nerve fibers and by correlation neurons that anatomical mechanisms are provided for innumerable modifications of any typical or primary reflex pattern. Which, if any, of these cross connections will be activated in any particular response will be determined by the aggregate of external and internal factors at the moment operating.

From these considerations it follows that the nervous system cannot be divided rigidly into mechanisms of correlation and coördination, for a part which serves one of these phases of reaction at one time may a moment later be so related to a changed aspect of the behavior that its rôle is quite different. Any simple cross connection between afferent and efferent paths in lower centers may be blocked by fatigue, by intercurrent stimuli, or otherwise, so that a present reaction is suspended while an overflow from the lower sensory centers passes up to higher centers of correlation, there to be redirected, perhaps into the same, perhaps into some different motor system, with reinforcement, inhibition, or other modifications. The lower centers in this event do not cease to work, but they no longer are the sole arbiters of the problem of conduct.

Conversely, an activity directed from the cerebral cortex may be in process when a strong intercurrent stimulus short circuits the lower centers and perhaps discharges into the same motor system which was before in action, thus capturing the final common path and transforming the deliberative act into a reflex one, or it may be that it discharges into a different motor system replacing the first activity by a totally different one. The turning point in the arc in the former case may be in the cortex and in the latter case it may be in the lowest primary sensory center, but in both cases the actual execution of the movement determined is relegated to a preformed neuromotor mechanism of efferent type.

Taking into account this inconceivable complexity of interwoven nervous pathways and the fluctuations from moment to moment in the course of nervous currents through these various connections and estimating the general or average character of the various regions into which the central nervous system is naturally divided, it is possible to lay down some general principles of structural arrangement which correlate with the physiological analysis here outlined. But it must not be forgotten that the schematic analysis which follows is not intended to express rigidly uniform conditions.

First of all, attention may again be called to the fact that, in general, neurons of the afferent or sensory systems differ structurally from those of the efferent systems (p. 110). The latter usually have, other things being equal, larger cell bodies with a richer supply of chromophilic substance and always in fixed and stained preparations this substance is arranged in definite discrete granules and not diffusely. This arrangement seems to facilitate more rapid and powerful nervous discharge. The motor pathways, too, are usually composed of long fiber tracts with minimum number of synaptic interruptions. This is especially true of the pyramidal tract, the voluntary motor path from the cerebral cortex (Fig. 29, p. 107).

Correlation in the brain stem. — The illustrations of extreme modification of the basic patterns of the reflex apparatus of the brain presented in Chapter 14 could be multiplied indefinitely. They are in all cases adaptations to particular modes of life by the exaggeration or reduction of certain elements of the action system, and the enlargements of individual primary centers do not imply any great increase in the complexity of living. The coöperation of several reflex units in the performance of adaptive reactions may be effected without the aid of higher correlation centers by simple connections between the primary centers themselves, as illustrated in Figures 118 and 119.

The simplest possible arrangement of this sort is seen in Figure 118, a transverse section through the medulla oblongata of a larval salamander (Herrick, 1914 a). Here fibers of tactile sensibility and fibers of gustatory sensibility terminate in their respective primary

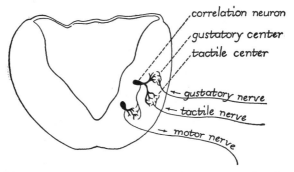

FIG. 118.—Diagram of some of the connections of nerves of touch and taste as seen in cross section of the medulla oblongata of larval Amblystoma.

centers. A neuron of the second order may send dendrites to both of these centers and its axon effects synaptic junction with a peripheral motor neuron. Now obviously the neuron of the sensory receptive field is a correlating element. If stimulated by something of possible food value simultaneously from both organs of touch and taste buds, the excitations may reinforce each other (if the food feels right and tastes right) or they may interfere by reason of antagonism between their normal or typical responses (if the food feels right but has an objectionable taste). As Sherrington expresses it, there is rivalry for possession of the final common path in the motor neuron and one or the other may obtain control. If they neutralize each other, no immediate reflex follows but inhibition of movement.

In Figure 119 there is a slightly more complex situation of the same sort. This diagram represents relations between the centers for taste and touch which I have observed (1906) in the medulla oblongata of the catfish.   Taste buds are abundantly distributed throughout the skin of these fishes (p. 185) and these cutaneous organs of taste are all supplied by branches of the facial nerve (Fig. 88, p. 188), while tactile sensibility is served by other nerves — the trigeminus in the head and spinal nerves in the trunk.   It has been shown experimentally (Herrick, 1903) that in the ordinary feeding reactions tactile and cutaneous gustatory organs coöperate.   All nerve fibers from the cutaneous taste buds end in the facial lobe of the medulla oblongata. Tactile nerves from the head enter the skin center (from which motor impulses may go out through neuron a of the diagram), and collateral branches of these fibers may pass directly to the gustatory center in the facial lobe.   Here correlation of the same type illustrated in Figure 118 may be effected, the efferent path being indicated by neuron b.   From the facial lobe cor-relation fibers ex-tend directly down-ward to the nuclei of the dorsal funiculi at the upper end of the spinal cord, a re-gion which is also a primary tactile cen-ter receiving spinal nerve fibers from the skin of the trunk and fins.   Essentially

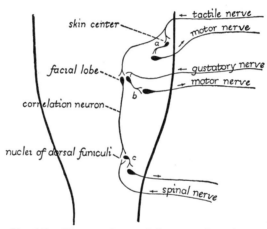

Fig. 119.—Diagram of some of the connections of nerves of touch and taste as seen in longitudinal section of the medulla oblongata of the catfish, Amiurus.

similar conditions, though with considerable differences in the de-tails, have been found in the codfish and its allies (p. 186, and Herrick, 1907).

In this arrangement there are represented no correlation centers of higher order than the primary sensory nuclei and yet provision is made for rather complex correlation and compounding of reflexes. The practical operation of this sort of correlation may be easily observed.   The catfishes are bottom feeders.   If the fish touches a desirable morsel of food, say a worm, the organs of touch and the cutaneous taste buds are simultaneously excited, the tactile and gusta-tory impulses reinforce each other in the centers where they converge, the three motor pathways indicated in Figure 119 are activated, and the complicated movements involved in seizing the worm and swallowing it are consummated. This is the normal response to appropriate food. The excitations are automatically shunted into the open pathways and, having reached the appropriate motor centers, they reinforce each other.

Let us suppose, again, that the food morsel feels right but has a noxious taste. The normal reaction to the first excitation is seizing and swallowing, to the second is inhibition of these movements. Obviously there will be conflict in the centers. If the animal is hungry and the taste not too objectionable, the positive reflex wins out, captures the motor mechanisms, and the food is eaten; under other conditions of internal physiological state the reverse reaction may follow from identically the same combination of stimuli.

Now, there are many things about this series of acts which are as yet entirely unexplained. We do not know how the open pathway "of less resistance" differs from other more obstructed systems of nerve fibers. We do not know the mechanism by which the positive or seeking reaction follows from a beneficial excitation and a negative or avoiding reaction follows from a noxious excitation. We know nothing at all about the essential features of the nervous mechanism of inhibition or reinforcement.[1] Nevertheless we do know that these physiological reactions take place as described. And we do know that the anatomical connections are present as indicated schematically in the diagrams. On the basis of this knowledge, limited though it is, we can map out within the nervous system functionally defined centers and fiber tracts which enable us to localize, in a general way at least, and in some cases very precisely, the apparatus for each of the chief systems of reflex activity and to observe the increasing complexity of the apparatus of compounding reflexes as we pass from lower to higher vertebrates.

Very recently Malone (1923, 1923 a) has called attention to the fact that in the medulla oblongata many, probably most, of the neurons which are intercalated between the primary sensory and motor centers are "premotor" in type, that is, they structurally resemble the peripheral motor neurons rather than the sensory neurons. This implies that correlation as we here define it is effected among the primary sensory centers. The tissue of the reticular formation which intervenes between sensory and motor centers is chiefly concerned with adjustments of the administrative type on the efferent side of the arc, that is to say with coördination rather than

---

[1] There is some experimental basis for conjecture in this field; see page 116.

with correlation. Apparently many of these bulbar reflex systems "turn the corner" from afferent to efferent type at the first synaptic junction.

The apparatus of correlation here described is typical for the brains of fishes and for the spinal cords of all vertebrates. In the brains of fishes, however, there begins to appear a correlation mechanism of another sort, namely, special correlation centers which do not receive any fibers directly from the periphery and are therefore not dominated by any particular sensory system. These centers are located chiefly in the forebrain and midbrain. They are very small and poorly separated from the primary sensori-motor centers already described; yet they are the precursors of the great centers of higher correlation and integration which give the human brain its immeasurable superiority over those of other animals.

Coördination in the brain stem. — The reticular formation, to which reference was made above, is a mixture of gray and white matter which contains the intercalary neurons and the connecting tracts through which primary sensory centers are connected with one another and with the motor centers from which peripheral motor nerves arise. The arrangements of these neurons determine the reflex patterns characteristic of each species of animal. The larger part of this formation lies below the limiting sulcus (p. 163) in the motor zone of the central nervous system. The more important of these coördinating neurons are grouped as the motor nuclei of the tegmentum (p. 195).

In lower brains correlations are to a large extent effected within and between the primary sensory centers and the motor tegmentum is for the most part organized in stable innate patterns concerned with the coördination of the effector apparatus in orderly fashion, such as the synergic muscles which must coöperate in the performance of any act. As we pass toward higher brains the correlations become more complex, special correlation centers are set apart, and the behavior becomes in corresponding measure more labile and more readily modifiable in terms of personal experience. This change is reflected in the relative sizes of the sensory and motor zones of the brain, that is, the regions lying respectively above and below the site of the limiting sulcus, as is illustrated by comparison of these zones in the lowest and highest members of the vertebrate series (Fig. 120). In the embryologic development of the human brain there is a similar increase in the relative mass of tissue on the sensory side of the limiting sulcus (compare Fig. 65 B with Fig. 120 B).

As we pass from lower to higher brains and from younger to older stages of the latter this notable increment in the relative amount of correlation tissue in the sensory regions is very significant. The complex adjusting mechanisms of the thalamus and cerebral hemispheres are all developed in the sensory zone. Within this region certain parts have secondarily acquired coördinating functions, notably the cerebellum of all vertebrates and the corpus striatum and motor cerebral cortex of mammals. But by far the larger part of the increment in relative brain weight of higher vertebrates is due to enlargement of correlation centers of sensory type.

The cerebellum (p. 190) offers problems of very special difficulty in this connection, for it clearly combines correlations and coördinations on the reflex plane of very characteristic types. In the main

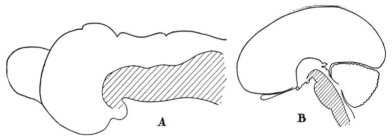

A   B

Fig. 120.—Diagrams of the relative extent of sensory and motor regions in A, cyclostome, B, man. The motor region is cross-hatched, the sensory region is unshaded. At the boundary between these two regions is the locus of the embryonic limiting sulcus, whose anterior end is drawn (after Kingsbury, 1922) somewhat farther back than was originally described by His (cf. fig. 65 B, p. 162).

it is an administrative apparatus (Malone, 1923 a), initiating nothing on its own account but regulating the movements of the body and its orientation in space.

The cerebellum is genetically derived from the vestibular nucleus;[1] it is primarily the balancing brain. Associated with this function are control of posture, regulation and coördination of all movements of precision of the skeletal musculature, and the maintenance of muscular tone. Its cortex seems to be a great reservoir of latent nervous energy which may be tapped for discharge into any neuromotor apparatus as needed. Its stabilizing influence may be compared with the action of a gyroscope on a large steamship, ensuring the steady progress of the vessel in its course by compensating the buffeting of wind and waves.

The rôle of the cerebellum as a proprioceptive adjustor may be

[1] On the phylogeny of the cerebellum see Herrick (1924).

clarified by another illustration. An experienced bareback rider is rarely thrown by sudden pitching or shying of his mount. If the horse while quietly trotting along the road suddenly jumps to one side, the rider, before the sidewise movement would be obvious to a spectator, senses the change in the rhythm of movement and the contraction of certain muscles of the horse not previously in action and on the basis of previous experience he makes compensatory adjustments in anticipation of the shying of the horse, thus keeping his seat when a novice would be thrown headlong.

So the cerebellum may be conceived as related to the lower neuromuscular apparatus. It is not merely in receipt of proprioceptive reports of bodily movements after they have happened as a chain reflex; but the primary sensori-motor centers and the correlation centers discharge collateral impulses into the cerebellum (especially from the cerebral cortex), so that this adjustor can anticipate the actual response and throw into gear all the motor apparatus necessary to execute it properly.

Sensory and motor differentiation.—The preponderance of coördination tissue of motor type in lower brains and of correlation tissue of sensory type in higher brains suggests some further reflections upon the significance in behavior of these anatomical patterns.

The senses of fishes are very highly developed and, while in some respects very different from those of man in adaptation to the aquatic life, they are probably on the whole not notably inferior in grade of organization to our own. The motor apparatus, on the other hand, while very efficient for swimming, feeding, breathing and the like, is far simpler than ours; for the motor activities of life in the water are rather uniform as compared with those required for running, climbing, digging, and the other varied industries of land animals.

This last point is significant, for biological efficiency, as we have seen (p. 13), is measured not by what the organism can receive from the environment through the sense organs but by the capacity for diversity of adaptive response and adjustment. It matters little how varied are the sensations and experiences of the individual so long as he is so circumscribed by hereditary organization or environment as to be unable to respond with appropriate behavior. What does matter is what he can do with his experiences.

The fish responds to more varied environmental agents than can the insect and the analysis of the sensory stimuli is doubtless carried much further. There is a corresponding improvement in general efficiency as measured by the standard which we have set up. But, with limited means of expression, with a narrowly confined range of possible reactions, there is no occasion for the elaboration of those higher association centers whose special province it is to choose from a large number of possible reactions which one best meets the emergencies of a present situation. It makes no difference whether this "choice" is effected physiologically and unconsciously by the resolution of a system of complex nervous excitations in a center of correlation or whether it is made intelligently after prolonged deliberation, the fact remains that neural mechanisms of the reflex type seem to be biologically more advantageous as long as the action system is limited to a relatively small number of possible responses, and that individually modifiable activity and intelligence in particular find scope for full development as the dominant factors in behavior only as diversity of bodily organization gives freer scope for expression (and in the case of man the supplementing of this by the use of tools). The centers of the higher correlations and associations are developed on the sensory side of the reflex arcs, but these do not attain to a high degree of complexity until on the motor side there is sufficient neuromuscular organization to provide for a wide range of possible responses.

The cerebral cortex. — The fishes, as has been pointed out, have no differentiated cortex, though cortical primordia have been recognized. These primordia are developed largely or wholly within the olfactory area, a region whose functions are dominated by a single receptor, the nose. The true cortex of higher animals is emancipated from any so direct relation with a single sensory system; it is rather an intermediary between these systems. In its definitive form the cortex is lifted away above the more primitive correlation centers of the brain stem out of which it has emerged and thus becomes a true suprasegmental apparatus (p. 166). The correlation centers of the segmental apparatus are adequate for the analysis of the sensory data of common experience and their resolution into motor responses so far as these fall within the range of the ordinary reflex or instinctive action system of the species of animal in question. But when this mechanism is inadequate to resolve an unusual or very complex situation the cerebral cortex may participate in the analysis, particularly by the weaving of the present sensory data in with memory vestiges of past experience.

This mnemonic function of the cortex is perhaps its most distinctive feature. The cerebral cortex has been compared with a big filing cabinet in which memories of individual experiences are laid away and indexed so as to be on call whenever related experiences arise. Whereas the physiological memories, that is, associative memories of non-corticated animals, may require scores or even hundreds of repetitions to become established, a cortical memory may be retained after a single such experience. True learning now takes the place of physiological habit or facilitation of path, psychological memory of physiological memory, association of correlation.

The following grades of these related physiological processes may be distinguished: (1) The immediate response of excited protoplasm to external stimuli. (2) The preservation for a longer or shorter time of structural changes induced by such responses — enduring modifications which facilitate repetition of the act, or physiological habit. (3) Permanent changes in the organic basis of heredity brought about by a combination of biological agencies — variation, mutation, natural selection, or others — giving rise to fixed uniform reflex and instinctive patterns of behavior. (4) Individually acquired correlations, associative memories, conditional reflexes, and similar modifications of innate reflex patterns growing out of personal experience and requiring tolerably well-developed nervous organization. (5) Cortical memories of particular experiences, with apparatus for interweaving such mnemonic vestiges with present experience in complex patterns — the rise of intelligent types of behavior. (6) Ideation, the formation of symbols and mental abstractions as intellectual tools permitting language, generalizations of experience, and forecast of future events. The last seems to be a distinctly human acquisition, at least in any but very rudimentary form, and to be dependent upon the elaboration of cortical association centers of human type.

The relationships in higher vertebrates of the centers of the brain stem, the cerebellum and the cerebral cortex may be illustrated somewhat crudely by the analogy of the departments of the national government. The correlation centers of the brain stem correspond with the legislative branch of government, determining in advance by virtue of their innate organization what actions may appropriately be performed in each particular type of frequently recurring situation. The subcortical centers of coördination comprise the administrative department, attending to the execution of the acts which have been previously determined and initiated in the other departments of government. The cerebellum is a higher administrative bureau, supervising and coördinating the functions of certain of the executive offices, with the aid of an extensive information service to which reports of the activities of these offices are sent both in advance of their execution and afterwards. The cerebral cortex is a sort of glorified judicial branch of government, integrating the total behavior by combining its elements into coöperative systems in view of all the factors of present and past experience, and with extensive powers of veto over inappropriate reactions which may have been inaugurated in the lower centers.[1]

We have a large body of information regarding the topographic distribution of cortical and subcortical centers of correlation and coördination and the courses of the fiber tracts through which these are kept in functional connection. Our manuals of neurology are devoted very largely to the exposition of these facts of cerebral architecture. But when it comes to a consideration of the actual events which take place in these tissues during processes of correlation, association, memory, etc., precise knowledge is lacking. We believe that these functions involve metabolism in brain tissue, and for this there is satisfactory evidence; but what may be the precise nature of these changes and how they differ in these various sorts of functional process as yet we do not know.

It is not improbable that all cortical functions, as well as all subcortical correlations, involve changes in dynamic equilibrium in a complex system all parts of which are connected by conductors of various degrees of permeability to nervous currents. A metabolic change at one point brought about by, let us say, a nervous discharge into the visual area of the cortex is widely irradiated through association tracts in a pattern which is determined by the existing pathways which are at the moment open. The pattern of these open pathways, in its turn, in any given case is determined partly by innate structure of the cortex and its association tracts, partly by previous individual experience which has facilitated transmission through certain paths, partly by concurrent stimuli of other senses which reinforce, inhibit, or otherwise modify the visually excited nervous discharges, partly by mnemonic vestiges in particular patterns in the association centers, partly by temporary physiological states of fatigue, lassitude, interest, etc., and it may be by countless other factors. When the equilibrium of the resting cortex is thus disturbed and nervous excitations irradiate from the focus of the initial excitation, the process will continue until a new equilibrium is established — it may be by motor discharge, it may be by fatigue with no practical outcome, it may be by the

[1] Compare Herrick (1922, p. 216). For further discussion of the cerebral cortex see the three last chapters of that work.

fabrication of a new pattern of cortical activity or a new enduring "set" of the reacting system which modifies all subsequent activity of this system and may appear in consciousness as an idea, a judgment, a decision, a purpose, or an ideal.[1]

These purely theoretical considerations do not carry us very far in the direction of a scientific analysis of cortical function and need not here be pursued further. But aside from all questions of the method of cortical function, it is clear that the cerebral cortex does control in very large measure the activities of the body as a whole, and in various vertebrates this control is roughly proportional to the mass of the cortex itself. It is a center of highest physiological dominance in the sense in which we have already employed this term. It is perhaps profitable to inquire further into the nature of this dominance.

[1] Compare my brother's discussion of "The Equilibrium Theory of Consciousness" (C. L. Herrick, 1910) and the references there given.

CHAPTER XVIII

MECHANISMS OF INTEGRATION AND DOMINANCE

Summary of integrative factors — Metabolism of nerve cells — Specificity in the nervous system

Summary of integrative factors. — We have now assembled some of the materials needful in establishing a foundation for a comprehensive scheme of animal behavior, and it may be well before going further to lay them out in order before us. The basic principle which must guide us in the selection and fabrication of these materials is the orderly or lawful character of vital processes.

The organism differs from inorganic bodies in its peculiar relation to surrounding objects and forces, reaching out in a selective way into its environment, assimilating from it material and energy which are made to do its bidding, and then when these have served their purpose yielding them up again in modified form. Throughout these complex cycles of nutrition, growth and reproduction the living body retains its specific pattern nearly unaltered but not quite, for there is evidence of more or less progressive change in the patterns of the form and behavior. Vital processes can, accordingly, be arranged under two general heads: (1) laws of uniformities, and (2) laws of change, progress, evolution, creation. In this chapter we shall review the first group of laws; in the following chapters progressive factors will be further considered.

The formulation of the uniform modes of action of living substance constitutes the science of physiology. These laws are in part identical with those of inorganic physics and chemistry; in part they are unique biochemical and biophysical modes of action, that is, combinations of elementary inorganic processes in patterns found only in living bodies. There are no elemental substances peculiar to living bodies, and there is as yet no satisfactory evidence of any primary manifestations of energy other then those known in inorganic nature. The postulation of a specific "vital force" is not justified by any known facts; but on the other hand there are numerous instances in the organic realm of the combination of elementary physico-chemical energies in patterns nowhere found in relation with lifeless matter. These are the true *organic modes* of action.

248

Each part of the living body has by virtue of the physiological division of labor a particular part to play and a corresponding specific protoplasmic structure. Thus arise the fixed tissues. These differentiations are stable heritable features of the organization and these locally specialized activities we have termed the local or · intrinsic functions (p. 49). They are sharply contrasted with certain more general types of action, the integrative functions, which are concerned primarily with the maintenance of the unity of the individual by keeping it in vital relation with surrounding forces and at the same time binding its component parts together as one body rather than a mob of separate cells and organs.

The integrative functions are of several sorts, most important of which from our standpoint are the phenomena of excitation and conduction, whereas the intrinsic functions are of as diversified physico-chemical character as are the tissues to which they pertain. The chief concern of the specific metabolisms is in general the chemical transformation or physical transfer of material, that of the integrative functions is the transfer of energy. (Of course, this is a relative matter only, for there are energy transfers in all metabolism and even in nervous conduction — a typical organismic process — there is some local chemical activity.)

Excitation is fundamentally protoplasmic reaction to stimulus involving rapid metabolism, a dynamic change which irradiates throughout the surrounding protoplasm in diminishing gradients (p. 53). This conductivity is the key to the integrating power of organismic functions of this type. It appears to be a cyclic phenomenon; a phase of intense physico-chemical activity is associated with a change in electric state which in turn excites chemical activity in the adjacent unmodified protoplasm, the whole process being largely self-contained so that energy of transmission is liberated with very slight loss of heat. The electric phenomena associated with excitation and conduction have been carefully studied and it is probable that the essential process is neither purely chemical nor purely electric, but a reciprocal relation between these two processes, each of which is essential to the initiation of the other (p. 54).

The mechanisms of excitation and conduction are very imperfectly understood on the biochemical plane, but their physiological significance has been very clearly brought to light. Their metabolism of excitation is known to exert a regulatory control over other bodily processes and this gives to excited regions a position of physiological dominance in the organization of the body as a whole. These are properties common to all living beings.

In lower organisms without nerves the imperfect conducting power of ordinary protoplasm involves definite limitations of bodily organization. Either the physiological processes are of simple patterns with rather imperfect integration of the bodily activities, as in most plants, or else the more active and mobile body is limited in size and the active parts remote from the center of chief physiological dominance become physiologically isolated as secondary centers of dominance, ultimately perhaps separating from the parent individual in a reproductive process (p. 136).

With the progress of differentiation of the conducting apparatus, animal bodies can grow to larger size with greater diversity of action of their parts without loss of the unity of the whole. If the protoplasmic bonds between the members are feeble, that is if the conductivity is poor and the physiological gradients are steep, the centers of secondary dominance may rise toward equality with the primary centers and we have not one body but a colony of connected individuals, as in some protozoans, sponges and cœlenterates, or else, if the equality is attained, reproduction by complete separation of the individuals ensues.

The unity of the organism in all complex animal bodies appears to be dependent upon the presence of a highly efficient conducting apparatus, namely, the nervous system, whose radius of transmission is wide, perhaps indefinite in higher animals, and within which the decrement of the energy of the physiological gradients from the center of highest dominance to the outlying organs is small or absent. Thus the dominant center in some measure controls the growth and activities of the entire body and ensures its integrity (Child, 1924, Chaps. 10, 12).

Primitively in organisms with simple axial gradients this is a one-sided arrangement; the apical end dominates the rest of the body. In the more complex animal bodies numerous centers of secondary dominance arise and the pattern of the gradients emanating from these centers becomes very intricate.

Child is of the opinion that in the less highly differentiated organisms (and perhaps in all) the physiological gradients are expressions of differences in rate of general metabolism, or as he says, of the rate of living of all of the protoplasm involved. In the nervous systems of higher animals there are certainly complicating factors which determine that the activity in question may be very readily transmitted along some lines, while others are relatively impermeable to it. This appears to be merely a matter of the relative conductivity of the different protoplasms. But this conductivity is the most essential property of the nerves and the metabolism involved here and in the nerve centers is of very special nature. The "rate of living" of a nerve fiber under excitation is expressed chiefly as nervous conduction and in a correlation center as adjustment of relative permeability at the interneuronic synaptic junctions. Here unquestionably we are dealing with a special kind of metabolism in a highly differentiated tissue, so that we may say that the physiological dominance of the nerve centers is dependent in part upon the nature of their intrinsic metabolism and in part upon the efficiency of the conducting apparatus leading away from them.

We may, therefore, believe that the actual control exerted by a particular nerve center is determined both by the gross pattern of arrangement of the related fiber tracts and by the specificity of its internal metabolism. In complex nervous systems metabolism of excitation-conduction type undoubtedly has higher regulatory and integrating value than do other kinds of metabolism in tissues not so favorably organized for transmitting the energies playing within them to remote parts.

The control exercised by the centers of dominance is not that of a *deus ex machina* imposing its ordinances upon obediently responsive organs, but rather it is a necessary consequence of the dynamic equilibrium of the body as a unit, in which every part is in physiological relation with every other part through the physiological gradients and otherwise. High metabolism of excitation-conduction type at one point gives to this region a dominant place in the general physiological equilibrium so far as the conductivity of the surrounding tissues permits the energies thus released to be transmitted and so to act upon other parts. Regulatory control of this type is a relationship between the dominant center of highest excitation and the activities of the specific protoplasmic mechanisms whose local affairs are to a greater or less degree influenced by the energies transmitted to them from the dominant center and a reciprocal and fluctuating relationship among the various centers of dominance which are widely distributed throughout the bodies of all higher animals.

In differentiation one of the earliest steps was the elaboration of more excitable protoplasm, which exhibits vigorous metabolism and exerts the highest physiological dominance, at the apical or leading end of the body with consequent establishment of a chief center of dominance and primary polar axis. This elaboration arises under the influence of more frequent or more intense excitation with consequent amplification of the vital process and increase in the mass, complexity and functional capacity of the excited protoplasm. Thus arose an arrangement of receptors and their related conductors which promotes differentiation of the head, or cephalization.

Organs of response were differentiated by an analogous process, being early separated from the remainder of the body and set apart through specificity of structure and kind of local metabolism. Their activities are of intrinsic rather than integrative type.[1] Fixed tissues serving for support, nutrition, excretion, movement, and the like made their appearance early in developmental history and their characteristic structural and functional patterns were incorporated into the hereditary organization of the phylum (p. 101).

This process of stabilizing of tissue patterns is regarded by Child (1915) as characteristic of senescence and protoplasm which has attained this grade of organization is termed "mature" or "old" in contrast with the "young" undifferentiated stuff which is labile in the sense that it is capable of further differentiation in any one of many different directions (p. 57).

To recur to the analogy of the river and its channel (p. 16), physiographers classify streams into young, mature and old phases. The first, found in geologically new regions, have steep gradients with great erosive power and occupy deep narrow valleys which are in process of still further sculpturing; the second flow through wide

---

[1] Compare page 58. The relatively low organismic or integrative value of the muscles, notwithstanding their high intrinsic metabolism under excitation, arises from the fact that the energy liberated during their contraction is largely expended locally as mass movement and heat. This is in marked contrast with the activities of the functional centers of the nervous system whose efferent nerve fibers provide open pathways for the ready transmission of the energy of their intrinsic activities away to remote parts. In higher animals, however, most muscles of the body possess a highly elaborate receptive apparatus within their own substance (the muscle spindles and associated sensory nerves) which reports back to the central nervous system the degree of contraction of the muscle—the proprioceptive innervation. The addition of this sensory apparatus gives to the muscles so equipped very great organismic value; that is, these muscles are the initial points of systems of physiological gradients passing back to the central nervous system in the reverse direction of their motor nerves. The enormous importance of these proprioceptive systems in the coördination and integration of bodily activities and as organic background of human behavior has only recently been fully appreciated (p. 42). The cerebellum (p. 190) has been differentiated chiefly under the influence of the proprioceptors (of various sorts) and its massive bulk in the more active vertebrates is an indication of the vital significance of these functions, whose ebb and flow go on almost entirely below the level of analytic consciousness.

valleys with gently sloping walls, erode their banks but slightly, and in general are of more stable form; the third meander through wide flood-plains which are constantly being built up by the deposition of silt carried down from higher levels. The streams of any area tend to degrade the uplifted regions to a uniform base level and in the course of this process they themselves pass through the phases described, their forms and currents undergoing modifications produced by their own action.

So the living body shapes its own destiny, creates its own form and dynamic patterns, and organizes its materials during and by means of its varied functions, maturity and senescence being characterized by changes in amount and pattern of energy change and by the accumulation of products of metabolism, all of which are expressions of progressive equilibration of the process of function reacting upon the structural materials of which the body is composed.

The history of differentiation, then, may be summarized under two general processes: (1) development, or the gradual fixation and stabilization of originally labile embryonic protoplasm into tissue systems specially modified for particular functions, with transformation of the character of the energy changes from those concerned with the intrinsic processes of assimilation and growth into those more directly excited, and (2) senescence, or the general lowering of metabolic activity by the accumulation of more inert substances which impede metabolism, either formed substances which play no part in the chemical interchanges or fixed tissues of low metabolism.

There is evidence (Child, 1915) that in the course of evolutionary history there has been a gradual change in the organization of the protoplasms of the different plant and animal phyla, tending toward the establishment of a definite and characteristic pattern of the fixed tissues and their related hereditary action systems in each phylum. This differentiation is to some extent an irreversible process, from which it follows that when such a definite pattern is once laid down in the hereditary organization the direction of the entire future course of evolution is to that extent predetermined. Here we can see something of the actual mechanism of that directive trend in evolution which has long been recognized under the name orthogenesis (Herrick, 1920). This is a factor in those progressive aspects of development to which the following chapters will be devoted.

In higher animals the nervous system is the apparatus par excellence of the integrative functions. The forces which maintain the unity of the body act largely (not exclusively) through the channels thus laid down. So far as the patterns of these activities are incorporated into the hereditary organization of the species they appear functionally as reflex and instinct, and on the structural side we have the corresponding specific configuration of sense equipment, nerves, correlation centers, and organs of response. To this extent the nervous tissues are "matured" and share in the intrinsic or local functions of the body. But even these fixed patterns of nervous circuits function only upon excitation from without their own substance, and by virtue of the nature of their organization they maintain their dominant position in the physiological gradients and so exert a real though limited control over the destinies of the individual.

The preservation of the unity of the organism, as we saw at the beginning, is dependent upon the maintenance of an equilibrium of material and energy intake and output between the body and its environment, and the unique position of the nervous system in the vital economy grows out of the essential part which it plays in the regulation of this adjustment of the body to the world in which it lives.

The primary function of nerves is conduction, and with the first appearance of a nervous network in cœlenterates but little is gained beyond the power to hold together a larger body by increasing the range of physiological influence of the primary centers of dominance through improvement of the conductivity between them and the other tissues (p. 94). But in this type of nervous system the primary physiological gradients which come to expression in the innate organization of the body are so weak, even in the nerve net, that they can be overcome by local stimulation and there is small permanent polarization of the nervous system.

In the worms we have the first appearance of the synaptic type of nervous system (p. 103). Here the cellular elements of which the nervous system is composed, the neurons, retain a certain measure of anatomical and physiological separateness, in contrast with the continuous nervous network of non-synaptic nervous systems. Neurons in general are more efficient conductors than are the protoplasmic strands of the nerve net. The point where two neurons come into physiological contact is termed the synapse and here there is a significant change in the conductivity of the transmitting mechanism. At this point there is always delay and apparently some impediment to transmission. The synapse, moreover, transmits nervous impulses in only one direction, that of the normal discharge from the sense organ toward the organ of response. This irreversibility of direction of conduction at the synapse gives to all synaptic nervous systems a permanent structurally defined polarity which stabilizes and greatly reinforces the functionally determined physiological gradients of the reflex arcs.

Reflex arcs are compounded in the correlation mechanisms so that numerous different sense organs can converge their excitations upon a single apparatus of response, or conversely so that an excitation or complex of excitations may be transmitted to any one of two or more different organs of response, thus increasing immeasurably the range and variety of possible reactions. Which of several possible final common paths leading out from a correlation center will be taken in any particular instance will depend in part upon the internal physiological state at the moment of excitation, and this in turn can be resolved into various factors, one of which is the past experience of the individual. The activation of any particular reflex path through a correlation center leading to an appropriate response to an excitation leaves that path in a more favorable "set" for a repetition of this response, that is, there is more or less permanent modification of future behavior resulting from this facilitation of path by use (pp. 56, 119). It is probable that a change in the permeability of the synapse to nervous transmission is a factor in this modification.

In synaptic nervous systems there is thus provided an apparatus (poorly developed in non-synaptic forms) which has the unique characteristic of capacity for differentiation in two very different directions. First, there is elaborated in the course of phylogeny a definite pattern of innate interneuronic connections giving to the species its characteristic reflex and instinctive behavior. And, second, there is at the synaptic junctions a labile and modifiable tissue, very impressionable to individual experiences, which maintains that plasticity and high susceptibility to excitation which is characteristic of "young" tissues.

The nervous system, therefore, exerts a dominant regulatory control over the entire body by a combination of two physiological features, both of which are present in the most primitive organisms, but which come to expression in higher animals in very distinct forms. These are: (1) innate arrangements of the tissues with related excitation-conduction gradients organized in very intricate patterns of sense organs, nerves, correlation centers, and organs of response and manifested in behavior as reflex and instinct; and (2) individual plasticity or modifiability of behavior, appearing in its higher forms as memory, association, intelligence.

In this very condensed summary we have stated in the most general terms and very dogmatically [1] some of the principles deduced in the course of the preceding discussions. A few specific cases have been cited in these discussions which illustrate the forms taken by the nervous system in correlation with diverse modes of life, in the course of which attention was called to the striking contrast between the fixed, stable and heritable factors in behavior (tropism, reflex, instinct) and the more plastic individually modifiable factors. This distinction between the innate and the individually acquired components of behavior is fundamental in any analysis of the more complex higher types. It is dimly foreshadowed even in protozoans and bulks larger and larger as we ascend the animal scale. In some groups the stable forms of behavior predominate, in others the more labile forms, and between these extremes we find them combined in diverse ways. In any particular activity they are usually inextricably blended; genetic and experimental studies are essential for the separation of the component factors.

Metabolism of nerve cells. — Mechanisms of integration in higher vertebrates present some very special features to which attention will next be directed. In neurons there are, broadly speaking, two types of metabolism. The first is that concerned with the growth and maintenance of the specific protoplasm. These processes vary with the nature of the cell and may include the accumulation of reserve materials capable of rapid consumption with sudden release of energy, much as fat serves as a reserve for the body as a whole, though more slowly utilized. The second type of metabolism is concerned with the process of conduction and is apparently fundamentally similar in all neurons. The first are intrinsic functions, the second is integrative.

Each neuron as a living cell must, of course, attend to its own metabolic needs; it must assimilate food, eliminate wastes, and in general maintain its protoplasmic organization. Under excitation it may be called upon, in addition to this, to liberate a great amount of energy very rapidly. Its protoplasm has, accordingly, been characterized as of the explosive type in contrast with that of most other tissue cells.

Cellular activities involve a complex series of dynamic interactions and exchange of materials between the protoplasm within the nuclear membrane and the general protoplasm of the remainder of the cell. The passage of substances through the nuclear membrane is a rela-

[1] See footnote 2 on page 52.

tively slow process. In nerve cells a substance chemically similar to the chromatin of the nucleus, the chromophilic substance (p. 108), is widely distributed in the cytoplasm of the cell body, so that under excitation the chemical interaction between this substance and the rest of the cytoplasm can take place simultaneously throughout the mass of the cell body with resultant speeding up of the metabolism.

The case is roughly analogous with the combustion of a grain of gunpowder contrasted with a piece of coal. The latter burns only at the surface where oxygen is available, but the gunpowder, when once the kindling temperature is reached, liberates oxygen internally so that combustion can take place simultaneously throughout the mass.

This "explosive" type of function is, as has been pointed out, a highly special form of intrinsic protoplasmic activity, not organismic. It is primarily concerned with the maintenance of the integrity of the cell under the strain of very rapid metabolism. The chromophilic substance is accumulated during periods of rest and during active function it is consumed. It is found only in the cell body and some of the larger dendritic processes and is probably an important source of energy. That it is not immediately involved in the metabolism of nervous conduction as such is shown by the fact that it is not present in the axon whose transmission is more perfect than is that of any other part of the neuron. During the intense functional upset of chromatolysis (p. 111) it tends to accumulate around the border of the axon hillock at the point where the axon leaves the cell body (Nicholson, 1923), a further evidence of the intrinsic nature of the activity of this substance, for during the reparative process following chromatolysis the intense activity of the axon is that of regenerative growth and not normal transmission of excitations.

The amount and arrangement of the chromophilic substance are correlated with the size of the cells, the length of their processes, and many other features, of which the most important is the type of function to be performed and the amount of energy required to initiate and maintain the active process. The motor neurons have more of this substance than do the sensory neurons, other things being equal (pp. 110, 237). Motor neurons are characterized by powerful and long continued discharges, frequently through very long axons (some are more than a meter long in the human body), and the sustenance of so extended a mass of protoplasm in high functional efficiency apparently puts a considerable physiological strain upon the nucleus and its related cytoplasm in the cell body. Nevertheless the sensory neurons occupy a higher place in the physiological gradient than do the motor neurons (p. 113) and it is probable that their actual metabolic rate in the aggregate is higher.

The neurons absorb nutrient materials from the surrounding fluids and give up wastes to them chiefly through their cell bodies and their dendrites; the axons probably participate in this function but little. Those parts of the brain which are composed chiefly of nerve fibers are white in color, while the so-called gray matter contains chiefly the cell bodies, their dendrites and the synaptic junctions. The amount of metabolism in the gray matter is much greater per unit weight than in the white matter, as shown by the richer blood supply and in other ways. The relative vascularization of various parts of the central nervous system has been quantitatively investigated by Craigie (1920, 1921) who finds that sensory centers are more richly supplied with blood vessels than are motor centers and that those parts of the cerebral cortex which are regarded as receptive in function are more vascular than the other parts.

The metabolism of the gray matter is evidently of a very special kind, and it appears that in connection with the points already mentioned there is an important new feature added in the higher correlation centers. The high metabolism of the gray matter is dependent upon three independently variable factors: (1) the chemical changes concerned with the nutrition and maintenance of the cell as a tissue element, (2) the highly special processes of accumulation of chromophilic substance and its rapid breakdown in active function, (3) the chemical changes involved in nervous transmission. The second and third items are closely related but they are not identical. The excitation of a nervous discharge in a resting neuron appears to require a considerable liberation of energy to overcome the inertia of the protoplasm and the sustaining of the activity also makes renewed demands on the energy reserves of the cell. Fatigue and cessation of transmission follow too prolonged continuation of the excitation and this is manifested histologically by the disappearance of the chromophilic substance. But once the process of transmission has entered the axon it is apparently self-propagating by a sort of circular reaction involving relatively little metabolism and small consumption of material. (The same applies to the long dendrites of peripheral processes of the neurons of the spinal and cranial ganglia, whose structure is similar to that of axons and which indeed are often called axons.)

The synaptic junctions are critical points in nervous metabolism. The "junctional tissue" appears to be notably susceptible to fatigue and to certain toxins. Especially in the correlation centers, where the selection of one out of several possible avenues of discharge is effected, the regions where the synaptic unions are made is richly vascularized and the evidence suggests that these are places of high metabolism of organismic type and centers of highest physiological dominance.

The details of the structure and functions of the "junctional tissue" are still obscure. The significance of these junctions in the polarization of the neuron and in the synchronizing and attunement of nervous impulses has been referred to in Chapter 9, but the mechanism employed is unknown. It may be merely a matter of relative permeability of the synaptic membranes, or it may be that some of the functions ascribed to the synapse reside in the protoplasm adjacent to these membranes in the neurons which are activated by passage of the excitation across the synaptic junction. The fact that there is a step-up of the energy of transmission in this region suggests that the second factor is important. At any rate it is clear that in general the gray matter has high metabolic rate and is the center of high dominance in the conduction systems, in accordance with the principles of excitation and conduction which we have seen in earlier chapters to be common to all forms of protoplasm. It also appears probable that in the regions of the synaptic junctions there is a sort of trigger action with release of latent energies (p. 263).

The physiological dominance of the higher correlation centers and their great importance as integrators of all bodily activities arise from a number of different features. One of these is undoubtedly the high intrinsic protoplasmic activity of their neurons and neuropil; a second is the presence of long nervous pathways of superlative conducting power leading out from them to the organs whose activities they control, thus eliminating that physiological isolation (p. 136) which in less perfectly innervated animals so much impairs the unity of the body; a third factor is probably the pattern of the arrangement of the neurons and their connections with one another, with provision for summation of stimuli, reinforcement, inhibition, and other complex interneuronic adjustments possible only at the synaptic junctions.

Specificity in the nervous system. — Unlike many other large organs of the body such as the liver which are relatively homogeneous throughout, the nervous system is characterized by a high degree of specificity in its different parts. There are innumerable "centers" concerned with particular functions, such as visual, auditory, olfactory reflexes, and the like. These centers are as distinctive structurally as they are functionally, and much attention has been devoted to the apparatus of this specificity.

The sense organs are clearly specific, both in form and function; each is attuned to respond to a particular limited range of external mainfestations of energy and to no others. Photosensitive protoplasm is chemically different from that of the sound receptors, and the anatomical arrangements of the accessory parts of the various sense organs are nicely adapted to facilitate the transformation of the particular physical excitants in question into nervous impulses.

The motor organs as a class are very different from any of the receptive organs and they also are so constructed as to perform each a particular act or series of acts. This specificity is partly a matter of internal organization of their protoplasms — the smooth muscle of the stomach is histologically different from the striated voluntary muscles and both of these are unlike the muscle of the heart. But all of these muscle fibers have a common plan of protoplasmic organization adapted for contraction; and amongst the skeletal muscles the particular movement performed by each is determined more by the mechanical arrangement of parts than by a specific internal structure of the protoplasm, that is, it is a matter of gross pattern of relation of bone and sinew rather than of internal physico-chemical organization.

So in the nervous system there are two factors involved in the specificity of function of different centers, first, the physico-chemical structure of the different protoplasms and, second, the arrangement in space of the different conduction systems with reference to one another and to their end-organs. Of the first factor our knowledge is very imperfect (p. 110 and Child, 1924, Chap. 11); yet every well-known functional center in the brain has so characteristic size, form and internal structure of neurons that the anatomical limits of the center can usually be determined by microscopic examination of its neurons. But the physiological significance of these facts and many similar cases that might be mentioned is still obscure. On the other hand, the process of physiological conduction seems to be essentially similar in all nerve fibers, whatever may be the differences in rate of transmission and final outcome in behavior.

By far the most important factor in the analysis of the functions of the nervous system is the way in which the neurons are articulated in functional chains extending from the sensory to the motor ends of the reflex arcs and bridging across from one reflex system to another in the correlation centers.

For this situation one may find a very rude analogy in the electric wiring of a large factory building to which reference has already been made (p. 50). The electric energy of the main feed wires (say 110 direct current) is of the same type no matter what kind of a generator or battery is used; so the nervous impulses actually transmitted by the nerve fibers appear to be fundamentally similar regardless of the nature or location of the exciting agent. As electric current may be drawn off from the same feed wires for a multitude of particular uses, each of which employs its own special apparatus — lamps, motors, heating units, etc. — so the response which follows the excitation of any nervous path is determined primarily by the pattern of the connections of the nerve fibers and the character of the end-apparatus rather than by any specific property of the nerve impulses as such.

All these patterns are matters of stable tissue differentiation with a large measure of intrinsic or local functional activity. The common organismic process of excitation and conduction by means of which these diversified activities are woven together in working systems which in the aggregate conserve the body are shot through the entire fabric. Thus the high physiological dominance of regions of more intense nervous activity is preserved notwithstanding that this tissue is structurally the most highly specialized ("matured") in the body.

These remarks apply to the highly stable stereotyped functional systems as well as to those of the most labile or modifiable type. In the latter, however, there is an added factor of great significance in this connection. Though much of the protoplasm of the nerve cells is, as has just been pointed out, highly differentiated or "matured" in the form of fixed mechanisms of excitation and conduction, in the higher correlation centers this is combined with a higher degree of plasticity or modifiability of reaction than is shown by any other tissue. This is brought about by the peculiar relations of neurons at their synaptic junctions which offer the possibility of a (physiological) choice of pathways to be taken by a given nervous impulse depending on variable internal factors such as fatigue, habit, etc. In this sense the nervous system is more plastic functionally than is the most undifferentiated embryonic tissue, and this is a feature which plays a large part in the more complex forms of regulatory control of behavior. In short, this is the apparatus of the highest physiological dominance.

CHAPTER XIX

THE APPARATUS OF MODIFIABLE BEHAVIOR

Physiological dominance in the nervous system — Dominance of the correlation centers — Intrinsic and integrative activities in the correlation centers — Distance receptors and the cortex — Functions of the cerebral cortex

Physiological dominance in the nervous system. — The characteristics of the nervous system which give to these tissues their commanding position as the apparatus of highest dominance and regulatory control can now be clearly seen. Taking as our point of departure the physiological gradients which enter into the stable organization of the bodies of the simpler non-nervous organisms and the resulting permanent polarization and axiation of these bodies, we find that when the nervous system first appears it is laid down within these preëxisting gradients and that its definitive form is to a considerable extent shaped in accordance with them (p. 97).

The physiological dominance of the head follows necessarily from the characteristics of the high points in the gradients (p. 251). With the appearance of the nervous system this head dominance is increased for several reasons, among which may be mentioned, first, the receptive organs which are the highest points in the simple gradients are especially elaborated in the head so that the metabolism of excitation is raised to a higher plane in this region, and, second, the improved conductivity of differentiated nerve fibers extends the range of the dominant excitation processes so that the activities of the entire body are more directly under regulatory control of these more excitable regions.

The transformation of the nervous system from the non-synaptic to the synaptic type introduces still other factors which favor head dominance. The irreversibility of the synapse, the high intrinsic metabolism of the cerebral neurons, the fact that one neuron may affect synaptic junctions with several others at higher or lower levels of the gradient of the reflex arc, and the fact that these synaptic junctions may have variable permeabilities to the transmission process—these and other features of the central adjusting apparatus which are especially highly elaborated in the brain involve a progressive increment in head dominance as we pass from simpler to more complex animal species. These processes are in part strictly organismic, in part they are local intrinsic activities which have small effect upon physiological gradients and general bodily regulation except as they are subsidiary to organismic functions of wider influence (Child, 1924, Chap. 12).

In the brains of higher vertebrates the innate mechanisms of stable action systems have attained a very high grade of complexity; the reflex and instinctive behavior of these animals is correspondingly amplified. But in addition to this complexity and superposed upon it there is more or less increase in capacity for individual modifiability of behavior. These two components of behavior, as we have seen, are independent variables, both always present but in varying proportions. Attention will next be directed to the mechanisms of this modifiability and the part which it plays in the physiological dominance of the brain in higher vertebrates.

Dominance of the correlation centers. — On the basis of careful experimental studies of the process of nervous conduction Lucas (1917) has advanced the hypothesis that every neuron, if excited at all, delivers its maximum energy of transmission; there are no grades of more or less energetic conduction in the nerve fibers, but the nervous impulse transmitted by any fiber is in every case the maximum impulse which that fiber is capable of conducting. This is the "all-or-none law" of nervous conduction which is widely accepted by physiologists (see Child, 1924, Chap. 11).

We do not know whether all nerve fibers have the same energy of transmission; presumably they do not, for nerve fibers differ greatly in structure, as do the entire neurons of which they are parts. But the nerve fiber appears to transmit its energy without appreciable decrement throughout its length, and in chains of functionally connected neurons each member of the series must deliver sufficient energy across the synaptic junction to overcome the internal resistance of the next element and so initiate its activity. Since each of these neurons has a certain latent reserve of potential energy, the chain may be conceived as made up of a series of charged elements each of which is set on a trigger whose release sets off a reaction of the "explosive" type already described (p. 256).

In the central nervous system there are numerous ways in which these principles are so applied as to result in a step-up of the energy of transmission at the synaptic junctions. Sherrington (1906, p. 120) in his study of the scratch reflex of the dog found that, if a subminimal stimulus which itself is incapable of provoking the reflex is supplemented by a second similar stimulus applied to a different part of the skin, the two stimuli reinforce each other and the reflex follows. The mechanism of such reinforcement is indicated in Fig. 121. Two subliminal excitations which converge into the same final common path are able to pass over a threshold of the motor apparatus

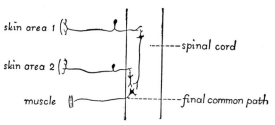

which neither acting alone can pass. The ineffectual energy of each of the sensory excitations is made effective through their conjoint action upon the motor neuron.

Fig 121.—Diagram of the mechanism of summation of stimuli in the spinal cord.

In the central olfactory pathways there is a series of very elaborate mechanisms for stepping up the energy of transmission (Fig. 122). Here several fibers of the olfactory nerve from the peripheral receptive surface converge into a single sensory cell, the mitral cell, whose axon carries the nervous impulse inward toward the olfactory correlation centers. Collateral branches of this axon end among very numerous minute granule cells which discharge their nervous impulses back into other mitral cells. Here are two very effective mechanisms of reinforcement. In the first place the combined action of several peripheral fibers upon a single mitral cell may over-step a threshold of the mitral cell too high for any one of them to do alone. In the second place the back-flow through the granule cells may rein-

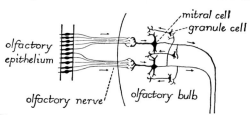

Fig. 122.—Diagram of the mechanism of summation and reinforcement of stimuli in the olfactory bulb.

force the action of the peripheral fibers upon other mitral cells and so perhaps activate cells which the combined action of the peripheral fibers was incompetent to excite. There are similar, though much more elaborate, devices for stepping up the energy of transmission in the gyrus dentatus of the olfactory cerebral cortex and these in the aggregate doubtless play a large part in giving to the sense of smell that extreme sensitiveness to which we have already referred (p. 40).

In these cases of central reinforcement of weak peripheral stimuli it may be that the sensory excitations are all of the same sort, as in the cases cited, or they may come from end-organs of different senses. We know experimentally (Herrick, 1903) that in fishes taste and touch thus coöperate in the normal feeding reactions and in fact this is the rule in most responses.   The correlation centers are primarily mechanisms for just this sort of convergence of afferent pathways of diverse functional sorts, and in them the physiological activity is raised to a high level, higher indeed than that of the receptive organs themselves.

There is another method of increasing the energy of transmission which is in some respects the converse of the process just considered. It is a very common thing for nerve fibers to divide so that a single

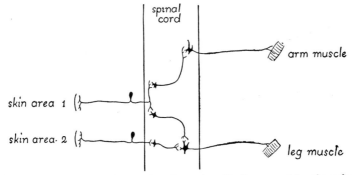

Fig. 123.—Diagram of the innervation of muscles of both arm and leg through the same cutaneous sensory neuron, from skin area 1.

neuron may activate many others.   Thus, a single sensory nerve fiber from the skin may connect centrally with motor neurons distributed to both arm and leg muscles (Fig. 123) so that both are activated from the same source.   Here the physiological gradient passes from skin area 1 to both muscles, but clearly the energy of the first neuron is not equally divided between the two efferent pathways, for there is no evidence of a decrement of nervous energy as it passes the synaptic barriers in cases where a single neuron simultaneously activates two or even a very large number of others.   Evidently there is a step-up of available energy of transmission at the synaptic junctions so that each muscle receives an adequate stimulus which is probably as great as if it were excited by an undivided pathway, as from skin area 2 in the diagram.   This follows from the all-or-none law, as Pike (1920) has shown.

In the correlation centers there are numberless instances of such divisions of nerve fibers with wide dispersal of the effects of excitation of a single neuron. In cases of this sort where one neuron excites a large battery of similar neurons which in turn discharge into the same final common path there is great increase in the total energy of transmission, this being in effect a combination of the two methods of step-up of energy just considered. This, which Ramón y Cajal calls "avalanche conduction," seems to be especially characteristic of the cortex of the cerebellum and also less obviously of all of the correlation centers, including the cerebral cortex.

This step-up of energy occurs in the gray matter and apparently at the synaptic junctions. In all regions where the mechanisms described are notably well developed there is unusually rich supply of blood vessels and other evidence of high metabolic activity. We are, therefore, confronted with the paradoxical situation that, whereas in a simple two-neuron reflex the nervous impulses follow a physiological gradient from a high level of metabolic activity at the receptive surface to a low level at the effector organ (with perhaps a slight increment in the center due to the high intrinsic activity of the cell body), in more elaborate systems where complex correlation centers are interpolated in the pathway the metabolic activity is higher midway of the course of the path (that is, in the correlation center) than at the initial point in the receptor. The correlation center is, as it has been said, set on a hair trigger; there may be a decrement from receptor to center, then the trigger is released with a notable increment of energy discharged, and a decrement appears again toward the effector, as expressed diagrammatically in Fig. 124.

If we use again the analogy of the energy of stream flow (p. 16), the diagram A would represent the pattern of erosive power in a mature stream with a tolerably even fall from source to mouth; the diagram B would represent the pattern of available energy in a stream which passes over a steep fall midway of its course with a strong increase in erosive power in the region of more rapid flow. This analogy, however, may be somewhat misleading, for in the stream flow the energy is acting all the time, while in the nervous circuits the activation is intermittent. The step-up of energy in the correlation centers here under consideration is not primarily consequent upon a high rate of uniform intrinsic metabolism of the centers, but it acts only during the transmission of the nervous impulse, that is, under excitation.

In these complex systems of conduction the pattern of the physiological gradient is dependent in part upon mere differences in amount of metabolism in different parts of the system, but in larger part upon the mode of the energy transformation, as was pointed out (p. 75) in discussing the gradients of the Protozoa. Certain types of activity have higher dynamic efficiency, capacity for doing work of wider usefulness in a given situation, than do other types which may rank as high or even higher in the equation of a calorimeter experiment. In terms of our fundamental conception of energetics (p. 46) the increase of entropy is retarded more in some kinds of dynamic complexes than in others, and the correlation centers perform this function in superlative degree. In so far as their activities

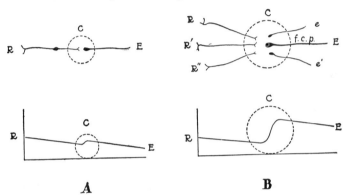

A   **B**

Fig. 124.—Diagram of the decrements in physiological gradients of two types. In A, the simple two-neuron reflex, the metabolism of excitation-conduction type falls off from the highest point at the receptor, R, to the effector, E, with small increment in the center, C, as indicated by the graph below. In B, where the excitations from several receptors, R, R', R'', converge into a common center, there is a great increase in the metabolic activity of the latter by summation of stimuli and otherwise until the final common path ($f.$ $c.$ $p.$) is activated, resulting in the adaptive reaction of E to the exclusion of other possible but inappropriate reactions, e and e'. The physiological dominance of the center is thus greater in the complex reflex system B than in the simple arc A, as indicated by the sharp rise of the graph in the center, C. These metabolic rates have not been quantitatively measured and the graphs are only rude approximations.

are available through the medium of the related fiber tracts for processes of binding together all bodily functions in systems of adaptive response they are of organismic type. And since they do control these functions in this way they are organs of highest physiological dominance.

Intrinsic and integrative activities in the correlation centers. — It has been pointed out that throughout the central nervous system there are fixed systems of reflex pathways and also innate patterns of association fibers even in the cerebral hemispheres. These fixed tissue systems exhibit a large measure of strictly intrinsic or local activity and their integrative processes are expressed in behavior as stereotyped (and doubtless in part inherited) reflex and instinctive acts. Permeating these fixed tissues, especially in the correlation centers, there is the synaptic apparatus of diffusion and summation of nervous impulses, avalanche conduction, integration of diverse sense modalities, analysis of excitation complexes, physiological choice and, in short, the more labile processes of correlation and association in general. The patterns of these processes are in large measure developed during individual growth under the influences of personal experience and they are rapidly modifiable during the course of further experience. These are regions of high metabolism of organismic type.

As has already been remarked, it is difficult, perhaps in many cases impossible, to determine just which components of a given reflex or instinctive pattern are inherited and which are of epigenetic origin; and for the purposes of this discussion it is unnecessary to do so. For both alike come to expression in permanent tissue organization; they are innate in the sense in which we have earlier used this term (p. 221), and the internal activities of the specific tissues involved include a large component of metabolism of intrinsic type. But these local intrinsic functions of the individual neurons are bound together in working systems by an organismic factor, namely, the excitation-conduction process which is shot throughout the whole organization. This factor is fundamentally the same wherever it operates; its behavioristic expression varies with the nature of the specific intrinsic mechanism through which it works.

The facile and very particularized reflex patterns of higher animals have emerged gradually, both in phylogeny and in ontogeny, from a generalized arrangement of nervous connections in the adjusting centers. The definitive reflex arc of the conventional sort is the end-product of this process and by no means to be regarded as genetically a starting point in the elaboration of the nervous system (Herrick and Coghill, 1915). But once having arrived, these definitive reflex pathways constitute a highly efficient mechanism of head dominance.

In the correlation centers, accordingly, there is very rapid metabolism in a labile and very unstable tissue of the "young" type associated with a highly differentiated diversity of more stable innate architectural patterns of the nervous connections, the latter being characteristic of the "mature" type of organization, as previously explained. The mature tissues may have high rates of metabolism under excitation, but their activities are sharply circumscribed in fixed action systems parallel with the inborn arrangement of the reflex arcs and their interconnections. This is a combination which permits the formation of a large amount of stable protoplasmic substance in fixed tissue patterns with definite and very restricted modes of action without interference with the more labile stuff whose activities maintain the dominant place of the correlation centers in the physiological gradients.

The plasticity of the complex tissue of the correlation centers is of very different sort from that of undifferentiated embryonic tissue. In the latter case external influences may shape the further course of development in most diverse ways, limited only by the inherited organization of the protoplasm characteristic of the species. But the pattern of the interneuronic connections of the correlation centers is much more sharply circumscribed, partly by inherited organization and partly by individually acquired, or habitual, avenues of neuro-motor discharge through nervous circuits opened up during and by means of repeated use.   At any particular stage of development or education there is a certain fixed equipment of possible neuromotor pathways which determines the limits within which the possible reactions to any stimulus will be confined. These limits, however, can be enlarged during the course of further development and education by the opening up of new combinations of the elements already laid down, so that the range of diversity of behavior is increased as long as this plasticity endures.

In the tissue under consideration there are two forms of plasticity which are dependent upon the peculiar organization of the synaptic nervous system. The first is the presence of a switch-board type of structure in the correlation centers which permits a considerable variety of possible responses to any stimulus depending upon the preëstablished arrangement of the correlation tracts, etc., and the internal physiological condition (fatigue, practice, attention, etc.) of the system involved at the moment of its activation. The second form of plasticity is the capacity for enlargement of the switch-board, through irradiation of nervous currents, facilitation by use, etc., resulting in an increase in the number of things one can do in response to a given sensory excitation. This is education.

These forms of labile behavior are expressions in part of the ana-tomic pattern of interneuronic connections and in part they are made possible by the peculiar properties of the protoplasm at or contiguous with the synaptic barriers, the "junctional tissue" of very mobile and impressionable nature.

The vertebrate nervous system is at the same time the most labile and (in some respects) the most stable organ in the body. Its labile components provide the mechanism for highly adaptive variable behavior, including intelligence, whose constant ebb and flow dominate the whole course of life. At the same time other parts of its protoplasm are so firmly stabilized as to resist loss of weight by starvation beyond most other tissues and to preserve with great tenacity the original patterns of the reflexes, instincts, and other innate functions.

The higher brain centers, including the cerebral cortex of man and many of the subcortical correlation centers, do not replace the lower reflex centers, but on the other hand the only way into these higher centers is through the lower (see Herrick, 1913, and 1922, Chap. 21). Physiologically this implies that the lower reflexes and instinctive reactions, which employ the direct passageways through the central nervous system, will always do the work when their stereotyped mechanisms are adequate to resolve any given stimulus complex into the appropriate and satisfying reaction. These lower centers are always first activated, but if they fail to solve the problem of conduct satisfactorily the flow of nervous energy will be dammed up in them and finding no appropriate outlet directly into the motor organs it will then be diverted upward into the higher correlation centers. Once these higher centers are activated, their own intrinsic processes liberate a large amount of latent metabolic energy of the very special type already described, resulting in a local summation or intensification of the excitation process.

In short, in the higher centers the physiological gradient is stepped up to a higher level with intensification of the control factor, much as an electric transformer may raise a current of low voltage to higher potential with greater range of action and efficiency for operating x-ray machines, etc. The result is that these brain centers become the organs of highest physiological dominance of the entire body. This is preëminently true of the cerebral cortex, whose dominant position is everywhere recognized. It is dominant, of course, only as regards those complex individually acquired functions which are superposed upon the simpler innate reflex and instinctive activities of the lower centers. Intelligence is the most important of these acquired functions, and since in mankind this shapes to a greater or less degree the entire course of life, cortical control has come to be the supreme factor in human behavior.

The preëminence of the human race in the control of the forces both of inorganic nature and of plant and animal life is undoubtedly directly correlated with the presence and physiological dominance of these higher cerebral centers. Of this there can be no question.

Distance receptors and the cortex. — Sherrington in a very illuminating way (1906, Chap. 9) has brought to our notice a very significant contrast between the immediate responses to contact stimulation and prolonged responses to objects at a distance. In the latter case there may be a long sequence of activities before satisfaction is achieved.

The reaction to a distant source of stimulation, say the prey of a carnivorous beast, involves these two phases: (1) the anticipatory reaction (pursuit of the prey and seizing it), and (2) the consummatory reaction (mastication and swallowing). During the anticipatory phase the acts, which are all directed toward a definite end, are constantly readjusting to new sense presentations and the whole process is one of intense nervous as well as muscular activity; and the more prolonged and complex the anticipatory phase becomes the more intricate the necessary associational processes must be. The chase may be extended with every sense alert to take note of each new turn made by the quarry and every advantage of the course, or the game may be stalked by careful approach with prevision of possible future contingencies.

In some of these reactions, like the pursuit of a minnow by a perch, every turn is a direct reflex response to the momentarily changing movements of the prey. Fishes, and indeed almost all other animals, thus utilize their preformed reflex circuits in a prolonged chase or other complex distance reaction. Fishes are also able, as we have seen (p. 197), to acquire specific associative memories, though only after many trials and prolonged training. These are obviously not reactions of cortical type, for they are exhibited by animals like fishes which possess no cerebral cortex.

There is much of this type of reaction, too, in the behavior of the hound as he follows the trail of a fox by scent. But the dog is not restricted to this narrow range of reactions to immediate sense excitations; he can at times forecast the probable future movements of the fox in terms of his remembrance of the topography of parts of the course not now within the range of his senses. And the success of the human hunter is measured very largely by his greater knowledge of the habits of the game and his skill in anticipating its probable behavior. This is more than reflex or any compounding of reflexes.

The dog can fabricate associations in terms of single experiences and utilize these past reactions by working their mnemonic vestiges into the present sensory complex during the anticipatory phase of a prolonged reaction, thus short-circuiting the process by the elimination of many trial-and-error or exploratory activities when direct sensory cues fail. This is a strictly cortical type of behavior.

In this situation vestigial traces of previous similar experiences and all sorts of acquired automatisms reinforce the sensory data of the moment and the whole nervous system is in a state of high neural tension which fluctuates continually as new sensory impulses from the periphery reverberate through its substance. The high synaptic resistance of the complex associational tissue raises the threshold of discharge from it and may delay the response until the residual data of previous experience can be incorporated into the dynamic system. Finally resolution takes place and the tension is relieved by discharge of neural energy into the appropriate lower administrative mechanisms which are already so adjusted as to execute the movements designated in the higher centers more or less mechanically and without the internal resistance characteristic of the higher association centers.

In this period of neural stress or tension of the anticipatory phase the psychic functions are born. So long as immediate reflex and instinctive modes of action are adequate they alone will be invoked, in accordance with the familiar law of parsimony. Reflex and instinctive action are biologically inexpensive. Their patterns are fixed and the apparatus is, as it were, manufactured wholesale and distributed by heredity to all members of the species. Individual conscious adjustment is much more costly; in fact, it is the most precious thing on our planet.

The cerebral cortex, then, becomes the chief organ of intelligence because it only is structurally adapted to serve the complicated correlations of sensory stimuli involved in the anticipatory reactions which alone call for special intelligent adaptations. And also because here alone is the apparatus necessary for the preservation of mnemonic vestiges of single previous reactions and the recall of the relevant parts of these to coöperate in the resolution of behavior problems arising from present stimuli.

Functions of the cerebral cortex. — The distance receptors and their cerebral centers, accordingly, not only dominate the behavior of the body from moment to moment, but they have shaped the course of its structural and functional evolution throughout the whole of its phylogenetic history. Their dominance as morphogenetic factors is evident in the lowest many-celled animals (*cf.* Herrick, 1910 a) and it increases as we ascend the series. With the unfolding of the cerebral cortex their central correlating apparatus takes on a new phase, and in higher mammals the most recently added cortical fields (the neopallium) serve these functions especially. Figure 125 illustrates the relative size of the cerebral hemispheres in a kangaroo and a man of approximately equal body weights. The contrast between the highest and well-nigh the lowest members of the mammalian series is almost wholly a matter of relative development of the neopallial cortical areas.

At the transition from brute to man there is another turning point in the progressive elaboration of the cortex. In the cerebral cortex we distinguish two series of cortical fields. First there are the projection centers, each of which is in direct fibrous connection with lower regions of the brain, either by ascending sensory fibers or by descending motor fibers — the visual, auditory and other sensory areas and the motor areas. Second, there are interpolated between the projection centers numerous association areas of great complexity.

Elliot Smith has called attention to the fact that in the larger anthropoid apes the projection centers are as extensive as in men of equal body weight, though the cerebral hemispheres as a whole are only half as heavy as the human.

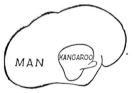

What is added in the human brain is far more complex association centers in the regions lying between the projection centers. These association centers, whose fibrous connections are for the most part related with other parts of the cerebral cortex itself, present a structural index of man's supremacy over the brutes. His senses are perhaps little

Fig. 125.—Outline projections (side view) of the relative sizes of the cerebral hemispheres of a man and a kangaroo of about equal body weights.

if at all superior to those of the apes, but he can do more with them because present and past sensory data can be associated in more complex patterns.

The most distinctive new mode of behavior colligated with the added association tissue in the human brain is the ability to form general symbols, notably those of language, which can be used as tools of thought in addition to the concrete data of sense. Upon this foundation is built man's supremacy in the realm of action as well as of thought. These symbolic instruments of thought are all individually acquired.

The correlation centers in general have been characterized as exhibiting in large measure the peculiarities of "young" as contrasted with "mature" tissue, that is, their activities are labile, plastic, modifiable. This is eminently true of the cerebral cortex and still more so of the association centers. These in mankind include the apparatus par excellence of modifiability, docility, adaptability, and the most complex adjustments to the physical, biological and social environment.

The cerebral cortex is the newest part of the brain both phylogenetically and ontogenetically considered. During the whole period of vertebrate evolution from Silurian times until now the basic reflex patterns of the brain stem have been laid down in stable form and progressively more firmly fixed in the hereditary organization (Child, 1924, Chap. 14). During the progress of the elaboration of the head (cephalization)

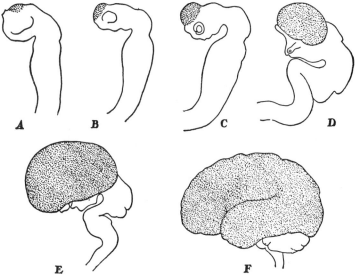

Fig. 126.—Sketches of side views of the human brain at different stages of development to illustrate the relative extent of the cortical area (stippled). The ages of the prenatal stages (A to E) are approximate. A, two weeks; B, three weeks; C, four weeks; D, eight weeks; E, six months; F, adult.

the correlation centers of highest physiological dominance have moved forward from the midbrain (fishes), through the thalamus and corpus striatum (reptiles and birds), to the cerebral cortex (mammals).

This history is recapitulated in the development of the human brain in ways whose full significance has only recently been brought to our attention (e. g., by Mott, 1922). Figure 126 shows six stages in the development of the human brain. In the youngest stage (A) the neural tube has just been formed from the neural plate. Here the medulla oblongata is very large, the midbrain is well formed, but the endbrain is still very small. In particular the part from which cerebral cortex will develop is minute (the dotted area). About two weeks later (C) the cerebral hemisphere has begun to form and the primordial cortical area is slightly expanded. Now the cortical field begins to grow more rapidly than the other parts of the brain, and in the adult (F) it overshadows all else. The growth of the cerebral cortex is not completed at birth, and for many years thereafter the internal structure of the cortex is rapidly developing in complexity.

The active processes of growth and differentiation of the cerebral hemispheres in late fetal and early postnatal life are expressions of their physiological dominance over the lower and now less actively differentiating regions. The newer and more plastic cortical tissue does not so soon "mature" and so the highest points in the physiological gradients are transferred from the brain stem to the cortex, and here they remain throughout the normal span of healthy mental vigor, for this tissue retains its plastic character as long as the powers of mind endure.

In the cortex itself during postnatal life there is further structural differentiation which is very closely correlated with the development of the cortical functions; in fact its progress is probably normally to a very large extent directly shaped by the energies of the nervous currents which irradiate throughout its texture during the progress of early education. There is a definite innate organization of the cerebral hemisphere, including a certain degree of elaboration of diversities in cortical structure in different regions and development of subcortical associational tracts which bind these regions together. To this there are added after birth the functional influences to which reference has just been made, a factor which will vary with the experience to which the child is subjected. Proper nutrition and opportunities for full physical and mental culture will promote normal unfolding of cortical potencies; deficiencies or perversions of these essential environmental aids will be apt to result in retarded or aberrant mental development with corresponding atypical cortical structure.

The converse aspect of this situation, too, is of great practical significance. If for any reason the innate organization of the cerebral hemisphere is defective or atypical, if the foundation upon which postnatal education must be built is weak or distorted, the most perfect postnatal culture cannot yield a normal product.

It is of the utmost importance that these two classes of defectives be recognized and given appropriate and different treatment for their own good as well as for the protection of society. This is by no means a simple or easy discrimination, but some progress has been made in the analysis of innate and acquired (postnatal) factors in development. This problem has been attacked by Bolton (1914) through a study of the relative development of the different parts of the human cortex at successive stages of embryonic development and in different degrees of congenital mental deficiency (amentia) and of mental deterioration (dementia).

When microscopic preparations of the cerebral cortex are examined the nerve cells are seen to be arranged in layers each of which is characterized by differences in the number, size, shape, internal structure and density of the cell bodies. This lamination differs in various parts of the cortex. Bolton recognizes five of these cellular layers (Fig. 127) in most parts of the cortex; other authors subdivide the cortex differently. Bolton's layers are: (1) the superficial layer, (2) layer of pyramidal cells (this includes layers 2 and 3 of Brodmann, 2, 3 and 4 of Campbell), (3) layer of granules, (4) layer of large cells or inner fiber layer, (5) layer of polymorphic cells. The third layer is of special significance in that it separates the cortex into infragranular and supragranular levels which in the opinion of Bolton have very different functional values. The conclusion, briefly stated, is that the infragranular layers are chiefly concerned with organic and instinctive (that is, innate) cortical functions, while the supragranular layers serve the acquired, associational, and in general the higher psychic functions.

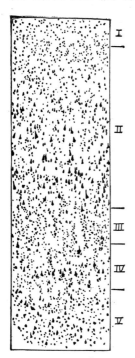

FIG. 127.—The cellular layers of the normal human cerebral cortex in the prefrontal region, magnified 38 diameters. Redrawn from Bolton.

In the development of the human brain the infragranular cortex matures earlier than the supragranular layers, and in comparing adult brains of different animals the lower mammals show well-developed infragranular cortex and very poorly developed supragranular cortex, the latter increasing in relative amount and complexity as the mammalian series is ascended. These relations are shown diagrammatically in Figure 129.

In extreme congenital imbecility the cortex is poorly organized, thin, and deficient in nerve cells, and the infragranular layers are less impaired than are the supragranular layers, as seen by comparison of Figures 127 and 128.

Bolton's second layer, of pyramidal cells, is the last to mature in individual development; viewed comparatively its elaboration in different mammals goes parallel with the degree of their intelligence; in human mental defectives (aments) its deficiency corresponds with the degree of mental arrest; and in the mental deteriorations (dementias) it is the first to show regressive changes. Mott (1922) is of the opinion that what he calls the primary dementias, which include many of the more common forms of mental disease, arise from genetic inadequacy resulting in a lowering of general vital efficiency, which manifests itself in the more susceptible supragranular cortex earlier than elsewhere in the nervous system.

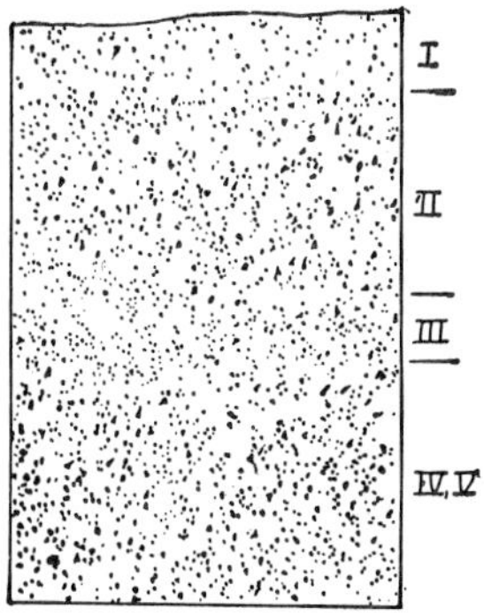

FIG. 128.—The cellular layers of the prefrontal cerebral cortex from a case of severe imbecility, magnified 42 diameters. The deficiency is especially marked in the second layer, whose constituent cells are fewer in number, defective in structure and irregular in position. Redrawn from Bolton.

Bolton's interpretation of the functional significance of the several layers of the cerebral cortex is by no means final; indeed, it has been actively controverted. The problems of cortical function are far too complex to be resolved by any one simple formula, yet these observations seem to be well founded and it is believed that they offer a very promising approach to some of the most baffling questions of human physiological psychology and neuropathology.

On these grounds it is concluded that the pyramidal neurons of the supragranular cortex serve the individually acquired associations and in general the higher mental processes. This supragranular cortex is, then, the highest apparatus of bodily control and the supreme center of physiological dominance.

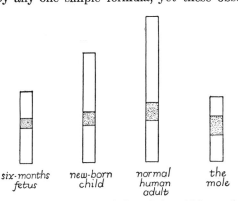

six-months fetus   new-born child   normal human adult   the mole

FIG. 129.—Diagrams of the relative thickness of the supragranular, granular and infragranular cerebral cortex in the six-months fetus, new-born child, normal human adult, and adult mole. The granular layer is dotted. Redrawn from G. A. Watson (1907).

This layer of the cortex differs widely in the various cortical areas and doubtless some of these areas are more important than others in the maintenance of this cortical dominance, but it is futile to look for any single center within the cortex which exerts a controlling power over the others, as Descartes conceived the pineal gland to function as seat of the soul. The essence of cortical function is correlation and this necessarily implies the conjoint action of several, perhaps many, different parts for the performance of any of these higher functions whatsoever. The facies of these correlation systems will differ from moment to moment and all of their phases may require the participation of numberless widely separated parts of the cortex and a different selection and combination of the parts at each phase of the process. Specific mental acts or faculties are not resident in particular cortical areas, but all conscious processes probably require the discharge of nervous energy throughout extensive regions of the cortex, and the character of the consciousness will depend in each case upon the dynamic pattern of this discharge and the sequence of function of its component systems. This pattern is inconceivably complex and only the grosser features are at present open to observation by experiment and pathological studies.

CHAPTER XX

FIXED AND MODIFIABLE BEHAVIOR

Behavior as regulation — The concept of modifiability — Modifiability of behavior in protozoans — Fixed and modifiable behavior in phylogeny — Conclusion

Behavior as regulation. — All of the activities of animals are, when viewed broadly, somehow fitted into the life pattern of the species exhibiting them. They are in general adaptive, or at any rate congruous with the organism's total life. Even though not positively useful they cannot be positively and irredeemably injurious, else they would be eliminated by natural selection. Maladjustments no doubt occur very frequently, as instanced by the appalling mortality from violent death seen in the animal world; yet these must be counterbalanced by compensating successful adaptations if the species is to survive. If a sturgeon lays a million eggs each season a system of adaptations which enables a single pair of eggs, from the total number produced during the parental reproductive period, to reach maturity is sufficient to maintain the species without diminution in number of individuals.

One phase of adaptation only need concern us at this point. This is the great complex of adjustments embraced by the term regulation. This concept is so fruitful that some further examination of it will be profitable.

The most distinctive characteristics of living things, as we saw at the beginning, are those concerned with the maintenance of the individuality of the organism, so that the forces of surrounding nature do not corrode and disintegrate it but on the other hand are incorporated into its organization to furnish the driving energy of the machine. The material and energy of the living body are in constant flux, yet the pattern of their manifestation persists. When this pattern is deformed by external violence or by changes of internal state it is said in current biological descriptions that there is a tendency to return to the typical condition. This restoration of the original pattern after deformation is termed regulation.

The term regulation was first used in biology to denote the organism's return to the original body form after an injury; this is form regulation and is an important factor in self-preservation, especially in lower organisms. The term regulation has since been much more widely applied to include all types of readjustment or return after disturbance to a condition permitting the ordinary vital processes to continue.[1] Though each regulatory act is a strictly individual adjustment, the mechanism of regulation and the pattern which is restored are parts of the hereditary organization. In view of the fact that the ordinary conditions of life involve constant changes in the relations of the body to its environment, regulation in the broad sense means simply the continuous readjustment of the organism to the flux of surrounding conditions.

Each species of animal and plant is so organized that in form and functional pattern it fits into a particular niche, so to speak, in the complex world of things. The hereditary form of the species is such as to enable it to thrive in some type of situation, from which it cannot be transplanted. The mole and the bat, for instance, are animals of very similar structure so far as the broad lines of organization go, yet each has very special adaptations to its mode of life which cannot be greatly changed. Many of these adaptations are of a very precise and rigidly determined nature. Some parasites are adapted to live only in one organ of a particular species of animal, and in some cases successive stages in the life history of the parasite must be spent in different unrelated hosts. The malaria parasite must spend part of its very complex life cycle in the stomach of a particular species of mosquito and part in the human red blood corpuscles. If infected mosquitos are not able to bite human beings, the parasite cannot be propagated and the disease disappears.

Just as every machine must be designed to fit the use to which it is put, so the form of every animal body is observed to fit its particular functional pattern. The preservation of its characteristic form (within narrowly circumscribed limits of variation) is the condition for the continued existence of both the individual and the species to which it belongs. This form is repeated in each generation and within the lifetime of each individual there is a regulatory tendency to return to the typical form pattern if this pattern is in any way distorted. This is fundamentally an expression of momentum, for the living body is no more a static thing than is a soap bubble or a gyroscope. It is momentum of dynamic pattern, not of mass.

Form regulation of this sort can be studied to advantage in many

[1] See Child (1924, Chap. 13) for a review and critique of the whole subject of regulation.

species of lower animals where after mutilation there is restoration of lost parts in the original form. A newt, for instance, will regenerate an amputated leg or tail, the lost part being finally restored perfectly (Holmes, 1904, 1907, Child, 1908). The human body with its much more complex tissues cannot restore lost parts so completely, though the healing of every wound illustrates some capacity for form regulation, and the perfect regeneration of severed peripheral nerves is the basis of some of the most illustrious triumphs of recent surgery.

Form regulation after loss of a part may be brought about by regenerating a new part in the place of the old or, as more commonly occurs in plants, the loss may be compensated by the development of another part in a different place. So in behavior the disturbance of the usual conditions may be corrected either by a return to the former state or by the acquisition of some quite different form of compensating activity, as, for instance, migration from a given locality after exhaustion of the local food supply. In each case after disturbance of the vital equilibrium a physiological readjustment occurs until a new equilibrium is established which is not necessarily the same as the original condition but which in general is adaptive or useful. The organism responds as a whole, in some measure, even to local disturbance, and in more complex adjustments the nervous system plays a leading rôle.

The regulation of behavior is a striking characteristic of all living things; indeed, Jennings says, "Behavior is adjustment or regulation" (1905, 1906, Chap. 21). The interpretation of this fundamental vital function lies at the basis of many vexed questions of theoretical biology. By some it has been assumed that no natural laws can be expected to cover so apparently purposeful responses and a metaphysical cause or principle is invoked. Thus the modern forms of the doctrine of vitalism have arisen. We may agree with Child (1911) that "regulation is the fundamental problem of life," and add that sufficient progress has been made in the analysis of the processes by which organisms are able to adjust their forms and behavior to their needs to justify the hope than an adequate scientific explanation is possible without transcending the laws of nature by invoking the aid of any metaphysical vital forces.

Historically the zoölogical study of form regulation preceded that of regulation of behavior, for the predominance of morphological study throughout the entire period of biological research has made most biologists structurally minded. Of course, form and function are in reality indissociable and the problems of form regulation, which have given morphologists a world of trouble, can best be approached from the functional side. All behavior is regulatory and these transient phenomena readily lend themselves to experimental control. The physiological principles thus discovered can then be applied to the problems of the slower and more recondite processes of form regulation with promise of return. In the present state of biological science dynamic formulations of problems and conclusions seem to be more willing guides than the more refractory and inert data of morphology.

Moreover, the distinction between form regulation and regulation of behavior is seen to be by no means fundamental, for these are in all cases inseparable. Restoration of form is possible only through equilibrated dynamic processes and the most transitory functional adjustments doubtless involve structural changes, though our available technique is inadequate to reveal these in many cases. Nevertheless the stable or "typical" form of every species is the visible expression of the accumulated results of past regulatory processes; and in default of a more direct method of approach the study of form reveals much of value regarding the dynamic factors which are (to speak crudely) precipitated in morphological patterns.

The behavior patterns of animals, like their form patterns, are innate and are adapted to the conditions of their natural habitats. Accordingly, every organism from the lowest to the highest has a certain congenital or innate pattern of behavior which is, of course, directly correlated with its specific structure. This behavior pattern, together with such fixed habitual modes of action as have been acquired in the course of individual life, constitute the action system as this term is used by Jennings.

But if either the internal or the external conditions are altered, the individuals are able, within certain limits, so to adapt their behavior to the changed conditions as to restore the former internal state and maintain their welfare. The approach of a thunderstorm drives the bees to the hive, and with us human folk sudden changes of temperature of the air are followed by changes in the circulation of the blood and secretion of perspiration so as to maintain a uniform internal temperature. To this physiological regulation we are able to add intelligently directed actions, such as building of fire and fabrication of clothing, houses with automatic thermo-regulators, etc. The last illustration is as truly regulatory as the first and our biology is incomplete, even misleading, until we are able to fit our human behavior into the general scheme of nature, thus completing the study of the natural history of man begun by Darwin.

The concept of modifiability. —Individual modifications of behavior, of course, can occur only if there is a certain capital of innate action system or reflex pattern with which to work. These two factors are never dissociated in practice. The innate patterns of any particular kind of animals have also grown up during use in the course of phylogeny and are in a sense functional modifications of earlier patterns. These patterns, however, have developed very slowly through biological agencies like natural selection which are able to effect relatively permanent changes in the organization of the protoplasmic "physical basis of life" and so are heritable. The individual modifications, on the other hand, are relatively quickly acquired and, while enduring for a time, do not involve any so permanent changes in the organization. They are in general not hereditary.

The term modifiability is used here in a very comprehensive sense. In all behavior we must distinguish: (1) the change in the environment of the reacting protoplasm, termed the stimulus, which causes the excitation; (2) the internal changes within the protoplasm itself which comprise the excitation and reaction. If internal changes persist after the completion of the reaction in such form as to alter the character of succeeding reactions, the protoplasm may be said to have been modified and these subsequent reactions which show the effects of this change may be classed as modifiable behavior.

Modifiability in this wide sense includes fatigue, acclimation, associative memory, and many other effects of past experience, in short, all of the internal factors of behavior except those immediately consequent upon the stimulus. Some modifications are evanescent, while others may persist throughout the life of the individual. This persistence of internal change is a true mnemonic function, ranging all the way from a transitory facilitation by use, through the so-called physiological memories of lower animals slowly acquired by numberless repetitions, to the lifelong memories of single events so characteristic of human experience. Obviously our interest in this context centers about the more sharply defined and enduring mnemonic functions of protoplasm. Facilitation by use and acclimation are very elementary forms of this series of modifiable behavior.

Child (1924, Chaps. 14, 15) has subjected the concepts of stability and modifiability of behavior to a searching analysis and he has shown that both rest ultimately upon similar laws of reaction of the living substance to external excitation. These responses involve structural changes which are more or less permanent and which necessitate change in the subsequent behavior, that is, they are aspects of organic memory. The possible range of this modifiability in any individual organism is determined by the potentialities of the inherited organization, but whether any particular possible modification will be called into actual being will depend upon the experience of the individual. Limitations of space forbid discussion here of the question of the origin of the stable inherited forms of behavior other than to call attention to Child's argument that, though they have arisen largely under the influence of excitation gradients, their fixation in the hereditary patterns does not necessarily imply a Lamarckian factor, as some have supposed.

In view of the similarity of the fundamental physiological nature of stable and modifiable behavior types, it is not surprising that in the lowest organisms these types tend to merge and lose their distinctive features. But in the more highly specialized animals the contrast between them becomes more and more significant. The origin and mechanism of the evolutionary and developmental modifications which have grown up slowly through the action of natural selection and similar biological factors need not concern us in this connection. We accept these as given and our present interest in them is merely to learn what they are in the species or race under consideration. This is important, for they furnish the individual with a certain capital of inherited action system or reflex pattern with which to work. His success in life will depend upon, (1) the perfection of the adjustment or adaptation of the stable innate action system to the actual environing conditions in which he lives and (2) the capacity of the organism to vary these native impulses in adjustment to new situations not provided for in the inherited action systems, that is individual modifiability of behavior.

This modifiability arises ordinarily from maladjustment. As long as the machinery of living is running smoothly and the innate organization of reflex and instinctive patterns is adequate to maintain the life and comfort of the body there is nothing to disturb the course of these reactions. But when external or internal conditions arise for which no apparatus of adjustment is already provided new combinations of the possible reflex elements may be made.

Nature, though prodigal in some of her moods, is very parsimonious in others; and in accordance with the law of parsimony general modes of behavior common to all members of a species, produced on a wholesale scale from the same pattern, are employed in all cases where they suffice. In lower forms with unlimited powers of rapid multiplication it appears to be more economical to standardize modes of behavior and limit these to a few rigidly determined types and to sacrifice the individuals who find themselves so situated that these circumscribed action systems break down.

Even the lowly organism does not yield to this fate without a struggle. Endowed with a certain capacity for general motility not specifically excited by an external stimulus, in an emergency for which no stereotyped response is directly provided in the innate action system it rapidly tries in turn all forms of response permitted by its organization, and if the outcome is successful the organization may be so altered as to facilitate a similar adjustment on repetition of the situation. The animal, we may say, has learned (physiologically) or has acquired a physiological habit which may persist for a longer or shorter time.

This kind of individually acquired modifiability is apparently biologically more expensive than the execution of reactions already standardized and provided with appropriate ready-made structural devices. It is very feebly developed in protozoans, and as we pass to higher forms the stabilized and the labile or modifiable types of behavior become more sharply differentiated, appearing on one hand as tropisms, reflexes and instincts and on the other hand as acclimation, habit, docility, intelligence.

The more labile behavior is higher as measured by the biological standard of more effective control of environmental forces. All that gives man his dominant position in the world is his preëminent capacity for modifying his conduct to suit the varying exigencies of life. Human education has as its prime purpose to supplement and often to supplant the inborn "natural" impulses of childhood by more appropriate intelligently acquired modes of action. This is in fact the characteristic human type of regulation of behavior.

The more highly complex forms of individual modifiability are termed associative memory and intelligence, and the latter is by definition consciously performed. Whether consciousness is present in the simpler forms of associative memory as these are demonstrated by students of animal behavior in lower animals, cannot be positively determined. In the behavior of lower animals there are no criteria which enable us to tell with certainty whether a given act is consciously performed or not, and therefore the lower limits of intelligence in the animal kingdom are problematical. But quite apart from the question of consciousness, the manifestations of modifiable behavior form a graded series from the simplest biologically regulated phenomena of the Protozoa to the highest human activities, so far as these are objectively manifested.

These two kinds of behavior are independent variables; both are always present in some measure, but in different proportions in the several species. Broadly speaking, in lower organisms the stable kinds predominate and the more labile assume greater importance in higher species, until in mankind individual modifiability takes the form of intelligent adjustment, learning by experience, and all the varied resources of physical and mental education with the powerful aid of accumulated traditional and documentary culture.

The second, or modifiable, form of behavior is sometimes called indeterminate in contrast with the more rigidly determinate or stereotyped reflexes, instincts, etc., of the first type; but, of course, this does not imply that the modifiable behavior is indeterminate in the sense of uncaused. The causes of reflex and instinct are acting uniformly on many individuals through long periods of time and the acts of all the members of a given species in a particular situation can be predicted with considerable precision so far as they are of this type. The causes of modifiable behavior, on the other hand, vary from moment to moment so that each act must be separately considered and no general formulation is possible. Moreover, most of these causes are obscure changes in internal physiological processes not readily open to observation or mental processes still more difficult of correlation with the physiological sequences.

That the so-called functional modifications of organisms, such as are illustrated by voluntary conscious reactions, and the biological alterations involved in the differentiation of reflex patterns with the corresponding changes in the structural architecture of the nervous system, and finally the fundamental processes leading to differentiation of tissues and organs in general — that these are all genetically related and shade into one another by insensible gradations has been clearly stated by Bok (1917). These are all reactions of living matter to excitation, some relatively transient and some long enduring or "chronic." He says (p. 281), "A certain lasting attitude can be caused by a permanent alteration of the surrounding world in the same way as it can for a moment be caused by an acute one. Hypertrophy of a muscle is seen with frequently repeated acute reflexes in consequence of a lasting alteration in the outer world." The physiological gradients, along with other factors, appear to be operative in all of these cases.

Stereotyped behavior implies sameness in all members of a species, innate similarities, as an outstanding feature. Modifiable behavior implies personally acquired differences. However much of uniformity there may be in all members of a race, there is superposed upon this an individuality which is personal and qualitatively different. The individual is not merely *other* than others in external (time and space) relations; he is different from the others in intrinsic nature, that is, in pattern of organization. This is the basis of human personality, which is the natural flower and fruitage of the elaboration of modifiable behavior, as Ritter (1921) has pointed out.

Besides the innate stable factors of behavior typified by tropism, reflex and instinct, there is also a personal acquisition of stabilized behavior, a tendency for acquired behavior, if oft repeated, to become ingrained as habit and so-called acquired automatisms. The failure to distinguish clearly between these two types of fixed or stable behavior has been responsible for a world of fruitless polemics in the domain of instinct. The first type is innate; the second is acquired, and if originally learned through conscious effort is a true "lapsed intelligence."

The lapsed intelligence is as adaptive as the reflex or the inherited instinctive action, but the conscious factor originally present may be wholly or partially lost. This kind of behavior has often been invoked to account for the origin of instincts of lower animals, but the indications are that most instinctive acts have a quite different origin. On the other hand, the lapsed intelligence type plays a major part in human behavior, for much of education and training is nothing other than the fixation of reaction types at first learned by close attention and conscious control at every step, so that ultimately they go off of themselves by "second nature," as we correctly say.

Modifiability of behavior in protozoans. — Since modifiable behavior is commonly thought of as especially characteristic of higher animals with well-developed nervous systems, it may be advisable at this point to inquire to what extent such individual adjustments are possible in protozoans. A few illustrations will show their type and limitations. Passing by the phenomena of fatigue and acclimation, we may say that, in addition to these elementary biological adjustments, there is some modifiability of the sort included in the more conventional idea of behavior, that there is some capacity for changing the customary reactions, at least temporarily, through previous function, that is through experience, and for the acquisition of habits. And from these humble beginnings we must trace the whole course of evolution of the capacity for individual improvement in the technique of living on the physiological plane through use, trial-and-error, habit, etc., and on a higher level through associative memory, and probably the whole realm of mind.

Most of the behavior of the lower organisms is definitely organized into stable action systems, either as tropisms or in the case of trial-and-error reactions by selection of the favorable response from among a limited number of possible acts, each of which is of stereotyped character. These stabilized acts are correlated with definite dynamic and structural patterns of the reacting substance which have arisen, as we have seen, in connection with the excitation-conduction gradients — a process requiring considerable time and many repetitions and in the case of multicellular forms the coöperation of natural selection or other factors capable of working through the germ cells.

Whether we can properly speak of hereditary characters in protozoans is perhaps a matter of definition not essential to our purpose. It may be objected that there can be no true heredity where each generation is so obviously merely the continuation of the life cycle with no separation of germ plasm from body plasm. But if the capacity to reproduce its like is taken as the general characteristic of heredity (Lillie, 1918 a), the analysis of this question is simplified (see Ritter, 1919, Chaps. 12, 13). In any case it is agreed that the intracellular organs of higher Protozoa are not merely transitory physiological phases, but they retain their forms and functions in stable patterns. In some cases they may dedifferentiate but return in the course of the life cycle to their former organization much as the higher animals do after passing through the egg stage.

It is true that the body forms of most of these species are exceedingly mobile. The ameba indeed assumes so rapidly varying shapes that it has been called the proteus animalcule, and even the higher protozoans have remarkable plasticity of form. Yet this form is within its limits of variability sufficiently constant to admit of definition and naming of species as in higher animals, and organs persist or reappear in due course in characteristic forms. There remains, however, always a certain measure of individual plasticity of behavior, or capacity for rapidly modifying the stable pattern of responses in the course of a diversified life. This arises usually from maladjustment, or the failure of the fixed action system to meet the requirements of the situation. Mobility or adaptability of behavior is as truly an essential feature of the life process as is the establishment of the stable pattern of response.

Mast (1910) has shown that an advancing ameba will not enter a beam of strong sunlight. After a few protrusions of the body have been thrust into it and withdrawn there is a change in the behavior from a local response to each excitation to a general avoiding movement of the body as a whole. The direction of locomotion is reversed.

This is a very rudimentary form of modifiability. The deleterious changes produced by the strong stimulation in the region directly excited are in a short time communicated to all of the body protoplasm and the immediate local response to the excitant is replaced by a total reaction of the body as a whole. The behavior has been transformed, as Child would say (1921, p. 235), from a simple local excitation gradient to an adaptive response of the whole body of the same physiological type as the higher reflexes. It is, however, evanescent and no structurally differentiated organs are involved, that is, there is no reflex arc as a permanent anatomical apparatus. The final response has become more than a local excitation phenomenon; yet the correlative and integrative capacity is manifested only under the immediate influence of the excitation gradient, and the adaptive behavior, having at its disposal no permanent organs, cannot long endure after removal of the exciting cause.

This is a typical avoiding reaction in two phases, each of which is reduced to lowest terms: (1) direct local response to a stimulus, and (2) correlated movements of the body as a whole following from the spread of the first activity and dependent upon preëxistent organization (of some kind) in the general body protoplasm. The modification endures for a very short time.

Positive seeking reactions of the ameba are well known and may be continued for as long as twenty minutes, as when the prey is pursued for considerable distances (Gibbs, 1908). In this case the series of reactions is sustained by constant changes in the external stimuli and no factor of modifiability can be recognized. But when the ameba upon entering a beam of sunlight first makes a series of local responses and then changes to a locomotor movement of retreat we have a different situation, for here the change in behavior occurs without any change in the external excitant and must, therefore, be internally determined.

Schaeffer (1917), among many others, has studied the feeding reactions of the ameba with interesting results, among which is the conclusion that in many cases past experience in receiving stimuli or in feeding is of more importance in the selection of food than the nature of the stimuli received from a present object. Selection is therefore a historical process resting largely on the experience of the individual.

In these cases the modifiability is of so low an order and so transient as scarcely to merit recognition; nevertheless in this transition from the simple excitation gradient to the reorganization of total bodily movement there is a necessary first step toward true habit formation and associative memory.

The behavior of Paramecium has been carefully studied by Jennings. The structure of the body is such that in the ordinary swimming movement it advances in wide spirals. In a strong avoiding reaction the movement is reversed and the animal swims backward, still in a spiral course. If now a Paramecium is confined in a capillary glass tube too narrow to permit the usual spiral mode of swimming, it swims forward by a rotary movement until the end of the tube is reached; it then reverses the movement several times and finally

turns about by a series of quick jerks (Fig. 130), as described by Stevenson Smith (1908). In the normal unconfined behavior this reaction never occurs. Day and Bently (1911), after more ex-

FIG. 130.—Diagram of the way Paramecium turns in a capillary glass tube, thus modifying the usual method of changing the direction of swimming. After Stevenson Smith (1908).

tended and precise observations by a similar method, conclude that Paramecium "learns" by experience to modify its behavior.

Jennings (1902) and many others have shown that transient habits of an adaptive sort can be acquired by various unicellular animals. The trumpet animalcule, Stentor, was especially studied. These delicate animals are among the larger Protozoa and are usually attached to the bottom by a slender base (Fig. 9, p. 69). They respond to an irritating stimulus by bending the body away. If the stimulus is not too severe they soon cease to respond at all, though experiments show that this is not due to fatigue. If it is an injurious stimulus, they soon contract the body away from it and if this is not effective in bringing relief, they loosen their hold on the bottom, swim away and attach in a new place. Jennings says, "Whether the animal reacts to a given stimulus or not, and how it reacts, depends upon previous subjection to this stimulus, and upon the previous method of reacting to it. If a stimulus continues, the animal gives a series of reactions which are not invariable in order or length of continuance; each reaction of this series is adapted, by a different method from the others, to getting rid of the stimulus." But these modifications of behavior are retained for only a short time.   The physiological memory is very short lived.

Fixed and modifiable behavior in phylogeny. — In our survey of behavior patterns of the various groups of animals from protozoans to men stable innate behavior has been seen to be in all cases blended with more labile individually modifiable manifestations.   It is unnecessary again to review this evidence here.   The fixed type is predominant in all the lower forms.   The higher groups of animals diverge in different directions, in some of which, as in insects, fixed types

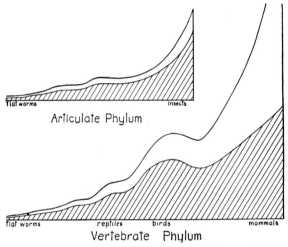

FIG. 131.—Two diagrams illustrating the relative development of the invariable and variable factors in the behavior of the articulate phylum and the vertebrate phylum of the animal kingdom.   In the articulates the invariable factor (represented by the shaded area) predominates throughout; in the vertebrates the invariable factor predominates in the lower members of the series, and the variable factor (represented by the unshaded area) increases more rapidly in the higher members, attaining its maximum in man, where intelligence assumes the dominant rôle.   From Herrick (1922), by permission of the publishers, W. B. Saunders Co.

continue to dominate the behavior throughout, while in others, as in vertebrates, the modifiable forms come to assume greater importance in the higher species.   The accompanying diagrams (Fig. 131) are intended to express these relations, though of course in the absence of any suitable standards of measurement they can make no pretense of accurate quantitative expression.

It is significant that in the vast majority of animal species, including those containing by far the largest number of individuals, the fixed modes of behavior clearly preponderate over the more labile or modifiable types.   The biological efficiency of these species in their respective habitats is obvious, but this is secured at the expense of enormous mortality of individuals which stray away from the niches for which they are adapted or are overwhelmed by adversity. It is of these that the Laureate spoke,

> So careful of the type she seems,
> So careless of the single life.

, With the enlargement in other branches of the animal kingdom of the capacity for individual adjustment to situations fraught with danger or offering opportunities for advantage, the entire facies of the evolutionary movement changes. Success is no longer measured in terms of dominant species but in terms of resourceful individuals. The individual ceases to be an insignificant unit among thousands of others, whose elimination has small influence upon the general welfare of the species because hosts of other identical units stand ready to take his place. With the increment of the value of the individual numbers are diminished and each member of the species comes to occupy a strategic position in the struggle for continued existence of the race. Just as in modern warfare, with all of its diabolically ingenious appliances for wholesale destruction, individual initiative and aggressiveness of the personnel count for more than mere numbers, so in life as a whole personality dominates mass action.

Now, the procedure through which this increase in personal efficiency comes to expression is to a large extent improvement in the capacity of the nervous system to adjust to the varied conditions of life, as has been exemplified in the preceding chapters. But it must not be forgotten that the nervous system is only one of many factors in bodily constitution which coöperate in bringing about this result. Of the other organismic factors which play leading parts in higher animals mention should especially be made of the ductless glands or endocrine organs (p. 58), whose activities are known to be in most intimate reciprocal relationship with those of the vegetative nervous system. The detailed consideration of this topic does not lie within the scope of this work, but as illustrative of the profound significance of endocrine activity for personal efficiency mention may be made of the work of Cannon (1915) and of the recent studies of Hammett (1921) on temperament and bodily constitution.[1]

[1] The entire field of endocrine physiology is now under very active investigation. So extremely complex are these relations that there is scarcely an observation whose full significance can be unambiguously evaluated and every generalization made is in controversy and should be held subject to possible revision. The two works cited above form no exception; but whether these specific conclusions stand

Hammett finds that in human beings of excitable temperament there is greater metabolic instability of the tissues, as measured by variations in the soluble nitrogenous constituents of the blood, than in persons of more unemotional or phlegmatic type. Wild rats in captivity and tame rats which for several generations have been constantly handled and gentled manifest somewhat similar temperamental differences, and these two groups of rats show very significant differences in their adjustments to experimental destruction of the parathyroid glands, the gentled rats being more resistant to the ill effects of the operation than the wild ones.

Many other illustrations might be cited which show the profound influence of temperamental tone on bodily constitution and conversely of bodily constitution on temperamental tone. That these things are not independent of the nervous system has just been pointed out, and Hammett comments upon "the practical value of the regulation of the expression of temperament by voluntary action to the smallest variability in response consistent with adequate adaptation." In other words, the practical value of voluntary emotional control is seen to rest upon demonstrable relations between the central nervous system, the visceral nervous system, the endocrine secretions and the regulatory effects of these on general metabolic efficiency.

Conclusion. — Regulation is a general name applied to the organism's capacity for return to the form or behavior characteristic of the species after any disturbance of this original pattern. The factors of regulation of behavior can be analyzed more readily than those of form and the latter are seen to be intimately bound up with the former. All behavior is regulatory in the sense that there is a typical action system adapted to meet the ordinary exigencies arising in the life of the species to which the organism returns after modification produced by unusual events. Even the ordinary reactions called forth by change in existing conditions tend to bring the system back to the former state and then cease. Trial-and-error, tropism, reflex, instinct, and various forms of modifiability of behavior may all participate on occasion in these regulatory processes.

In the analysis of the more complex types of behavior of higher animals utter confusion has prevailed and there is no agreement to-day regarding the relative parts played here by reflex, instinct and intelligence nor upon the definition of these terms. Recognition of the different values for behavior of the inborn and acquired factors

or fall, the indications are that the significance of endocrine activity in general in the development of the personality is not here exaggerated.

and of the differences in the apparatus employed will do much to clarify these muddy waters of controversy and to enable us to see through to some important underlying principles. The confusion of individually acquired habits and intelligently learned automatisms with the inborn "original nature" is another prolific source of fallacious reasoning.

Where the behavior is largely an expression of innate reflex and instinctive patterns, the individual and social organization is necessarily very different from those cases in which more individual plasticity and freedom of conduct is the rule.

The attempt not infrequently made now-a-days to express the whole of life, including the human mind, in terms of successive hierarchies of reflex and other similarly determined modes of behavior can lead only to failure to grasp essential factors of the evolutionary process. The *elements* of these complex processes are, it is freely granted, reaction types whose nature is fixed or predetermined in the innate organization of the body; but the particular form in which these elements are combined in any situation which may arise is by no means necessarily so determined, but rather, to a large extent at least, by the past experience of the individual. And this, as a matter which can be subjected to direct social and individual control, has far different significance than any innate factors whatsoever.

Keeping in mind our biological point of view, the differences between various kinds of organisms are seen to be in the main incidental to the extent and character of their relations with the forces of their surroundings. In discussing the criteria of functional rank it was stated that a species which can adjust itself to few elements of its environment we call low; one that can adapt itself to a wide range of environmental conditions in a great variety of ways we call higher. The supremacy of the human race is directly due to our capacity for diversified living. If man finds himself in an unfavorable climate, he may either move to a more congenial locality or adapt his mode of life by artificial aids, such as clothing, houses and fire. And in these adaptations he is not limited to a narrow range of inherited instincts, like the hive of bees, but his greater powers of observation and reflection enable him to discover the general uniformities of natural process (he calls these laws of nature) and thus to forecast future events and to prepare himself for them intelligently. And this higher type of adjustment to the conditions of life is largely an individual acquisition. It is not bred into us and born with us, but is the product of individual contact with the world about and conflict with it.

CHAPTER XXI

PROGRESSIVE FACTORS IN EVOLUTION

Diversification versus progressive evolution — Critical stages in progressive evolution — Uniformity of fundamental organismic processes — The progressive factors — Habit formation in education — Creative intelligence — The definition of behavior and its limits — The future of human evolution

Diversification versus progressive evolution. — In the preceding chapters reference has been made to evolutionary trends in two directions which have often been distinguished by previous writers. These are:

(1) Diversification, or differentiation of structure and behavior in adaptation to particular environmental or other conditions without that increase in complexity of organization and variety or range of vital adjustment which was set down at the beginning of our discussion as the criterion of advance in biological rank. This may lead to great increase in number of species and individuals and to great biological efficiency of the group as a whole but not necessarily to a higher range of capacity of the individuals.

(2) Progressive increase in the complexity of organization of the individual arising from more refined analysis of the diverse forces of surrounding nature by the sense organs, more efficient use of the sensory data through elaboration of the apparatus of correlation and integration, and more complex neuromotor apparatus of response. This gives to the individual ability to adjust to more varied conditions and a fuller and richer life.

Both of these evolutionary movements show evidences of adaptation. But fitness may be effected either by precise adaptation on a low plane to a limited environment or by enlarging the individual's control of the total environment and so lifting him into a higher sphere of activity.

There is no proof that the limit of evolution has been reached in either of these directions. Highly successful organisms are continually spreading out into new environments and adjusting themselves to unaccustomed conditions by diversification on their original biological levels, as illustrated by the introduction into a new continent or island of old-world weeds, sparrows, rabbits, etc. And in mankind the progressive evolutionary advance is sustained by ever widening control of the inorganic and organic environment with increased capacity for diversified living on the part of each individual.

Critical stages in progressive evolution. — Evolutionary progress of both of these types appears to have been far from uniformly accelerated. Climatic changes were undoubtedly important factors in fixing the times of some of these pulses of differentiation (Lull, 1918) as were also changes in the configuration of the land and water surfaces of the globe. Since, moreover, the existing organization of any species at any period of its development to some extent predetermines the limits within which further differentiation can take place (pp. 98, 253), it naturally follows that periods of rapid evolutionary advance in the second sense as defined above can occur only when a structural pattern has been attained which can serve as a point of departure for variations or mutations in radically new directions as contrasted with minor changes in the preëxisting pattern in adaptation to local environmental conditions. This structural pattern, futhermore, must combine sufficient complexity of organization with plasticity or capacity for radical change.

In view of these requirements it is not surprising to find that the step from a lower to a higher type advances from the most generalized members of a lower group, not from the most highly specialized species, for the latter have already passed beyond the plastic stage and their stabilized complex bodily patterns cannot be dedifferentiated sufficiently to serve as points of departure for fundamentally different patterns.

In the series of organic forms which have led up to the culmination of evolution in mankind the following critical points may be mentioned as conforming to the conditions necessary for the appearance of radical departures from the established pattern:

1. From the inorganic to the organic.

2. From unicellular to multicellular bodies.

3. From generalized structure to specially differentiated tissues.

4. From ordinary protoplasmic to nervous apparatus of excitation and conduction.

5. From non-synaptic to synaptic type of nervous system.

6. From relatively diffuse ganglionic to the dorsal tubular pattern of central nervous system with cephalization and bilateral symmetry (vertebrate type).

7. From aquatic to terrestrial mode of life with increase in complex-

ity of sensori-motor equipment and extensive evagination of cerebral hemispheres from the primitive neural tube.

8. Differentiation of superficial cortex in the cerebral hemispheres and rise of intelligence.

9. Elaboration of cortical association centers with powers of symbolic thinking, ideation and conscious personal and social control.

In the early stages of each of these advance movements there appears to have been nothing of revolutionary character. The starting point in every case was, as has been pointed out, a very generalized type which had attained a given level of organization without a high degree of specialization in that level and with corresponding plasticity of structure. The distinguishing feature of all of these critical points is that further differentiation does not lead into a cul-de-sac (as in tunicates), nor merely to spreading out on the horizontal plane into a multiplicity of forms of similar grade of organization (as in insects and teleosts), but sooner or later into fundamental changes in organization making possible more varied and efficient relations with environing forces.

Uniformity of fundamental organismic processes.— It is significant that throughout all of these varied progressive movements the fundamental factors of organismic regulatory control of behavior as a whole appear to have been preserved with (in the higher forms) inconceivable complexity of interrelated parts and hierarchies within hierarchies of equilibrated systems of correlation and integration, but with no change in the basic type of process by which these activities are realized. The functions of the human brain, so far as exact physiological knowledge of these processes has gone, can all be reduced to phenomena of excitation and conduction not radically different in fundamental character from those of a protozoan or a polyp. The differentiation of the nervous tissues, their condensation into a central nervous system, the specialization of sense organs, nerves and correlation centers, the development of synaptic barriers, the unfolding of the cerebral cortex and the fabrication within it of association centers and tracts of marvelous complexity and mysterious capacities — all of these are largely matters of increasingly complex patterns of excitation-conduction systems and differences of excitation thresholds, facility and rate of conduction, modifiability through use, and capacity to retain the modifications.

The man is more than a polyp, but his enlarged capacities come to expression in similar types of physiological gradients, in head dominance and regulatory control of bodily functions through mutual interaction between the chief center and the innumerable subsidiary centers of varying physiological dominance, in the same dependence of all of these functions upon the maintenance of active vital relations between the organism and its environment. And the measure of the worth and the fullness of life in the case of the man not less than the polyp is expressed in terms of the individual's capacity to appropriate for his own use the natural wealth by which he is surrounded, to assimilate it, and to return again to the world in which he lives the impress of his own nature.

Thus we see that the continuity of process throughout the whole course of progressive evolution is marked by the preservation at every stage of certain fundamentals common to all life. Living bodies contain no chemical elements not found in inorganic nature. Certain elemental physical forces can be recognized throughout the organic series — chemical affinities, osmosis, surface tensions, electrolytic dissociations, and numberless others are constantly at work in our own bodies. But in living protoplasms these are combined in new and progressively more complex patterns. Progressive evolution is nothing other than this recombination, always under the influence directly or indirectly of agencies from without the affected protoplasm but always shaped by the existing structure of the protoplasm itself which in turn has been determined by its past.

The progressive factors. — Growth and propagation are universal biological features; they are matters of internal organization, controlled from within, for the uncontrolled environing forces tend only toward disintegration. Continuous activity reaching out for external goods and appropriating these, and self-aggrandizement are universal progressive biological factors. The organism tends to expand, to enlarge its sphere of action, to grow, to "be fruitful, and multiply, and replenish the earth, and subdue it." This is a real élan vital, though no more mysterious or metaphysical than are other well-recognized vital properties. This is merely another way of phrasing the struggle for life so universal in the biological realm.

The good, the indifferent and the evil traits as we view them are alike propagated and enlarged unless prevented by pressure from without, for what is good in one place may be evil in another. The "problem of evil" is part and parcel of the problem of life.

But these progressive, expansive movements are not haphazard. They are to a large extent limited, as already mentioned, by the factor of orthogenesis and to this extent their directions are predetermined. Moreover, variation in a direction which is prejudicial to a species in a given environment will be eliminated in accordance with the principle of natural selection (it is an "evil") unless the species changes its habitat, in which case the variation may be "good," possibly forming the starting point for a new and progressive series of evolutionary changes.

An evolutionary trend toward rigidly instinctive behavior may be amplified in this direction with almost no admixture of the intelligent type of behavior (as in insects) or with a considerable addition of the latter type (as in birds). In both cases the instinct is "good"; it practically does conserve the welfare of the species so long as it remains in the appropriate environment. On the other hand, a trend toward greater plasticity of behavior may lead up to heights of intellectual achievement and social organization in which the instinctive impulses must at first be utilized to the full but at length largely suppressed or subordinated and redirected.

Now human progress is clearly in the latter direction and its successful march is to a large extent dependent upon striking the proper balance in the early plastic years of childhood between the powerful blind impulsions of the "original nature," that is, the innate organization of reflex and instinctive type, and the two personally acquired factors of rational control and social control of conduct. How frequent and how serious may be the failure to make this adjustment in early life is obvious from even casual inspection of the miserable wrecks of humanity who clog the machinery of social progress in every community.

Attention has been called to the fact that the individually modifiable type of behavior is biologically more expensive than the rigidly determinate types, and this is particularly true of the acquired rational and social controls which make civilization possible. The line of less resistance is always in the direction of reversion to the instinctive impulsions. We have recently seen under the stress of war how quickly the thin veneer of human kindness and conventional morality may be abraded and to what depths of bestiality even highly accomplished and learned men may sink.

Habit formation in education. — There is another aspect of this theme which is not so much in the public eye, but at the present time is perhaps of greater moment. It is a truism that elementary education consists largely in the acquisition of correct habits. That is, much of what is painfully learned by concentrated effort must become so automatized that it no longer requires the undivided attention, thus freeing the mind to go on with more significant matters while the acquired neuromotor automatisms are at work with the petty administrative details of the performance. No musician can rise to the higher levels of artistic expression until the elementary technique of his art is so perfectly mastered as to require practically no attention.

We thus (all of us) gain by practice so complete a mechanization of the common duties of life, such as walking, speaking, driving motor cars, and the details of daily routine, that they are performed by "second nature" with almost, if not quite, as great economy of effort as are the instinctive acts of our "original nature." In fact, it is so difficult to analyze this routine behavior of the adult man into its innate and habitual factors that there is still great uncertainty as to just how many instincts there are in mankind and to what extent these persist as factors in adult behavior (Thorndike, 1913).

Though a large part of the educational career, especially in its early stages, is necessarily concerned with this process of habit formation, it is important to remember that this is only the framework upon which the priceless fabric of mental culture is to be woven.

The educational process which is arrested at the stage of habit formation, it matters not how extensive the repertoire and how perfect the mastery of the letter of the lesson assigned, is scarcely begun. In fact, it is a failure. True education must use the knowledge and skill thus acquired and mechanized merely as the tools for constructing out of the experiences of life new and individual methods of response, powers of logical analysis, critical appreciation and personal ideals.

Human progress is never through reversion to rigid mosaic patterns of stereotyped automatisms. And here a practical matter may be mentioned. The shop efficiency expert who standardizes production by gearing every operator to his machine and determining by shop tests the precise motions and the precise speeds of operation by which the conjoined dead and living machines can be made to yield the largest return per hour is treading on dangerous ground. It is reported that the operatives of one large factory which pays higher than standard wages and gives the employees unusually favorable advantages in other ways claim that it is impossible to stand the strain of standardized efficiency of this sort for more than a few years. The monotonous repetition of a few simple movements at high speed during even a short working day "gets them," and they are compelled to seek other and less remunerative employment or break under the strain. The necessity for relief from the benumbing influence of shop routine and for the quickening of creative interest in the work is a factor not always recognized by the so-called efficiency experts.

Creative intelligence. — And what shall we say of a psychology which subsumes under habit formation the whole of the rational process? This is not merely a perversion of the scientific analysis of mind; it is a complete negation of those constructive factors which alone make mental or any other progress in mankind possible. Habit faces backward, while thought reaches forward into the future and gives zest and piquancy to an otherwise dull and listless repetition of the necessary routine of daily life.

Human progress builds to-day upon the past of yesterdays gone, and the activity of to-day at its close will in turn be laid down as another static foundation stone on which to-morrow's building will be done. Creative intelligence shapes these building stones of character. They are not pushed up from below ready formed by the forces of the past, but each is hewn into its place by the strenuous labors of a mind alert to see how to shape each new fact of experience so as to fit it into the building already laid down in such a way as to enhance and not to mar the strength and symmetry of the whole. When this type of intelligent effort ceases progress comes to an end. The building may be widened by adding more material of the kind already designed, but it can be built no higher nor can its plan be fundamentally changed. The true education of the individual is complete, though further training may improve the technique of the performance.

This intelligence is creative in a literal sense (Dewey, 1917). The old elements of experience are recombined in new patterns. The energy required to lift a great weight with a simple lever is the same as that employed when a six-pulley-block is used, but in the latter case a small child can lift with ease what the utmost exertion of many men could not have accomplished with the lever. The invention of the dynamic pattern of the pulley-block was a real cause whose effects will continue as long as men use machines. Doubtless there was some metabolism of cortical nervous matter during the inventive procedure, for which an energy equation could be written if our knowledge of cerebral physiology were complete. But the relatively trivial amount of energy change involved in this process in comparison with the mechanical advantage gained during the entire subsequent period in which pulley-blocks have been used illustrates the importance of the factor of pattern of performance in all equations of energetics.

So in the living machine all organismic functions occupy a high place as causative factors, whether or not they involve large quantities of energy change, because of the unique part played by these processes in determining the form of the behavior pattern. Now, we have no scientific evidence that the physiological functions of the cerebral cortex differ in fundamental nature from the organismic functions of other parts of the nervous system, and the fact that the most interesting and important of these functions can be only very incompletely investigated by the ordinary physiological methods now in vogue should not lead us to refuse to observe them by the one method that is available, namely, by introspection (Herrick, 1915). This seems perfectly obvious regardless of one's philosophical views regarding the relations between mind and body.

Much valuable information was gained regarding the laws of nervous conduction by the study of the accompanying electric currents (the negative variation or action current) before anything was known regarding the processes going on within the nerve fiber itself. We now believe that the action current is more than an indicator of internal change; it is an integral part of the process of nervous conduction. In an analogous way introspective evidence has value at least as an indicator of the presence of some cerebral process of great significance to the organism; and the evidence is to some of us quite as convincing that conscious processes play as real a part in shaping human conduct as does the action current in maintaining nervous transmission. And to the plain man of science unversed in the subtleties of traditional metaphysics mind seems to be a function of brain in much the same sense that contraction is a function of muscle.

To an unprejudiced observer mind appears to be as truly a cause of certain bodily actions as muscular contraction is a cause of bodily movement. The evidence is of the same kind and as convincing in the one case as in the other. Now in biology we do not recognize disembodied functions as causes of anything. It is the functioning organ which is the cause, and it seems to be at least a plausible inference that the observed effects of mind on body are in reality effects of one functioning organ (the brain thinking) on other organs of the body. This is no more an objectionable materialism than is the statement of any other physiological correlation between an organ and its function. The question of the essential nature of the relation between structure and function in general the biologist may set aside for future consideration or very cheerfully hand over to the philosopher to do with as he sees fit.

The definition of behavior and its limits. — These reflections, which have carried us far outside the traditional boundaries of biology, suggest another theme. In an earlier approach (p. 11) to the problems set at the beginning of this paragraph the field of behavior was extended on the biological side well beyond the conventional limits. The question may now be raised whether a similar removal of old landmarks may not be in order on the opposite border, the one that faces toward psychology.

The "behaviorists" of the modern school have set for themselves the task of a scientific formulation of what animals do with their bodies. They have naturally approached this stupendous undertaking at certain favorable points with an extensive laboratory equipment for the measurement of sensori-motor reactions and other activities which readily yield to quantitative statement. In the elaboration of this program they have already had a gratifying measure of success and the field of their labors is rapidly being extended.

The analysis of the activities of the higher animals, including those classified as of the intelligent and emotional types, can be elaborated as our knowledge is extended along the present lines of objective physiological inquiry without limit. But pervading this so-called objective psychology there is necessarily the recognition, tacit or explicit, of the fact that the man or other higher animal under investigation is aware to some extent of what is going on during his behavior. And in view of the further indubitable fact that this awareness is in some of the cases demonstrably a causative factor in the behavior complex, it is bad scientific method to ignore it or to set it aside as an irrelevant epiphenomenon.

Doubtless there is cerebral metabolism, which in due time we may be able to measure quantitatively and for which chemical equations may be written, while I read a telegram announcing the birth of my first child and the conscious processes ensuing are as real causes of my subsequent behavior as is the metabolism, and they can no more be ignored in a consideration of the total situation than can the heat generated during muscular work be left out of account in the equation of a calorimeter experiment.

Of the various discussions of the place of consciousness in behavior from the standpoint of the radically objective school, the recent paper by Lashley (1923) on "The Behavioristic Interpretation of Consciousness" is in some respects the most critical and catholic that has come to my notice.

With the author's attack on dualistic interpretations I am in full sympathy, but the disparagement of the behavioristic (or any other?) value of introspective experience is not the proper alternative course to pursue. His attempt to show from the introspective evidence itself that the physiological account of behavior will also be a complete and adequate account of all the phenomena of consciousness must be reckoned a failure. The awareness which he is at so great pains to expunge reappears under another and even less intelligible name, to wit: "All that can be said is that some process, relation, or what not, gives rise to the phenomena of content, and determines the character of the field of consciousness."

My contention is that this "field of consciousness" is not some metaphysical psyche, but that it is an integral and necessary part of certain higher behavior complexes, a part whose essential attribute (awareness) knits in with the rest of the complex in a way no more unphysiological than the way the negative variation knits in with the process of conduction in a nerve fiber. Consciousness is, in short, an organic mode in the strictly biological sense in which this term was used on page 248. If this be true, to neglect adequately controlled introspective data in a complete survey of the behaviorist's program is unphysiological.

I like to believe that I am a behaviorist. As such I like to carry my physiological method farther into the psychological field than the radical behaviorists seem to be able to follow. And by so doing I feel that I am salvaging something from introspective psychology which is quite worth while for Behavior.

Consciousness, then, is a factor in behavior, a real cause of human conduct, and probably to some extent in that of other animals. We have endeavored to show that it belongs to the general class of individually modifiable action, whose manifestations in some form are coextensive with life itself. This series of activities as viewed objectively forms an unbroken graded series from the lowest to the highest animal species. And since in myself the awareness of the reaction is an integral part of it, I am justified in extending the belief in the participation of consciousness to other men and to brutes in so far as the similarities of their objective behavior justify the inference. How far down the organic scale this inference is permissible is a matter of opinion. Panpsychism is certainly not the only possible solution of the problem. We have enumerated on page 296 a number of critical periods in animal evolution where new organic modes were introduced by the recombination of simpler elements in patterns hitherto not present, and clearly it is not impossible that at some level of organization awareness of action similarly came into being as a new biological pattern.

But these turbid waters are too deep for us; we can neither walk safely upon the solid bottom of verifiable observation nor sail upon the troubled and uncharted surface by dead reckoning, for in the exploration of the unknown expanse of psychogenesis we lack both compass and chronometer.

Returning, then, to the question of the limitations of the field of animal behavior, it is clear that we gain nothing but on the other hand may lose much, if we are content to base our conclusions upon only a part of the data at our hand. It is, no doubt, far easier going on the relatively level ground of objective physiological experimentation; but the wider view obtainable from the summits beyond will justify the additional labor demanded by the ascent. And if at the top we find to our disappointment that the anticipated prospect is obscured by clouds whose murk we cannot penetrate, the undismayed explorer can only try again in the hope that another peak or another and fairer day may bring success.

The conclusion is that if consciousness, when present, is a real factor in the causative complex resulting in behavior, as I believe it to be, obviously this factor cannot be ignored in the scientific analysis of the field of behavior as a whole. To be sure, one may abstract from the total complex any factor desired for special study apart. This is the usual method of experimental analysis. Recent students of animal behavior have, for the most part, wisely chosen to investigate the objective aspects of the question apart from possible conscious factors, and the brilliant results of their labors have abundantly justified the procedure adopted. But from this it does not follow that the properly controlled study of the introspective factors, when this is possible, may not assist greatly in the final evaluation of certain higher types of behavior.

The future of human evolution. — Turning now to the specific problem of the evolution of human behavior, it is everywhere recognized that with the advent of man on earth evolution took a new direction. The lineage of the human body has been traced upward through a line of generalized forms, and except in brain texture it retains to-day its generalized character. With the expansion of the cortical associational mechanisms, progressive evolution of the remainder of the body apparently came to an end, though lateral diversification of races may have gone on until now. Even this has probably reached its limit and intercrossing of races will tend to swamp the existing differences (Conklin, 1922, p. 174).

Whether evolution of cortical texture is still in process is a controverted matter. So-called social heredity, or the transmission from generation to generation of accumulated cultural material by example and precept, has so far supplemented the physical or protoplasmic heredity of cerebral differentiation that it is impossible to separate the factors.

Certain it is that in civilized communities the social factors have so overshadowed the individual factors that it may safely be said that further evolutionary advance will be measured by social efficiency rather than by personal efficiency alone (Conn, 1914, Conklin, 1915, Chap. 6). But the highest social efficiency is impossible without a high average of personal efficiency. What, then, is the integrating bond in such a society?

The individual whose brutish desire for personal profit is unrestrained by the needs and rights of his fellows reverts to barbarism. If a bandit he is outlawed; if a politician he is — usually reëlected, with resulting retrogression of the entire social organization.

The individualizing tendencies of the various parts of the animal body as expressed in local centers of physiological dominance are kept in hand, so to speak, by the integrating organismic forces. And the more highly differentiated are the tissues and organs of the body the more efficient must be the center of chief dominance and the organismic apparatus of conduction which binds the whole together. So the highest social organism is composed of units each of which has great individual efficiency with strong impulses toward self-preservation and self-aggrandizement which are kept in check by the ties of interdependence, loyalty and devotion to the public welfare. Commercial interchange, patriotism and altruism, in short, are as truly organismic factors as are the physiological gradients in a flatworm (Child, 1924, Chaps. 16 and 17).

This argument cannot be elaborated here. The point is raised merely to emphasize the fact that, though human evolution has taken an entirely new direction through social control, yet this is not something apart from the rest of the general process. On the contrary, the social factors in human progress are rooted deeply in the lives of our earliest mammalian ancestors.

In parental care are the rudiments of that widening of the self which has culminated in the metamorphosis of a narrow self-seeking into the altruistic ideal of the highest attainable self-culture in the interest of increased value to the community as a whole. Nothing of self-interest is sacrificed in this irradiation of the personality to include in its scope the welfare of the remotest human circle (*cf.* p. 3), for experience has shown that the welfare of the individual is bound up with that of the society of which he forms a part. Indeed, enlightened self-interest goes further than this and includes intelligent conservation of the natural resources of forest, soil and mineral and even scenic beauty.

And so the self to be cherished and fostered has enlarged to include the family, clan, tribe, nation and (let us hope) the community of nations. Each organic unit from the cells of which the body is composed, through the tissues, organs, bodies, and human societies of successively higher rank, up to the nations which have partitioned among themselves the habitable land of the globe, is bound to the others in reciprocal organismic relationship of such a character that the welfare of each individual is essential to that of the whole and the integrity of the whole to that of even the humblest unit.

The two factors which seem to be playing the largest part at present in progressive human evolution are: (1) the greater control over nature through intelligence, ideation, and prevision of the future course of events; and (2) the progress from high individual efficiency to the still more potent coöperative unit of society. This is nothing new under the sun, for the biological origins of both of these factors can readily be traced. The integrating factor here, as in the multicellular body and the hive of bees, is the harmonious interrelationship of the units of the organization under the guidance of certain groups of units which dominate by reason of their greater dynamic efficiency (Child, 1924, Chap. 16).

And the power exercised by these dominating units in a well-ordered society, as in a living body, is not that of a tyrannical overlord appointed by an outside power to exploit his subjects, but a natural regulatory control developed within the community itself. Those individuals whose broader vision and executive ability command the respect and confidence of their fellows come by common consent to occupy strategic positions in the social organization with benefits to all concerned.

So also in the relationships of social units with each other, of nation with nation, the day has not yet dawned when brute force can be suspended as the arbiter of international differences and yet the utter futility of this brutish method is already apparent. War breeds war, not peace. Not for long can lust of conquest, whether of land or goods or the spirits of men, contend on equal terms against the more enlightened social consciousness of the age. And the factors of this progressively widening social consciousness are no longer either personal or national self-seeking alone.

Honor, fidelity, justice, mercy, charity, the good, the true, the beautiful, in short, the finer "humanities" — these are essential threads in the warp of this noble pattern of human culture, as essential as are strength, courage and aggressive power. These finer traits are not something added to the grosser clay of man's animal heritage. They are part of that heritage, the smaller part perhaps, but the most precious treasures in his legacy from the past; and his success in the future cycles of the evolutionary movement will depend to a large extent upon the balance which he strikes between the narrower interests of his purely personal, family or national welfare and the wider relationships with his entire social environment through commerce, interchange of intellectual, esthetic and moral ideals, and sympathetic intercourse of all sorts.

The key to success here, as everywhere, is the *mutual* advantage arising from such relationships, whether these be with peoples of relatively backward social development or with those who have already progressed beyond us in material or cultural advance.

Finally, let it not be forgotten that orthogenetic factors do not cease to operate when the evolutionary process is transferred from the elementary biological to the social plane. Altruism and idealism grow, expand and propagate as truly as do cunning, acquisitiveness, selfishness and greed; and when once society has definitely set its face toward the higher standards of social relationship no single community can obstruct the general movement. Nor can any advanced people revert to the barbaric standard of isolated self-sufficiency. They must adjust to the general movement and advance with it or perish from off the earth. If any individuals or nations are unable to recognize this trend in human affairs or feel unwilling to pay the price demanded in order to retain a place in the van of this train of progressive evolution and so desire to drop behind, let them in the interest of self-preservation, if they would avoid imminent disaster, remember the maxim, "Face forward when alighting."

If we would forecast the future of progressive evolution on this planet, the question is not whether the individual human mind of to-day has greater intellectual capacity than had those of the ages of antiquity. For this we have no proper standard of measurement in any event. But the question is irrelevant. What we want to know is, does the culture of to-day exhibit better team-work than of old, is the machinery of coöperative effort more efficient, are we more neighborly, and have we a proper understanding of the searching question, who is my neighbor?

BIBLIOGRAPHY

ALLEE, W. C., and STEIN, E. R. 1918. Light reactions and metabolism in mayfly nymphs. *Jour. Exp. Zoöl.*, vol. 26, pp. 423–458.

ANDREWS, E. A. 1911. Observations on termites in Jamaica. *Jour. Animal Behavior*, vol. 1, pp. 193–288.

ASHWORTH, J. H. 1909. The giant nerve cells and fibers of Halla parthenopeia. *Phil. Trans. Roy. Soc.*, B, vol. 200, pp. 427–521.

ATWATER, W. O., and BENEDICT, F.C. 1903. Experiments on the metabolism of matter and energy in the human body. *Bul. no. 136, U. S. Dept. Agriculture*, Office of Experiment Stations, Washington.

BAGLIONI, S. 1900. Physiologische Differenzierung verschiedener Mechanismen des Rückenmarkes (Frog). *Arch. f. (Anat. und) Physiol.*, 1900, Suppl., pp. 193–242.

————— 1905. Physiologische Differenzierung verschiedener Mechanismen des Zentralnervensystems. II. (Squid) *Zeits. f. allg. Physiol.*, Bd. 5, pp. 43–65.

BARKER, L. F. 1901. *The nervous system and its constituent neurones.* New York.

BARTELMEZ, G. W. 1915. Mauthner's cell and the nucleus motorius tegmenti. *Jour. Comp. Neur.*, vol. 25, pp. 87–128.

————— 1920. The morphology of the synapse in vertebrates. *Arch. Neurol. and Psychiatry*, Chicago, vol. 4, pp. 122–126.

BEHRE, E. H. 1918. An experimental study of acclimation to temperature in Planaria dorotocephala. *Biol. Bul.*, vol. 35.

BELLAMY, A. W. 1919. Differential susceptibility as a basis for modification and control of early development in the frog. *Biol. Bul.*, vol. 37, pp. 312–361.

————— 1922. The same. II. Types of modification seen in later developmental stages. *Am. Jour. Anat.*, vol. 30, pp. 473–502.

BETHE, A. 1899. Die Locomotion des Haifisches (Scyllium) und ihre Beziehungen zu den einzelnen Gehirntheile und zum Labyrinth. *Pflüger's Archiv*, Bd. 76, pp. 470–493.

BIANCHI, L. 1922. *The mechanism of the brain and the functions of the frontal lobes.* Edinburgh, E. and S. Livingstone.

BINGHAM, HAROLD C. 1922. Visual perception of the chick. *Behavior Monographs*, vol. 4, no. 4.

BLACK, DAVIDSON. 1917. The motor nuclei of the cerebral nerves in phylogeny. A study of the phenomena of neurobiotaxis. Part 1. Cyclostomi and Pisces. *Jour. Comp. Neur.*, vol. 27, pp. 467–564.

————— 1917 a. The same. Part 2. Amphibia. *Ibid.*, vol. 28, pp. 379–424.

————— 1920. The same. Part 3. Reptilia. *Ibid.*, vol. 32, pp. 61–98.

————— 1922. The same. Part 4. Aves. *Ibid.*, vol. 34, pp. 233–275.

311

Bok, S. T. 1915. Die Entwicklung der Hirnnerven und ihrer zentralen Bahnen. Die stimulogene Fibrilation. *Folia Neurobiologica*, Bd. 9, pp. 475–565.

———— 1917. The development of reflexes and reflex tracts. I. The reflex-circle. *Psych. en Neurol. Bladen*, 1917, no. 4, pp. 281–303.

Bolton, Joseph Shaw. 1914. *The brain in health and disease.* London.

Bovard, John F. 1918. The transmission of nervous impulses in relation to locomotion in the earthworm. *Univ. of Calif. Pub. in Zoölogy*, vol. 18, no. 7, pp. 103–134.

———— 1918 a. The function of the giant fibers in earthworms. *Ibid.*, vol. 18, no. 8, pp. 135–144.

Breed, F. S. 1911. The development of certain instincts and habits in chicks. *Behavior Monographs*, vol. 1.

Broman, Ivar. 1920. Das Organon vomeronasale Jacobsoni, ein Wassergeruchsorgan. *Anat. Hefte*, Abt. 1, Bd. 58, pp. 137–191.

Buchanan, J. W. 1922. The control of head formation in Planaria by means of anesthetics. *Jour. Exp. Zoöl.*, vol. 36, pp. 1–47.

Bunting, Martha. 1922. A preliminary note on Tetramitus, a stage in the life cycle of a coprozoic amœba. *Proc. Nat. Acad. Sci.*, vol. 18, pp. 294–300.

Bütschli, O. 1912. *Vorlesungen über vergleichende Anatomie.* 2 Liferung. Leipzig.

Cannon, W. B. 1915. *Bodily changes in pain, hunger, fear and rage.* New York.

Carey, Lewis R. 1916. The influence of the marginal sense organs on the rate of regeneration in Cassiopea xamachana. *Jour. Exp. Zoöl.*, vol. 21, pp. 1–32.

———— 1917. Studies on the physiology of the nervous system of Cassiopea xamachana. *Carnegie Inst. of Washington, publ. no. 251*, pp. 123–170.

Carmalt, Churchill. 1901. Preliminary report on a case of cyclopia. *Proc. 14. Ann. Session Assoc. Am. Anatomists, Session of 1900*, pp. 93–104.

Chamberlin, T. C. 1900. On the habitat of the early vertebrates. *Jour. Geology*, vol. 8, pp. 400–412.

Child, C. M. 1908. The physiological basis of restitution of lost parts. *Jour. Exp. Zoöl.*, vol. 5, pp. 485–501.

———— 1910. The central nervous system as a factor in the regeneration of polyclad Turbellaria. *Biol. Bul.*, vol. 19, pp. 333–338.

———— 1911. The regulatory processes in organisms. *Jour. Morph.*, vol. 22, pp. 171–222.

———— 1911 a. Experimental control of morphogenesis in the regulation of Planaria. *Biol. Bul.*, vol. 20, pp. 309–331.

———— 1914. The axial gradients in ciliated Infusoria. *Biol. Bul.*, vol. 26, pp. 36–54.

———— 1914 a. Susceptibility gradients in animals. *Science*, n. s., vol. 39, pp. 73–76.

———— 1915. *Senescence and rejuvenescence.* Univ. of Chicago Press.

———— 1915 a. *Individuality in organisms.* Univ. of Chicago Press.

CHILD, C. M. 1916. Axial susceptibility gradients in Algæ. *Bot. Gaz.*, vol. 62, pp. 89–114.

———— 1916 a. Studies on the dynamics of morphogenesis, etc., IX. The control of head form and head frequency in Planaria by means of potassium cynanide. *Jour. Exp. Zoöl.*, vol. 21, pp. 101–126.

———— 1919. The axial gradients in Hydrozoa. II. *Biol. Bul.*, vol. 37, pp. 101–114.

———— 1920. Studies on the dynamics of morphogenesis, etc., X. Head frequency in Planaria dorotocephala in relation to age, nutrition and motor activity. *Jour. Exp. Zoöl.*, vol. 30, pp. 403–418.

———— 1921. *The origin and development of the nervous system.* Univ. of Chicago Press.

———— 1921 a. The axial gradients in Hydrozoa. IV. *Biol. Bul.*, vol. 41, pp. 78–97.

————1921 b. Studies on the dynamics of morphogenesis, etc., XI. Physiological factors in the development of the planarian head. *Jour. Exp. Zoöl.*, vol. 33, pp. 409–433.

———— 1924. *Physiological foundations of behavior.* New York.

CHILD, C. M., and HYMAN, L. H. 1919. The axial gradients in Hydrozoa. I. Hydra. *Biol. Bul.*, vol. 36, pp. 183–223.

CHILD, C. M., and McKIE, E. V. 1911. The central nervous system in teratophthalmic and teratomorphic forms of Planaria dorotocephala. *Biol. Bul.*, vol. 22, pp. 39–59.

CHURCHILL, E. P., JR. 1916. The learning of a maze by goldfish. *Jour. Animal Behavior*, vol. 6, pp. 247–255.

COGHILL, G. E. 1902. The cranial nerves of Amblystoma tigrinum. *Jour. Comp. Neur.*, vol. 12, pp. 205–289.

———— 1924. Correlated anatomical and physiological studies of the growth of the nervous system in Amphibia. III. The floor plate of Amblystoma. *Jour. Comp. Neur.* (in press).

COLE, A. E. 1921. Oxygen supply of certain animals living in water containing no dissolved oxygen. *Jour. Exp. Zoöl.*, vol. 33, pp. 293–320.

CONKLIN, E. G. 1915. *Heredity and environment in the development of men.* Princeton Univ. Press.

———— 1921. Problems of organic adaptation. *The Rice Institute Pamphlet*, vol. 8, pp. 299–380.

———— 1922. The trend of evolution. Chapter VI in *The evolution of man.* New Haven.

CONN, H. W. 1914. *Social heredity and social evolution.* New York.

CRAIG, WALLACE. 1908. The voices of pigeons regarded as a means of social control. *Amer. Jour. Sociology*, vol. 14, pp. 86–100.

———— 1909. The expression of emotion in the pigeons. I. The blond ring-dove (Turtur risorius). *Jour. Comp. Neur.*, vol. 19, pp. 29–80.

———— 1911. The same. II. The mourning-dove. *The Auk*, vol. 28, pp. 398–407.

———— 1911 a. The same. III. The passenger pigeon (Ectopistes migratorius Linn.). *The Auk*, vol. 28, pp. 408–427.

CRAIGIE, E. H. 1920. On the relative vascularity of various parts of the central nervous system of the albino rat. *Jour. Comp. Neur.*, vol. 31, pp. 429–464.

———— 1921. The vascularity of the cerebral cortex of the albino rat. *Jour. Comp. Neur.*, vol. 33, pp. 193–212.

CROSBY, ELIZABETH C. 1917. The forebrain of Alligator mississippiensis. *Jour. Comp. Neur.*, vol. 27, pp. 325–402.

CROZIER, W. J., 1917. The photoreceptors of Amphioxus. *Anat. Rec.*, vol. 11, p. 520.

CROZIER, W. J., and AREY, L. B. 1919. Sensory reactions of Chromodoris zebra. *Jour. Exp. Zoöl.*, vol. 29, pp. 261–310.

DANIEL, J. FRANK. 1922. *The elasmobranch fishes.* Berkeley, Univ. of Cal. Press.

DARWIN, C. 1883. *The formation of vegetable mould through the action of worms, with observations on their habits.* New York.

DAWSON, A. B. 1920. The intermuscular nerve cells of the earthworm. *Jour. Comp. Neur.*, vol. 32, pp. 155–171.

DAY, LUCY M., and BENTLY, M. 1911. A note on learning in Paramecium. *Jour. Animal Behavior*, vol. 1, pp. 67–73.

DENDY, A. 1910. On the structure, development and morphological interpretation of the pineal organs and adjacent parts of the brain in the tuatara (Sphenodon punctatus). *Phil. Trans. Roy. Soc.*, B, vol. 201, pp. 227–331.

DERCUM, F. X. 1922. *An essay on the physiology of mind.* Philadelphia.

DEWEY, JOHN. 1917. *Creative intelligence.* Essay I. The need for a recovery in philosophy. New York.

EASTMAN, MAX. 1917. The will to live. *Jour. Philos.*, vol. 14, pp. 102–107.

EDINGER, FRITZ. 1913. Die Leistungen des Zentralnervensystems beim Frosch (Sammelreferat). *Zeits. f. allg. Physiol.*, Bd. 15, H. 3, pp. 15–64.

EDINGER, L. 1908. *Vorlesungen über den Bau der nervösen Zentral-organe.* 7 ed., vol. 2. Leipzig,

———— 1911. *The same.* 8 ed., vol. 1. Leipzig.

EVE, FRANK C. 1923. In the beginning. An interpretation of sunlight energy. *The Atlantic Monthly*, vol. 131, pp. 664–677.

EYCLESHYMER, A. C., and SHOEMAKER, D. M. 1917. *Anatomical names, especially the Basle Nomina Anatomica ("B. N. A.") with biographical sketches by* R. L. MOODIE. New York.

FOÀ, C. 1911. Ricerche sul ritmo degli impulsi motori che partono dai centri nervosi. *Zeits. allg. Physiologie*, Bd. 13, pp. 35–68.

FORBES, A., and GREGG, A. 1915. Electrical studies in mammalian reflexes. *Am. Jour. Physiol.*, vol. 39, p. 172.

FORTUYN, A. B. DROOGLEEVER. 1920. *Vergleichende Anatomie des Nervensystems. I. Teil. Die Leitungsbahnen im Nervensystem der wirbellosen Tiere.* Haarlem.

FRIEDLÄNDER, B. 1894. Beiträge zur Physiologie des Centralnervensystems und des Bewegungs-Mechanismus der Regenwürmer. *Arch. f. ges. Physiol.*, Bd. 58, pp. 168–206.

GASSER, H. S., and ERLANGER, JOS. 1922. A study of the action currents of nerve with the cathode ray oscillograph. *Am. Jour. Physiol.*, vol. 62, pp. 496-524.

GASSER, H. S., and NEWCOMER,H.S. 1921. Physiological action currents in the phrenic nerve. An application of the thermonic vacuum tube to nerve physiology. *Am. Jour. Physiol.*, vol. 57, pp. 1-26.

GERARD, MARGARET WILSON. 1923. Afferent impulses of the trigeminal nerve. The intramedullary course of the painful, thermal and tactile impulses. *Arch. Neurol. and Psychiatry*, Chicago, vol. 9, pp. 306-338.

GIBBS, DAVID. 1908. The daily life of Amœba proteus. *Am. Jour. Psychol.*, vol. 19, pp. 232-241.

GOLGI, C. 1907. La dottrina del neurone, teoria e fatti. *Arch. Fisiol.*, vol. 4, pp. 187-215.

GRIFFIN, LAWRENCE E. 1922. *A guide for the dissection of the dogfish* (Squalus acanthias). 3 ed. Privately printed by the author. Portland, Oregon.

GROŠELJ, P. 1909. Untersuchingen über das Nervensystem der Aktinien. *Arb. Zoöl. Inst. Wien.*, Bd. 17.

GROSS, ALFRED O. 1921. The feeding habits and chemical sense of Nereis virens, Sars. *Jour. Exp. Zoöl.*, vol. 32, pp. 427-442.

HACHLOY, L. 1910. Die Sensillen und die Entstehungs der Augen bei Hirudo medicinalis. *Zoöl. Jahrb.*, Bd. 30, pp. 261-300.

HAMILTON, W. F. 1922. A direct method of testing color vision in lower animals. *Proc. Nat. Acad. Sci.*, vol. 8, pp. 350-353.

HAMMETT, F. S. 1921. Temperament and bodily constitution. *Comparative Psychology*, vol. 1, pp. 489-494.

HARPER, E. H. 1905. Reactions to light and mechanical stimuli in the earthworm, Perichæta bermudensis (Beddard). *Biol. Bul.*, vol. 10, pp. 17-34.

HARRIS, W. H. 1904. Binocular and stereoscopic vision. *Brain*, vol. 27, p. 106.

HARVEY, E. NEWTON. 1912. The question of nerve fatigue. *Carnegie Inst. Yearbook*, no. 10, for 1911, pp. 130-131.

———— 1922. Some recent experiments on the nature of the nervous impulse. *Jour. Nerv. Ment. Dis.*, vol. 55, pp. 503-505.

HAVET, J. 1922. La structure du système nerveux des actinies, leur mécanisme neuro-musculaire. *Libro en honor de D. S. Ramón y Cajal*, vol. I, pp. 477-504. Madrid.

HECK, L. 1919-20. Ueber die Bildung einer Assoziation beim Regenwurm auf Grund von Dressurversuchen. *Lotus*, Prag. Nos. 67-68.

HEIDENHAIN, M. 1911. Plasma und Zelle. 2 Lieferung, Jena. (In Bardeleben's Handbuch der Anatomie des Menschen, Bd. 8.)

HERRICK, C. JUDSON. 1899. The cranial and first spinal nerves of Menidia: A contribution upon the nerve components of the bony fishes. *Jour. Comp. Neur.*, vol. 9, pp. 153-455.

———— 1903. The organ and sense of taste in fishes. *Bul. U. S. Fish. Com.*, vol. 22, pp. 237-272.

———— 1903 a. The doctrine of nerve components and some of its applications. *Jour. Comp. Neur.*, vol. 13, pp. 301-312.

———— 1903 b. On the phylogeny and morphological position of the terminal buds of fishes. *Jour. Comp. Neur.*, vol. 13, pp. 121-138.

HERRICK C. JUDSON. 1905. The central gustatory paths in the brains of bony fishes. *Jour. Comp. Neur.*, vol. 15, pp. 375–456.
———— 1906. On the centers for taste and touch in the medulla oblongata of fishes. *Jour. Comp. Neur.*, vol. 16, pp. 403–439.
———— 1907. A study of the vagal lobes and funicular nuclei of the brain of the codfish. *Jour. Comp. Neur.*, vol. 17, pp. 67–87.
———— 1907 a. The tactile centers in the spinal cord and brain of the sea-robin, Prionotus carolinus L. *Jour. Comp. Neur.*, vol. 17, pp. 307–327.
———— 1908. On the phylogenetic differentiation of the organs of smell and taste. *Jour. Comp. Neur.*, vol. 18, pp. 159–166.
———— 1910. The evolution of intelligence and its organs. *Science*, N. S., vol. 31, pp. 7–18.
———— 1910 a. The relations of the central and peripheral nervous systems in phylogeny. *Anat. Rec.*, vol. 4, pp. 59–69.
———— 1913. Some reflections on the origin and significance of the cerebral cortex. *Jour. Animal Behavior*, vol. 3, pp. 222–236.
———— 1914. The cerebellum of Necturus and other urodele Amphibia. *Jour. Comp. Neur.*, vol. 24, pp. 1–29.
———— 1914 a. The medulla oblongata of larval Amblystoma. *Jour. Comp. Neur.*, vol. 24, pp. 343–427.
———— 1914 b. Cranial nerves. In Wood's *Reference Handbook of the Medical Sciences*, 3 ed., vol. 3, pp. 321–339.
———— 1915. Introspection as a biological method. *Jour. Philos.*, vol. 12, pp. 543–551.
———— 1919. The senses of fishes. *Nat. History*, vol. 19, pp. 322–324.
———— 1920. Irreversible differentiation and orthogenesis. *Science*, N. S., vol. 51, pp. 621–625.
———— 1921. A sketch of the origin of the cerebral hemispheres. *Jour. Comp. Neur.*, vol. 32, pp. 429–454.
———— 1921 a. The connections of the vomeronasal nerve, accessory olfactory bulb and amygdala in Amphibia. *Jour. Comp. Neur.*, vol. 33, pp. 213–280.
———— 1922. *Introduction to neurology.* 3 ed. Philadelphia.
———— 1922 a. Some factors in the development of the amphibian nervous system. *Anat. Rec.*, vol. 23, pp. 291–305.
———— 1922 b. What are viscera? *Jour. Anat.* (London), vol. 56, pp. 167–176.
———— 1922 c. Functional factors in the morphology of the forebrain of fishes. *Libro en honor de D. S. Ramón y Cajal*, Madrid, vol. I, pp. 143–204.
———— 1924. Origin and evolution of the cerebellum. *Arch. Neurol. and Psychistry.* (In press.)
HERRICK, C. JUDSON, and COGHILL, G. E. 1915. The development of reflex mechanisms in Amblystoma. *Jour. Comp. Neur.*, vol. 25, pp. 65–85.
HERRICK, C. JUDSON, and CROSBY, ELIZABETH C. 1920. *A laboratory outline of neurology*, 2 ed. Philadelphia.
HERRICK, C. L. 1910. The metaphysics of a naturalist. Philosophical and psychological fragments (posthumously published). *Bul. Sci. Lab.* Denison University, Granville, Ohio, vol. 15.

HERRICK, F. H. 1905. *The home life of wild birds.* Rev. ed. New York.
———— 1911. Nests and nest-building in birds. *Jour. Animal Behavior,* vol. 1, pp. 158–192, 244–277, 336–373.

HERTWIG, O. 1918. *Das Werden der Organismen. Zur Wiederlegung von Darwin's Zufallstheorie durch das Gesetz in der Entwicklung.* 2 ed. Jena, G. Fischer.

HESS, C. 1912. *Vergleichende Physiologie des Gesichtssinnes.* Jena.

HESSE, R. 1896. Untersuchungen über die Organe der Lichtempfindung bei niederen Thieren. I. Die Organe der Lichtempfindung bei den Lumbriciden. *Zeits. wiss. Zoöl.,* Bd. 61, pp. 393–419.

HILL, A. V. 1921. The tetanic nature of the voluntary contraction in man. *Jour. Physiol.,* vol. 55, *Proc. Physiol Soc.,* pp. xiv–xvi.

HILTON, W. A. 1917. The central nervous system of simple Crustacea. *Jour. Comp. Neur.,* vol. 28, pp. 429–440.

HINES, MARION. 1922. Studies in the growth and differentiation of the telencephalon in man. The fissura hippocampi. *Jour. Comp. Neur.,* vol. 34, pp. 73–171.

HOLMGREN, NILS. 1922. Points of view concerning forebrain morphology in lower vertebrates. *Jour. Comp. Neur.,* vol. 34, pp. 391–459.

HOLMES, S. J. 1904. The problem of form regulation. *Arch. f. Entwicklungsmechanik,* Bd. 17, pp. 265–305.
———— 1907. Regeneration as functional adjustment. *Jour. Exp. Zoöl.,* vol. 4, pp. 419–430.

HOUGH, TH. 1915. The classification of nervous reactions. *Science,* N. S., vol. 41, pp. 407–418.

HOWARD, A. D. 1908. The visual cells in vertebrates, chiefly in Necturus maculosus. *Jour. Morph.,* vol. 19, pp. 561–632.

HUDSON, W. H. 1918. *Far away and long ago. A history of my early life.* New York.

HUNTER, WALTER S. 1915. The auditory sensitivity of the white rat. *Jour. Animal Behavior,* vol. 5, pp. 312–329.

HUXLEY, T. H. 1902. Evolution and Ethics. In vol. 9 of Huxley's *Collected essays.* New York.

HYMAN, LIBBIE H. 1916. An analysis of the process of regeneration in certain microdrilous oligochætes. *Jour. Exp. Zoöl.,* vol. 20, pp. 99–163.
———— 1917. Metabolic gradients in Amœba and their relation to the mechanism of amœboid movement. *Jour. Exp. Zoöl.,* vol. 24, pp. 55–99.
———— 1920. The axial gradients in Hydrozoa. III. *Biol. Bul.,* vol. 38, pp. 353–403.
———— 1922. *A laboratory manual for comparative vertebrate anatomy.* Univ. of Chicago Press.

HYMAN, LIBBIE H., and BELLAMY, A. W. 1922. Studies on the correlation between metabolic gradients, electrical gradients, and galvanotaxis. I. *Biol. Bul.,* vol. 43, pp. 313–347.

HYMAN, LIBBIE H., and GALIGHER, A. E. 1921. Direct demonstration of the existence of a metabolic gradient in annelids. *Jour. Exp. Zoöl.,* vol. 34, pp. 1–16.

INGVAR, SVEN. 1918. Zur phylo- und ontogenese des Kleinhirns, nebst einem Versuche zu einheitlicher Erklärung der zerebellaren Funktion und Lokalisation. *Folia Neurobiologica*, Bd. 11.

———— 1920. Reaction of cells to the galvanic current in tissue cultures. *Proc. Am. Soc. Exp. Biol. and Med.*, vol. 17, p. 198.

JAMES, WM. 1890. *The principles of psychology.* 2 vols. New York.

JANET, CHARLES. 1912. *Le volvox.* Limoges, Ducourtieux et Gout. 151 pp.

———— 1922. *Le volvox. Deuxième memoire.* Paris, Presses Univ. de France. 66 pp.

JENNINGS, H. S. 1902. Studies on reactions to stimuli in unicellular organisms. IX. On the behavior of fixed Infusoria (Stentor and Vorticella) with special reference to the modifiability of protozoan reactions. *Am. Jour. Physiol.*, vol. 8, pp. 23–60.

———— 1905. The method of regulation in behavior and in other fields. *Jour. Exp. Zoöl.*, vol. 2, pp. 473–494.

———— 1905 a. Modifiability in behavior. I. Behavior of sea anemones. *Jour. Exp. Zoöl.*, vol. 2, pp. 447–472.

———— 1906. *Behavior of the lower organisms.* New York.

———— 1906 a. Modifiability in behavior. II. Factors determining direction and character of movement in the earthworm. *Jour. Exp. Zoöl.*, vol. 3, pp. 435–455.

JOHNSON, G. L. 1901. Contributions to the comparative anatomy of the mammalian eye. *Phil. Trans. Roy. Soc.*, vol. 194 B, pp. 1–82.

JOHNSON, H. M. 1913. Audition and habit formation in the dog. *Behavior Monogr.*, vol. 2, no. 3.

———— 1914. Visual pattern discrimination in the vertebrates. II. Comparative visual acuity in the dog, the monkey, and the chick. *Jour. Animal Behavior*, vol. 4, pp. 340–361.

JOHNSON, S. E. 1917. Structure and development of the sense organs of the lateral canal system of selachians (Mustelus canis and Squalus acanthias). *Jour. Comp. Neur.*, vol. 28, pp. 1–74.

JOHNSTON, J. B. 1901. The brain of Acipenser. *Zoöl. Jahrb.*, Bd. 15, pp. 1–204.

———— 1902. The brain of Petromyzon. *Jour. Comp. Neur.*, vol. 12, pp. 1–86.

———— 1902 a. An attempt to define the primitive divisions of the central nervous system. *Jour. Comp. Neur.*, vol. 12, pp. 87–106.

———— 1905. The cranial nerve components of Petromyzon. *Morph. Jahrb.*, Bd. 34, pp. 149–203.

———— 1906. *The nervous system of vertebrates.* Philadelphia.

———— 1909. The central nervous system of vertebrates. Spengel's *Ergebnisse und Fortschritte der Zoölogie*, Bd. 2, Heft 2, Jena.

———— 1911. The telencephalon of selachians. *Jour. Comp. Neur.*, vol. 21, pp. 1–113.

———— 1915. The cell masses in the forebrain of the turtle, Cistudo carolina. *Jour. Comp. Neur.*, vol. 25, pp. 393–468.

———— 1923. Further contributions to the study of the evolution of the forebrain. Parts I to IV. *Jour. Comp. Neur.*, vol. 35, pp. 337–481; Part V, vol. 36, pp. 143–192.

JOHNSTONE, JAMES. 1921. *The mechanism of life.* London, Edward Arnold.

KAFKA, G. 1914. Einfürhrung in die Tierpsychologie auf experimenteller und ethologischer Grundlage. *Bd. I. Die Sinne der Wirbellosen.* Leipzig.

KAPPERS, C. U. ARIËNS. 1913. Cerebral localization and the significance of sulci. *Proc. 17th Intern. Congress of Medicine. Anat. and Embryol.* London.

———— 1914. Ueber das Rindenproblem und die Tendenz innerer Hirnteile sich durch Oberflächen-Vermehrung statt Volumzunahme zu vergrössern. *Folia Neurobiol.*, Bd. 8, pp. 507–531.

———— 1917. Further contributions on neurobiotaxis. IX. An attempt to compare the phenomena of neurobiotaxis with other phenomena of taxis and tropism. The dynamic polarization of the neuron. *Jour. Comp. Neur.*, vol. 27, pp. 261–298.

———— 1920–1921. *Die vergleichende Anatomie des Nervensystems der Wirbeltiere und des Menschen.* 2 vols. Haarlem.

———— 1922. Dixième contribution a la théorie de la neurobiotaxis. *L'Encephale*, no. 1, 1922, pp. 1–19.

KATSANUMA. 1915. Zur Frage der Naphtolblauoxydase-reaction des Nervensystems. Ziegler's *Beiträge*, Bd. 60.

KINGSBURY, B. F. 1922. The fundamental plan of the vertebrate brain. *Jour. Comp. Neur.*, vol. 34, pp. 461–491.

KINGSLEY, J. S. 1907. *The dogfish (Acanthias), an elasmobranch*, New York.

KLEINENBERG, N. 1872. *Hydra. Ein anatomisch-entwicklungsgeschichtliche Untersuchungen.* Leipzig.

KOFOID, C. A., and SWEZY, OLIVE. 1919. Studies on the parasites of the termites. I–IV. *Univ. of Calif. Pub. in Zoöl.*, vol. 20, nos. 1–4, pp. 1–116.

KRAWANY, J. 1905. Untersuchungen über das Zentralnervensystem der Regenwürmer. *Arb. Zoöl. Inst. Wien*, Bd. 15, pp. 281–316.

LAMEERE, A. 1922. The origin of insect societies. *Ann. Rep. Smithsonian Inst.* for 1920, pp. 511–521. Transl. from *Rev. Gén. des Sciences*, Aug. 15–30, 1915.

LANDACRE, F. L. 1914. Embryonic cerebral ganglia and the doctrine of nerve components. *Folia Neurobiol.*, Bd. 8, pp. 601–615.

LAPICQUE, L. 1907. Plan d'une théorie physique du fonctionnement des centres nerveux. *C. R. Soc. Biol.*, vol. 63, pp. 787–790.

LAPICQUE, L., M. et MME. 1908. Sur le mécanisme de la curarisation. *C. R. Soc. Biol.*, vol. 65, pp. 733–735.

———— 1912. Curarisation par la vératrine; antagonismes dans la curarisation. *C. R. Soc. Biol.*, vol. 72, pp. 283–286.

LASHLEY, K. S. 1923. The behavioristic interpretation of consciousness. *Psych. Rev.*, vol. 30, pp. 237–277, 329–353.

LEE, F. S. 1898. The functions of the ear and the lateral line in fishes. *Am. Jour. Physiol.*, vol. 1, pp. 128–144.

LILLIE, R. S. 1917. The formation of structures resembling organic growths by means of electrolytic local action in metals, and the general physiological significance and control of this type of action. *Biol. Bul.*, vol. 33, pp. 135–186.

LILLIE, R. S. 1918. Transmission of activation in passive metals as a model of the protoplasmic or nervous type of transmission. *Science*, N. S., vol. 48, pp. 51–60.

———— 1918 a. Heredity from the physico-chemical point of view. *Biol. Bul.*, vol. 34, pp. 65–90.

———— 1919. Nervous and other forms of protoplasmic transmission. *Sci. Mo.*, vol. 8, pp. 456–474, 552–567.

———— 1920. The place of life in nature. *Jour. Philos.*, vol. 17, pp. 479–493.

———— 1922. Transmission of physiological influence in protoplasmic systems, especially nerve. *Physiol. Reviews*, vol. 2, pp. 1–37.

———— 1922 a. Growth in living and non-living systems. *Sci. Mo.*, Feb. pp. 113–131.

———— 1923. *Protoplasmic action and nervous action.* The University of Chicago Press.

LILLIE, R. S., and JOHNSTON, E. N. 1919. Precipitation structures simulating organic growth. II. A contribution to the physico-chemical analysis of growth and heredity. *Biol. Bul.*, vol. 36, pp. 225–273.

LOEB, J. 1894. Beiträge zur Gehirnphysiologie der Würmer. *Arch. f. ges. Physiol.*, Bd. 56, pp. 247–269.

LOTKA, ALFRED J. 1922. Contribution to the energetics of evolution. *Prcc. Nat. Acad. Sci.*, vol. 8, pp. 147–151.

———— 1922 a. Natural selection as a physical principle. *Prcc. Nat. Acad. Sci.*, vol. 8, pp. 151–154.

LUCAS, K. 1917. *The conduction of the nervous impulse.* London.

LULL, R. S. 1918. The evolution of the earth and its inhabitants. Lecture IV. *The pulse of life.* Yale Univ. Press, New Haven.

McCRACKEN, ISABEL. 1907. The egg-laying apparatus in the silkworm (Bombyx mori) as a reflex apparatus. *Jour. Comp. Neur.*, vcl. 17, pp. 262–285.

McINDOO, N. E. 1922. The senses of insects. *Ann. Rep. Smithsonian Inst.*, for the year ending June, 1920, pp. 461–483.

———— 1922 a. The auditory sense of the honey-bee. *Jour. Comp. Neur.*, vol. 34, pp. 173–199.

MALONE, E. F. 1913. Recognition of members of the somatic motor chain of nerve cells by means of a fundamental type of cell structure, and the distribution of such cells in certain regions of the mammalian brain. *Anat. Rec.*, vol. 7, pp. 67–82.

———— 1913 a. The nucleus cardiacus nervi vagi and the three distinct types of nerve cells which innervate the three different types of muscle. *Am. Jour. Anat.*, vol. 15, pp. 121–129.

———— 1923. The cell structure of the superior olive in man. *Jour. Comp. Neur.*, vol. 35, pp. 205–211.

———— 1923 a. Efferent characteristics of reception centers. *Science*, N. S., vol. 57, pp. 449–450.

MARINESCO, G. 1919. Recherches histologiques sur les oxidases. *C. R. Soc. Biol.*, vol. 82, no. 2.

———— 1922. Du rôle des ferments oxydants dans les phénomènes de la vie. *Libro en Honor de D. S. Ramón y Cajal*, Madrid, vol. I, pp. 361–413.

MARSHALL, A. M., and HURST, C. H. 1899. *Practical zoölogy.* 5 ed. London.

MAST, S. O. 1907. Light reactions in lower organisms. II. Volvox globator. *Jour. Comp. Neur.*, vol. 17, pp. 99–180.

———— 1910. Reactions of Amœba to light. *Jour. Exp. Zoöl.*, vol. 9, pp. 265–277.

———— 1911. *Light and the behavior of organisms.* New York.

———— 1911 a. Habits and reactions of the ciliate, Lacrymaria. *Jour. Animal Behavior*, vol. 1, pp. 229–243.

———— 1915. The relative stimulating efficiency of spectral colors for the lower organisms. *Proc. Nat. Acad. Sci.*, vol. 1, pp. 622–625.

———— 1916. The process of orientation in the colonial organism, Gonium pectorale, and a study of the structure and function of the eye-spot. *Jour. Exp. Zoöl.*, vol. 20, pp. 1–17.

———— 1923. Eyes in Volvox and their function (Abstract). *Anat. Rec.*, vol. 24, p. 397.

MATHEWS, A. P. 1903. Electrical polarity in the hydroids. *Am. Jour. Physiol.*, vol. 8, pp. 294–299.

———— 1915. *Physiological chemistry.* New York.

MAYER, A. G. 1906. Rhythmical pulsation in Scyphomedusæ. I. *Carnegie Inst. Publ.*, no. 47.

———— 1908. The same; II, *Ibid.*, no. 102.

MAXWELL, S. S. 1897. Beiträge zur Gehirnphysiologie der Anneliden. *Arch. f. ges. Physiol.*, Bd. 67, pp. 263–297.

———— 1920. Labyrinth and equilibrium. *Jour. Gen. Physiol.*, vol. 2, pp. 123–132, 349–355, vol. 3, pp. 157–162.

———— 1923. *Labyrinth and equilibrium.* Philadelphia.

METCALF, M. M. 1904. *An outline of the theory of organic evolution.* New York.

MEYER, A. 1898. Critical review of the data and general methods of modern neurology. *Jour. Comp. Neur.*, vol. 8, pp. 113–148, 249–313.

MÖBIUS, K. 1873. Die Bewegungen der Thiere und ihr psychischer Horizont. *Schrift d. Naturwiss. Ver. f. Schleswig-Holstein.* Bd. 1, p. 113.

MONTGOMERY, THOS. H. 1906. *The analysis of racial descent in animals.* New York.

MOORE, A. R. 1916. The mechanism of orientation in Gonium. *Jour. Exp. Zoöl.*, vol. 21, pp. 431–432.

———— 1917. Chemical differentiation of the central nervous system in invertebrates. *Proc. Nat. Acad. Sci.*, vol. 3, pp. 598–602.

———— 1919. The respiratory rate of the sciatic nerve of the frog in rest and activity. *Jour. Gen. Physiol.*, vol. 1, pp. 613–621.

———— 1923. Muscle tension and reflexes in the earthworm. *Jour. Gen. Physiol.*, vol. 5, pp. 327–333.

MORRILL, A. D. 1895. The pectoral appendages of Prionotus and their innervation. *Jour. Morph.*, vol. 11, pp. 177–192.

MOTT, F. W. 1907. The progressive evolution of the structure and functions of the visual cortex in Mammalia. Mott's *Archives of Neurol.*, vol. 3, pp. 1–48.

———— 1921. The psychopathology of puberty and adolescence. *Jour. of Mental Science*, vol. 67, pp. 279–318.

MOTT, F. W. 1922. The genetic origin of dementia præcox. *Jour. of Mental Science*, vol. 68, pp. 333–347.

NICHOLSON, F. M. 1923. The changes in amount and distribution of the iron-containing proteins of nerve cells following injury to their axones. *Jour. Comp. Neur.*, vol. 36, pp. 37–87.

NISSL, F. 1903. *Die Neuronenlehre und ihre Anhänger.* Jena.

NORRIS, H. W. 1908. The cranial nerves of Amphiuma means. *Jour. Comp. Neur.*, vol. 18, pp. 527–568.

———— 1913. The cranial nerves of Siren lacertina. *Jour. Morph.*, vol. 24, pp. 245–338.

NORRIS, H. W., and HUGHES, SALLY P. 1920. The cranial, occipital, and anterior spinal nerves of the dogfish, Squalus acanthias. *Jour. Comp. Neur.*, vol. 31, pp. 293–402.

OLMSTED, J. M. D. 1918. Experiments on the nature of the sense of smell in the common catfish, Amiurus. *Am. Jour. Physiol.*, vol. 46, pp. 443–458.

———— 1922. The rôle of the nervous system in the regeneration of polyclad Turbellaria. *Jour. Exp. Zoöl.*, vol. 36, pp. 49–56.

———— 1922 a. The rôle of the nervous system in the locomotion of certain marine polyclads. *Jour. Exp. Zoöl.*, vol. 36, pp. 57–66.

OPPEL, A. 1896–1914. *Lehrbuch der vergleichenden mikroskopischen Anatomie der Wirbeltiere.* Jena.

OSBORN, H. F. 1917. *The origin and evolution of life.* New York.

PARKER, G. H. 1903. The skin and the eyes as receptive organs in the reactions of frogs to light. *Am. Jour. Physiol.*, vol. 10, pp. 28–36.

———— 1905. The stimulation of the integumentary nerves of fishes by light. *Am. Jour. Physiol.*, vol. 14, pp. 413–420.

———— 1905 a. The function of the lateral-line organs in fishes. *Bul. U. S. Fish Com.*, vol. 24, pp. 183–207.

———— 1908. The sensory reactions of amphioxus. *Proc. Am. Acad. Arts Sci.*, vol. 43, pp. 415–455.

———— 1908 a. The origin of the lateral eyes of vertebrates. *Am. Nat.*, vol. 42, pp. 601–609.

———— 1908 b. The sense of taste in fishes. *Science*, N. S., vol. 27, p. 453.

———— 1910. The olfactory reactions of fishes. *Jour. Exp. Zoöl.*, vol. 8, pp. 535–542.

———— 1910 a. Influence of the eyes, ears and other allied sense organs on the movements of the dogfish, Mustelus canis (Mitchell). *Bul. Bureau of Fisheries*, vol. 29, pp. 45–57.

———— 1911. The olfactory reactions of the common killifish. *Jour. Exp. Zoöl.*, vol. 10, pp. 1–5.

———— 1914. The directive influence of the sense of smell in the dogfish. *Bul. U. S. Bureau of Fisheries*, vol. 33, pp. 61–68.

———— 1917. Actinian behavior. *Jour. Exp. Zoöl.*, vol. 22, pp. 193–229.

———— 1918. A critical survey of the sense of hearing in fishes. *Proc. Am. Philos. Soc.*, vol. 57, no. 2.

———— 1918 a. The rate of transmission in the nerve net of the cœlenterates. *Jour. Gen. Physiol.*, vol. 1, pp. 231–236.

PARKER, G. H. 1918 b. Some underlying principles in the structure of the nervous system. *Science*, N. S., vol. 47, pp. 151–162.

———— 1919. *The elementary nervous system.* Philadelphia.

———— 1922. *Smell, taste and allied senses in the vertebrates.* Philadelphia.

PARKER, G. H., and ARKIN, L. The directive influence of light on the earthworm, Allobophora foetida. *Am. Jour. Physiol.*, vol. 5, p. 151.

PARKER, G. H., and BURNETT, F. L. 1900. The reactions of planarians with and without eyes to light. *Am. Jour. Physiol.*, vol. 4, pp. 373–385.

PARKER, G. H., and VAN HEUSEN, A. P. 1917. The responses of the catfish, Amiurus nebulosus, to metallic and non-metallic rods. *Am. Jour. Physiol.*, vol. 44, pp. 405–420.

———— 1917 a. Reception of mechanical stimuli by the skin, lateral-line organs and ears of fishes, especially in Amiurus. *Am. Jour. Physiol.*, vol. 44, pp. 463–489.

PARKER, G. H., and SHELDON, R. E. 1913. The sense of smell in fishes. *Bul. U. S. Bureau of Fisheries*, vol. 32, pp. 35–46.

PARKER, T. J. 1900. *A course of instruction in zoötomy (Vertebrata).* London.

PARMELEE, M. 1913. *The science of human behavior.* New York.

PECKHAM, G. W. and E. G. 1905. *Wasps, social and solitary.* Boston.

PIGHINI, G., and others. 1912. Chemische und biochemische Untersuchungen über das Nervensystem unter normalen und pathologischen Bedingungen. *Biochem. Zeits.*, Bd. 42, pp. 124–149.

PHILLIPS, E. F. 1917. *Beekeeping. A discussion of the life of the honeybee and of the production of honey.* New York.

PIKE, F. H. 1920. The efferent path of the nervous system regarded as a step-up transformer of energy. *Science*, N. S., vol. 52, pp. 111–112.

PÜTTER, A. 1911. *Vergleichende Physiologie.* Jena.

RAMÓN Y CAJAL, PEDRO. 1922. El cerebro de los batracios. *Libro en Honor de D. S. Ramón y Cajal*, Madrid, vol. I, pp. 13–59.

RAMÓN Y CAJAL, S. 1911. Histologie du Système nerveux, vol. 2, Paris.

RAND, H. W. 1915. Wound closure in actinian tentacles with reference to the problem or organization. *Arch. f. Entwickelungsmechanik*, Bd. 41, pp. 160–214.

RANSON, S. W. 1920. *The anatomy of the nervous system.* Philadelphia.

RAU, PHIL and NELLIE. 1918. *Wasp studies afield.* Princeton Univ. Press.

REES, CHARLES W. 1922. The neuromotor apparatus of Paramecium. *Science*, N. S., vol. 55, pp. 184–185.

REICHERT, E. T. 1913. The differentiation and specificity of starches in relation to genera, species, etc. *Carnegie Inst. Washington, pub. 173.*

———— 1914. The germplasm as a stereochemic system. *Science*, N. S., vol. 40, pp. 649–661.

REICHERT, E. T., and BROWN, AMOS P. 1909. The differentiation and specificity of corresponding proteins and other vital substances in relation to biological classification and organic evolution. The crystallography of hemaglobins. *Carnegie Inst. of Washington, pub. 116.*

RITTER, WM. E. 1919. *The unity of the organism, or the organismal conception of life.* Boston.

———— 1921. Scientific idealism. *Sci. Mo.* for Oct., pp. 327–340.

Rogers, Fred T. 1922. Studies of the brain stem. VI. An experimental study of the corpus striatum of the pigeon as related to various instinctive types of behavior. *Jour. Comp. Neur.*, vol. 35, pp. 21–59.

———— 1922 a. A note on the excitable areas of the cerebral hemispheres of the pigeon. *Jour. Comp. Neur.*, vol. 35, pp. 61–65.

Sabussow, H. 1904. Ueber den Bau des Nervensystems von Tricladen aus dem Baikal-See. *Zoöl. Anz.*, Bd. 28, pp. 20–32.

Schaeffer, A. A. 1917. Choice of food in ameba. *Jour. Animal Behavior*, vol. 7, pp. 220–258.

Sharp, Robert G. 1914. Diplodinium ecaudatum, with an account of its neuromotor apparatus. *Univ. of Calif. Pub. in Zoöl.*, vol. 13, pp. 43–122.

Sheldon, R. E. 1909. The reactions of the dogfish to chemical stimuli. *Jour. Comp. Neur.*, vol. 19, pp. 273–311.

———— 1911. The sense of smell in selachians. *Jour. Exp. Zoöl.*, vol. 10, pp. 51–62.

Sherrington, C. S. 1906. *The integrative action of the nervous system.* New York.

Slonaker, J. R. 1897. A comparative study of the area of acute vision in vertebrates. *Jour. Morph.*, vol. 13, pp. 445–502.

Smith, B. G. 1912. The embryology of Cryptobranchus alleghaniensis, including comparisons with other vertebrates. Part II. *Jour. Morph.*, vol. 23, pp. 455–579.

Smith, G. Elliot. 1902. *Descriptive and illustrated catalogue of the physiological series of comparative anatomy contained in the Museum of the Royal College of Surgeons of England.* 2 ed., vol. 2. London.

———— 1910. Some problems relating to the evolution of the brain. *The Lancet* for Jan. 1, 15 and 22, 1910.

———— 1912. The evolution of man. *Nature* (London) for Sept. 26, 1912. Reprinted in *The Smithsonian Report for 1912*, pp. 553–572, Washington, 1913.

———— 1919. A preliminary note on the morphology of the corpus striatum and the origin of the neopallium. *Jour. Anat.*, vol. 53, pp. 272–291.

Smith, Grant. 1906. The eyes of certain pulmonate gasteropods, with special reference to the neurofibrillæ of Limax maximus. *Bul. Mus. Comp. Zoöl.*, vol. 48, pp. 233–283.

Smith, Stevenson. 1908. The limits of educability in Paramecium. *Jour. Comp. Neur.*, vol. 18, pp. 499–510.

Sprenkel, H. Berkelbach van der. 1915. The central relations of the cranial nerves in Silurus glanis and Mormyrus cashive. *Jour. Comp. Neur.*, vol. 25, pp. 1–63.

Starbuck, E. D. 1921. The intimate senses as sources of wisdom. *Jour. of Religion*, vol. 1, pp. 129–145.

Stockard, C. R. 1909. The development of artificially produced fish — "The magnesium embryo." *Jour. Exp. Zoöl.*, vol. 6, pp. 285–338.

———— 1921. Developmental rate and structural expression: An experimental study of twins, double monsters, and single deformities, and the interaction among embryonic organs during their origin and development. *Am. Jour. Anat.*, vol. 28, pp. 115–277.

STRONG, O. S. 1895. The cranial nerves of the Amphibia. *Jour. Morph.*, vol. 10, pp. 101–230.

SUMNER, FRANCIS B. 1919. Adaptation and the problem of "organic purposefulness." *Am. Nat.*, vol. 53, pp. 193–217, 338–369.

TASHIRO, S. 1917. *A chemical sign of life.* Univ. of Chicago Press.

———— 1922. Studies on alkaligenesis in tissues. I. Ammonia production in the nerve fiber during excitation. *Am. Jour. Physiol.*, vol. 60, pp. 519–543.

TAYLOR, CHARLES V. 1920. Demonstration of the function of the neuromotor apparatus in Euplotes by the method of microdissection. *Univ. of Calif. Pub. in Zoöl.*, vol. 19, pp. 403–470.

THOMPSON, CAROLINE B. 1913. A comparative study of the brains of three genera of ants, with special reference to the mushroom bodies. *Jour. Comp. Neur.*, vol. 23, pp. 515–572.

———— 1916. The brain and frontal gland of the castes of the "white ant," Leucotermes flavipes, Kollar. *Jour. Comp. Neur.*, vol. 26, pp. 553–603.

———— 1917. Origin of the castes of the common termite, Leucotermes flavipes, Kol. *Jour. Morph.*, vol. 30, pp. 83–153.

———— 1919. The development of the castes of nine genera and thirteen species of termites. *Biol. Bul.* vol. 36, pp. 379–398.

———— 1922. The castes of Termopsis. *Jour. Morph.*, vol. 36, pp. 495–535.

THORNDIKE, E. L. 1899. A note on the psychology of fishes. *Am. Nat.*, vol. 33, p. 923.

———— 1913. *The original nature of man.* Published by Teachers College, Columbia Univ., New York.

TRIPLETT, N. B. 1901. The educability of the perch. *Am. Jour. Psychol.*, vol. 12, p. 354.

TURNER, C. H. 1907. The homing of ants, an experimental study of ant behavior. *Jour. Comp. Neur.*, vol. 17, pp. 367–437.

VIALLETON, L. 1911. *Éléments de morphologie des vertébrés.* Paris.

VINCENT, S. B. 1912. The mammalian eye. *Jour. Animal Behavior*, vol. 2, pp. 249–255.

WASHBURN, MARGARET F. 1908. *The animal mind.* New York.

WATSON, G. A. 1907. The mammalian cerebral cortex, with special reference to its comparative histology. I. Order Insectivora. *Mott's Archives of Neurology*, vol. 3, pp. 49–118.

WATSON, J. B. 1907. Kinæsthetic and organic sensations: their rôle in the reactions of the white rat to the maze. *Psych. Rev. Monographs*, vol. 8, No. 2.

———— 1914. *Behavior, an introduction to comparative psychology.* New York.

———— 1919. *Psychology from the standpoint of a behaviorist.* Philadelphia.

WEISMANN, A. 1904. *The evolution theory.* 2 vols. London.

WHEELER, W. M. 1913. *Ants, their structure, development and behavior.* New York. Columbia Univ. Press.

———— 1923. *Social life among the insects.* New York.

WHITE, GERTRUDE M. 1919. Association and color discrimination in mud-minnows and sticklebacks. *Jour. Exp. Zoöl.*, vol. 27, pp. 443–498.

WHITMAN, C. O. 1892. The metamerism of Clepsine. *Festschr. f. Rudolf Leuckharts*, pp. 384–395. Leipzig.

———— 1919. Orthogenetic evolution in pigeons. Vol. III. *The behavior of pigeons.* Edited by Harvey A. Carr. Carnegie Inst. of Washington.

WILLARD, W. A. 1915. The cranial nerves of Anolis carolinensis. *Bul. Mus. Comp. Zoöl.*, vol. 59, pp. 17–116.

WILSON, C. W. 1916. On the life history of a soil Amœba. *Univ. of Calif. Pub. in Zoöl.*, vol. 16, pp. 241–292.

WINTREBERT, P. 1921. La contraction rhythmée aneurale des myotomes chez les embryons de sélaciens. I. Observation de Scyllorhinus canicula L. Gill. *Arch. Zoöl. Exp. et Gen.*, vol. 60, pp. 222–459.

WOLFF, MAX. 1904. Das Nervensystem der polypoiden Hydrozoa und Scyphozoa. *Zeits. f. allg. Physiologie*, Bd. 3, pp. 191–281.

YERKES, R. M. 1902. A contribution to the physiology of the nervous system of the medusa, Gonionemus murbachi. *Am Jour. Physiol.*, vol. 6, pp. 434–449, vol. 7, pp. 181–198.

———— 1907. *The dancing mouse.* New York.

———— 1912. The intelligence of earthworms. *Jour. Animal Behavior*, vol. 2, pp. 332–352.

YERKES, R. M., and WATSON, J. B. 1911. Methods of studying vision in animals. *Behavior Monographs*, vol. 1, no. 2.

YOCOM, HARRY B. 1918. The neuromotor apparatus of Euplotes patella. *Univ. of Calif. Pub. in Zoöl.*, vol. 18, pp. 337–396.

INDEX AND GLOSSARY

References are to pages or to the first page of a longer passage. Numbers of pages on which the item is figured are printed in **black-face type**. To facilitate cross reference the key word of a polynomial term is capitalized wherever it occurs in this Index and Glossary. Terms which are defined in this Glossary are printed in **black-face type**. The condensed definitions aim in many cases to suggest only the particular meanings of technical terms as they are applied in this work.

327